T. H. HUXLEY'S PLACE IN NATURAL SCIENCE

T. H. HUXLEY'S PLACE
IN
NATURAL SCIENCE

Mario A. di Gregorio

Yale University Press
New Haven and London

Published with assistance from the foundation established in
memory of Philip Hamilton McMillan of the Class of 1894, Yale
College.

Designed by Nancy Ovedovitz and set in Trump Medieval type by
The Composing Room of Michigan, Inc. Printed in the United
States of America by Edwards Brothers, Inc., Ann Arbor, Michigan.

Library of Congress Cataloging in Publication Data
Di Gregorio, Mario A.
    T. H. Huxley's place in natural science.
    Bibliography: p.
    Includes index.
1. Huxley, Thomas Henry, 1825–1895. 2. Naturalists—Eng-
land—Biography. I. Title.
QH31.H9D5 1984   574'.092'4 [B]   84-2375
ISBN 0-300-03062-2

The paper in this book meets the guidelines for permanence and
durability of the Committee on Production Guidelines for Book
Longevity of the Council on Library Resources.

10   9   8   7   6   5   4   3   2   1

*I dedicate this work to
Katharine, Lady Darwin*

Quoi! Vous ne tenez pas véritable une chose établie par tout le monde, et que tous les siècles ont révérée?

—Molière, *Le Malade imaginaire*

CONTENTS

ACKNOWLEDGMENTS

This book is a thoroughly revised version of my Ph.D. thesis, *On the Side of the Apes, T. H. Huxley and the Method and Results of Science,* presented at University College, London.

I wish to thank my former supervisor, Dr. W. F. Bynum, for his constant help and encouragement during its completion; and the British Council, the Accademia Nazionale dei Lincei, and the Royal Society of London, which have all in different periods generously supported my research.

I am also very grateful to Dr. Sydney Smith for his invaluable advice concerning the first three chapters. Dr. M. Bartholomew's criticisms have helped me to focus on some aspects that I had developed insufficiently and the late Professor J. S. Wilkie made useful comments. Dr. M. Hoskin, who introduced me to the British academic world, was of great help and assistance at the beginning of my studies in his country. Dr. F. Mondella of the Faculty of Philosophy at Milan University and professors S. Ranzi and G. Lanzavecchia of its Institute of Zoology greatly encouraged me before the start and during the early stages of my research. My friend Dr. M. Ferraguti, lecturer in general biology in Milan, read and criticised chapters 1, 3, and 4. I also had an interesting and stimulating correspondence with Professor J. Ostrom of Yale University concerning some aspects of chapter 3; the BBC sent me the typescript of their program "The Hot-Blooded Dinosaurs," which was relevant to the same chapter. A special thanks to Mr. P. Martin and Mr. N. Gill, students at Darwin College.

A grateful thought also to Mrs. J. Pingree, archivist of Imperial College, London, where the Huxley Papers are preserved. Her assistance was vital in the deciphering of Huxley's handwriting—without her help, I should not have been able to produce a large part of the unpublished material which appears in these pages. Many thanks also to her secretary, Mrs. Felton. I cannot forget the staffs of the libraries I visited: the library of the Department of History and Philosophy of

Science and the Balfour and Newton Library of the Zoology Department, Cambridge; the D.M.S. Watson Library at University College,
London; the library of the Wellcome Institute, London; the British Museum (Natural History), where I saw the Owen Papers, and, of course,
the Cambridge University Library, above all the Manuscript Room with
Mr. P. Gautrey and Mr. Purvis, who were of great help with the Darwin
Papers. I thank all the libraries concerned for granting me permission to
quote from the unpublished material in their possession.

At Cambridge I also had the chance to meet Professor F. Burkhardt
and Dr. D. Kohn, who are editing Darwin's correspondence, and whose
company, friendship, and comments I have greatly enjoyed. I had interesting talks with Professor Sir Andrew Huxley and Professor J. G.
Paradis, whose recent book on Huxley is of great interest. It was very
kind of the late Professor D. Ospovat to make me acquainted with some
of his work while it was in progress. Many thanks also to P. L. Farber and
J. P. Regelmann.

Darwin College elected me into a research fellowship. I am extremely grateful to the master, fellows, students, and staff of the college
for the very pleasant and encouraging environment they have provided
for me in my work.

A special thought goes to Mrs. Celia Goodman and her family. I have
spent a marvellous time at 9 Latham Road, Cambridge, thanks to their
warmth and kindness.

I wish also to remember Professor L. Geymonat, emeritus professor
of the philosophy of science at Milan University, whose lectures persuaded me to become a professional historian of science rather than an
operatic bass.

Last but not least I want to express my gratitude to my parents,
without whose lifelong support nothing would have been possible.

NOTES ON THE
PRINCIPAL SOURCES

Because pagination of *The Life and Letters of Thomas Henry Huxley* differs from edition to edition, I consistently cite the date and the correspondent wherever known. I have quoted directly from Huxley's memoirs as reprinted in *The Scientific Memoirs of Thomas Henry Huxley*, edited by G. Foster and E. R. Lankester; in the bibliography I have also quoted the original journal in which they were published. The only exception is Huxley's review of Chambers's *Vestiges of Creation*, for which I refer directly to the original source.

Since Huxley's *Collected Essays* are readily available, I have referred to them when a lecture or discourse has been reprinted there, but I have mentioned the original sources, where traceable, in the bibliography.

Except where a good English translation is available, I have retained all non-English quotations in the original language. I have quoted Rádl's book in German, because the English translation is also an abridgment. I refer to the *Huxley Papers* as *HP*, and to the manuscripts collected by Mrs. J. Pingree in *T. H. Huxley: List of His Scientific Papers* as *HM*. The abbreviation *Dar.* identifies quotations from the collections of Darwin's manuscripts at Cambridge, and *OP* those from the Owen collection in the British Museum (Natural History).

All the items in the bibliography are numbered and keyed into the text by those numbers. I have maintained the original spelling in all quotations, including cases where scientific terms are spelled differently from their modern spelling. The modern spellings are used in the text.

Introduction
On the Side of the Apes

In 1864 Disraeli delivered a famous speech in which he declared, "The question is this—is man an ape or an angel? My Lord, I am on the side of the angels" (477, p. 1).

Awareness of their social status, and successful enterprises in political, diplomatic, and commercial activities, convinced most Victorians that their place was with Disraeli "on the side of the angels." This study endeavours to describe the scientific outlook of one of the leading protagonists "on the side of the apes" in the controversy over the relationship between mankind and other living beings which divided nineteenth-century scientists, thinkers, and vociferous laymen.

Thomas Henry Huxley, through hard work in science and success in debate, rose from being a basically self-taught man of the lower middle class to the supreme honour of the presidency of the Royal Society. He was the leader of the most powerful group of scientists of his lifetime (480, 504), and the founder of one of the most influential families in the cultural life of his country (415).

Study of his treatment of the questions of life science throws light on the methods of, and results achieved in, that branch of research by a remarkably important section of scientists operating in the so-called Victorian age, which also included Tyndall, Romanes, Clifford, and several others. All these scientists, to different degrees, had in some way to come to terms with the works of the great pivotal figure of Charles Darwin. They all flourished in his shadow.

This is not a biography of T. H. Huxley. For a truly biographical account, one should refer primarily to his son Leonard's classic work, *The Life and Letters of Thomas Henry Huxley* (472), or to the books by T. C. Mitchell (511) and C. Bibby (394; 395). My aim is rather to outline Huxley's major contributions to science, his attitude to Darwinism, and the reasons and causes which led him to hold those views. This book is therefore intended to revive interest in Huxley as a *scientist*, rather than a controversialist, and makes no claim to provide a "definitive" account of all his views. For Huxley's social and philosophical views, I recommend the recent study by Professor Paradis, an outstanding piece of Huxleyana (527).

This book derives from my Ph.D. thesis, but the structural modifications have been so radical that it stands as quite a different work. I endeavour to treat two major questions whose solution seems to me the key to the understanding of Huxley's place in the history of science:

Did Huxley make any original contributions to biological science, regardless of his controversies on behalf of Darwinism?
Was Huxley a genuine Darwinian?

To answer question 1 in the affirmative is easy: Huxley's contributions to science have been neglected because his strong personality and multifarious interests are somehow more readily approachable by readers not closely conversant with the development of biological science.

Question 2 is more intriguing, especially after the publication of M. Bartholomew's article "Huxley's Defence of Darwin" (380), which claims that there was no real turning point in Huxley's science after 1859. Bartholomew's arguments present a very useful criticism of the traditional interpretation of Huxley as "Darwin's bull-dog" (472, vol. 1, p. 391), a sort of general agent of Darwin's ideas (661, vol. 1, p. 131); although I agree with them only in part, they helped me considerably in reaching my own conclusions on this central problem.

It seemed to me that the best approach to question 2 was via the outcome of question 1; namely, I considered Huxley's scientific works and saw to what extent their results were compatible and consistent with Darwin's theory of evolution by natural selection. I trusted Huxley's actual work rather than his own public statements about it.

I do not deny Huxley's importance as a populariser of evolutionary ideas. Irvine is indeed right to ask:

What would the evolutionary controversy have been without Huxley? No doubt Darwin's reputation would have been nearly as great . . . but science would not have enjoyed such dazzling prestige among politicians and businessmen, nor figured, perhaps, so prominently in the late-nineteenth-century school curriculum. [477, p. 118]

But if we consider Huxley's scientific works, we realise that he was an outstanding scientist in his own right, and that many of his views were independent of—and sometimes quite different from—Darwin's.

With a few notable exceptions in chapters 2 and 5, my work is based entirely upon Huxley's *Scientific Memoirs* (355) and private papers. I commence by considering his research in the fields of zoology and palaeontology and then assess the impact of the *Origin of Species* upon these studies. Huxley spent his early years in science—from the late 1840s to the early 1850s—mainly in the field of invertebrate morphology; undoubtedly these were the formative years in his career, during which his mind was moulded by influences which were to last for the rest of his life (433; 536).

Huxley's attitudes to the general problems of biology before 1859 are considered first of all. There we see how uneasy he felt about some of the theoretical implications of the concept of the type, which he (and many of his contemporaries) used as the unifying principle in zoology. Huxley rejected the Platonic implications of the type concept, but was not prepared to deploy the notion of actual modifications of animal forms towards the solution to his unanswered questions. Obviously a general frame was needed for all the zoological discoveries in the first part of the nineteenth century. By rejecting Platonism, Huxley cleared the way for his later qualified acceptance of Darwinism, but prior to the publication of the *Origin of Species* he had rejected all evolutionary views propounded (for example, those of Chambers and Lamarck), either as philosophical speculations rather than true science or as highly defective science. German science exerted a great influence upon Huxley throughout his career. Von Baer, Rathke, and Johannes Müller are the representatives of the German school to whom Huxley came closest; Goethe was his favourite author (443). Von Baer is especially important. His embryological method became Huxley's central approach to biological problems, as E. S. Russell has pointed out (879, pp. 159–61). This is described in chapter 1, which also introduces Huxley's "archenemy," Richard Owen, whose views on biology, evolution, and integrity are briefly sketched. Many aspects of Huxley's career have to be seen in the light of his antagonism to Owen.

Huxley was desperately searching for a pattern which could guarantee the harmony and order of nature. The type concept, as interpreted by Huxley after von Baer, did provide such a pattern; and Huxley never actually abandoned the concept. On the other hand, Huxley's interpretation of the type was remarkably different from that of his contemporaries—notably Richard Owen—insofar as Huxley rejected the Platonic assertion of the "existence" of the type itself, *all* living organisms being variations or developments of the type. Huxley referred to the type as an empirical working tool. A theory which preserved the harmonious pattern of nature and was empirically based was sure to meet his approval.

During his voyage on board HMS *Rattlesnake*, Huxley applied the type concept to his researches in invertebrate zoology, and made some important contributions to the knowledge of the coelenterates and the ascidians. The only relevant publications known to me which deal with the aspects considered here are Sir Julian Huxley's commentary on his grandfather's diary of the voyage (354) and M. P. Winsor's valuable *Starfish, Jellyfish, and the Order of Life* (581). A curious episode, the clash between Huxley and Owen over the anal structure of *Terebratula,* a brachiopod, is a further example of Owen's recurrent lack of integrity in scientific observations, a fault which certainly contributed to the blackening of his name.

During the later 1850s, Huxley shifted from invertebrate morphology to vertebrate palaeontology: the move was to be decisive for his approach to the problems of zoology after the publication of the *Origin of Species.* Huxley's reaction to Darwin's book is known, but I have included an analysis of its impact upon him, because the conclusions reached here are essential preparation for the unravelling of the issues involved in the second question above.

I argue that Huxley supported Darwin for three reasons:

1. he thought that Darwin had provided actual causes of evolution;
2. the theory could be empirically tested; and
3. Darwin's doctrine was a hypothesis of the order of nature, and as such capable of guaranteeing the harmonious pattern Huxley demanded.

On the other hand his acceptance was not wholehearted, for two reasons: the central principle, natural selection, was not experimentally proved; and he believed that the final value of the theory had to be treated as "absolute," while Darwin's attitude came closer to pragmatism.

The dates of Huxley's palaeontological memoirs reveal that it was only from 1868, long after the publication of the *Origin of Species,* that Huxley began to apply evolutionary concepts to his own work. Moreover, he made an increasingly confident use of phylogeny, even while officially proclaiming it a doubtful method.

What happened between 1859 and 1868 to persuade Huxley to put into practice what he had (with some reservations) claimed to be true but had not hitherto applied? It is my belief that Huxley was convinced by Haeckel, whose *Generelle Morphologie* appeared in 1866 (716), and whose *Schöpfungsgeschichte* (717) was published two years later and was reviewed by Huxley (168). Huxley and Haeckel met in London in 1866. According to Haeckel's report (461), Huxley was deeply impressed by his colleague's work.

I detect two reasons, strictly connected, for Haeckel's "success" where Darwin had "failed": First, whereas Darwin's hypothesis was based upon the unproven principle of natural selection, Haeckel's view emphasised the aspect of descent, for which the evidence would be palaeontological—the so-called missing links, some of which Huxley indeed went on to provide. And second, according to the views expressed by the zoological school of Jena, whose major representatives were Haeckel and Gegenbaur (913), it was possible to replace the relationships between the types with genealogical connections (645)—thus preserving Huxley's favourite type concept within an evolutionary framework.

Huxley's enthusiasm for evolution did not extend to the invertebrates, which as late as 1868 (155) and even 1875 (226) he still regarded as quite separate from the vertebrates—a remnant of his old belief that there was a complete separation between the major types. He appeared confident only of the evolution of the crustaceans—a view shared by many nineteenth-century evolutionists.

It seems to me that throughout his career Huxley maintained many of the beliefs he had acquired prior to his acceptance of evolution. This explains why his attitude sometimes appears ambiguous and helps to elucidate his frequent reliance on more traditional, "static" views of life science, a good example being his concept of morphological species, which he uses in his textbooks. Huxley's language is always clear and comprehensible (468). If there is confusion, it concerns the thought rather than its expression.

That in Huxley's ideas there remains much of the pre-Darwinian science is proved even by *Man's Place in Nature* (110), allegedly his most important Darwinian work. Undoubtedly it was an interesting work, but its *historical* importance, if we consider the reaction it triggered and the influence it exerted upon anthropologists contemporary with Huxley, lay primarily in its definitive acceptance of Linnaeus's classificatory scheme of the primates; although it is true that this was a major element in the acceptance of Darwin's views of human evolution, it was not a direct, necessary, or deliberate move in that direction. Paradoxically, *Man's Place in Nature* was better received in the twentieth century than when it was written. It seems to me that here Huxley had a glimpse of one of the fundamental principles inherent in the Darwinian view of evolution: the connection of the complex network of specific adaptations to the structure/function relationship. But this was not the way Huxley's contemporaries interpreted the book, as its reviews show.

The final chapter is concerned with a rather unfamiliar aspect of Huxley's scientific interests, the field of ethnology. Huxley contested the philological approach to ethnology then fashionable, propounded in Britain by Max Müller at Oxford. Like his contemporaries Huxley assumed the superiority of the "white" races over the others, but his attitude toward race was relatively mild by comparison with that of other Victorians, even Hooker, one of his best friends. In the field of ethnology, Huxley tended to introduce value judgments into the realm of science—an attitude which elsewhere he strongly opposed. Certainly in his time most of the concepts that social anthropologists work with today were still to be elaborated. One section of this chapter considers Huxley's interesting intervention in the heated debate among European intellectuals concerning the colonisation of Europe by "Aryans." This debate presents an opportunity not only to see how Huxley argued against the philological approach to anthropology in favour of a more physical view, but also to glimpse the racialist and nationalist bias of European culture at that time.

In my opinion this was the cardinal sin of Victorian science: the introduction of values into the most controversial and passionately debated branch of human knowledge. The scientific programme set up by the new scientific wave, of which Huxley was one of the leaders, largely failed here, although the degree of failure varied widely according to the degree of awareness of the problem on the part of individual scientists.

Huxley and his friends were convinced that science could and should be "neutral," independent of any ideological or other generally extra-scientific considerations. Our conclusions must depend entirely upon the consistency of the method we apply throughout our scientific research and ought not to be influenced by our hopes and wishes (see 736; 737; for a different opinion, see 944). There was nothing novel in this attitude, which had its roots in Galileo's arguments with Catholic authority and was nourished by the British empiricists—Locke, Hume, Mill, and later Russell and Ayer. The conception of the neutrality of science was taken by Huxley, who was philosophically an empiricist (433, pp. 465–528), as the necessary condition of his programme. Important steps in the realisation of this programme were his intervention at the Oxford meeting of the British Association in 1860, and his "last words" on science in Evolution and Ethics (343, 345; for a different view see 463). Both the Oxford incident with Bishop Wilberforce and Evolution and Ethics fall outside the scope of the study of Huxley's scientific contributions, so I will restrict myself to a brief comment here.

Wilberforce was scientifically altogether more sophisticated than we traditionally suppose from reports of the incident blatantly in Huxley's favour (411; 543). He represented a clear attitude to science which one might call "ideological." Such a view is opposed to the "neutral" view, which was defined by Galileo in his clash with the Catholic Church. The ideological view reappears from time to time in the history of science, and we have two interesting examples in our own century, Lysenko's biology and Nazi anthropology. Needless to say, Darwinism can easily be interpreted ideologically, as happened at the time and indeed still does; but for Huxley the correctness of the results of science is independent of ideological concerns. Huxley's main theoretical concern was to show that true scientific method is independent of one's wishes and hopes. The word *dangerous* is for him scientifically meaningless; what is important is to reach certain conclusions which can be tested empirically by a logically sound method. If the results, once properly checked, contradict our beliefs, it is our beliefs which must be given up. *Evolution and Ethics* and especially the "Prolegomena" (345) Huxley prefaced to its reprint in his *Collected Essays* are his manifesto on the neutrality of science, with the emphasis on the independence of knowledge (i.e., science) from value (i.e., ethics).

Now, when they came to the very branch of knowledge in which wishes and personal interest were stronger than anywhere else—the study of cultures different from, and often in suicidal conflict with, their own—Victorian scientists, and Huxley with them, were unable to let their programme work, and polluted their science with values. Huxley "failed" to a lesser extent than, say, James Hunt; but even if his was an enlightened mind, he still failed to suppress an expression of scorn for customs different from his. Being liberally inclined, he supported women's emancipation, but thought that women were biologically inferior to men, a view then a commonplace. He accused Governor Eyre of overstepping the boundaries of English law in hanging a black rioter, but held the Negro to be biologically inferior to the white (then a widespread belief)—though not so inferior as to constitute a link between man and the apes, as Hunt thought.

This work is addressed primarily to historians of science, but I should be pleased if it also interested scientists. The reader is expected to have some prior knowledge of biology and of Darwin's theory and its historical circumstances, since Darwin is a presence throughout. Huxley worked in such proximity to Darwin that this study may also contribute, albeit indirectly, to the understanding of the reception of the works and ideas of the author of the *Origin of Species,* one of the most original thinkers of our age, whose influence (605), together with that of his colleague Huxley, has extended far beyond the strictly scientific limits for which it was intended.

PART ONE
Zoological Science

We must not recoil with childish aversion from the examination of the humbler animals. Every realm of nature is marvellous: as Heracleitus, when the strangers who came to visit him found him warming himself at the furnace in the kitchen and hesitated to go in, is reported to have bidden them not to be afraid to enter, as even in the kitchen divinities were present, so we should venture on the study of every kind of animal without distaste; for each and all will reveal to us something natural and something beautiful.

—Aristotle, *De Partibus Animalium*

1
The Making of a Zoologist

Gleich einem leuchtenden Strahle schoss es mich durch die Seele, dass der Typus im Bau der Wirbelthiere sich allmählig im Embryo ausbildet.
                                         —Karl Ernst von Baer to Heinrich Christian Pander

Early Works

The Medusae

Huxley's first publication, at the age of twenty, was an interesting memoir, "On a Hitherto Undescribed Structure in the Human Hair Sheath" (1). This memoir constitutes his first contribution to histology, one of the many branches of biological science in which he was involved during his career.* He describes a layer of human hair he had detected as consisting of "very pale epithelium-like nucleated cells. If the eye be now carried again over the fenestrated membrane . . . this layer will be found to be traceable over the fenestrated membrane and to be in close connection with it" (1, p. 2). This structure was henceforth called Huxley's Layer.

Huxley's "official" scientific career, however, began with his voyage on board HMS *Rattlesnake*, during which he kept a diary (354) which his grandson Julian edited in 1935. At the beginning of the diary, the young, self-confident man reveals his plans. He wants to start as a student and finish as a teacher (p. 15). His entry of 10 December 1846 reads: "The study of the habits and structure of the more perishable or

---

*Huxley returned to histology in 1856 with "Tegumentary organs" (45). This memoir was originally a series of fascicles published between August 1855 and October 1856 in R. Todd's *Cyclopedia of Anatomy and Physiology*. Here Huxley follows the method of the great morphologist Xavier Bichât, whose classification of living tissues was based upon macroscopical and functional distinctions (614). Each tissue must be considered as an organ; in fact Huxley decides "to regard these organs as a system in the sense of Bichât—as a sort of zoological class—whose members, the tegumentary organs of particular animals, are but special modifications of one general plan" (45, p. 365).

rare marine productions [is] most likely to be profitable. Naturalising for systematic purposes is not *à mon gré"* and is good only for people sitting in museums (pp. 15–16). "But what I *can* do and they *cannot* and where therefore the chief value of my position is: I can observe. 1. the "habits" of living bodies. 2. their mode of development and generation. 3. their anatomy by dissection of fresh specimens. 4. their histology by microscopic observation."

The zoological results of the voyage were later published in a monograph entitled *The Oceanic Hydrozoa* (70). The circumstances that accompanied its publication were unfortunate. On his return to England, the young scientist was still by no means established, despite the good reception of a paper (3) sent to the Royal Society, of which he became a fellow in 1851 thanks to the support of his friend and mentor Edward Forbes. Huxley met many difficulties in getting his projected monograph published (472, vol. 1, pp. 80–82). The cost of the publication would be about £300, he tried to explain to the Admiralty, "a sum small in itself but beyond the means of a private individual" (*HP* 30.10; 30 March 1852). Preoccupied with the problems of publication, he refused to embark on another voyage, and this caused a breach with the Admiralty which might have jeopardised his career.

In the monograph, Huxley had compiled the best of the results achieved during the voyage, which had also been reported in a series of scientific memoirs between 1846 and 1850. The book, finally published in 1859, is presented as a general survey of the Hydrozoa, without sufficient distinction between Huxley's own contributions and those of other scientists. Moreover, a scientific monograph which is published almost ten years after being written is bound to be stale and of lesser interest. It can be useful only as a textbook. As Huxley wrote to Leuckart in January 1859:

The book ought to have been published eight years ago. But for three years I could get no money from the Government, and in the meanwhile you and Kölliker, Gegenbaur and Vogt, went to the shores of the Mediterranean and made havoc with my novelties. Then came occupations consequent on my appointment to the chair I now hold; and it was only last autumn that I had leisure to take up the subject again. [472, vol. 1, pp. 175–76]

In view of these circumstances, I shall not refer to the monograph but directly to the original scientific memoirs.

In 1849 Huxley wrote "On the Anatomy and the Affinities of the Family of the Medusae" (3). In it he claimed that very little was known about those animals, probably in order to emphasise the originality of his contribution, which is indeed remarkable. Important studies on the Medusae had however been carried out by other scientists, such as

Sars, Ehrenberg (678), and Forbes (689). Huxley's paper is important because it is an attempt to describe all the biological aspects of the class. The first section, which presents a description of the anatomy of the Medusae (pp. 10–23), reveals immediately a central aspect of Huxley's scientific approach. If we anticipate extremely detailed descriptions in his enquiry, we shall be disappointed. Most other naturalists, such as Milne-Edwards and Owen, were more accurate and precise in most of their descriptions of anatomical detail. But Huxley is not interested merely in description of structures in greater or lesser detail; the core and aim of his enquiry is always to discover and analyse a single problem, say of animal morphology, and from it to draw general conclusions of wider zoological interest. Without Huxley's enquiry in this field, Kowalewsky's greater work would scarcely have been possible.

Huxley's analysis of the Medusae starts by considering their gastrovascular cavity ("stomach"). Although it varies in size and shape, he claims, this structure is always made of two membranes, an inner and an outer (p. 10). In zoology it is always a sound technique to find some structure which can be used as a basis for comparisons, which reveal morphological relationships; Huxley's interest is preeminently a morphological one. From the single morphological problem of the structure of the gastrovascular cavity, Huxley passes on to the general statement that the organs of the Medusae consist of two membranes:

I would wish to lay particular stress upon the composition of this and other organs of the Medusae out of *two distinct membranes*, as I believe that it is one of the essential peculiarities of their structure and that a knowledge of the fact is of great importance in investigating their homologies. I will call these two membranes as such, and independently of any modification into particular organs, "foundation membranes." [3, p. 11]

It is in fact one of Huxley's most notable contributions to the knowledge of invertebrate animals that he found the Hydrozoa to be composed of two layers, and only two, inner and outer. It is a fact which one finds nowadays in any textbook of zoology, but which was a novelty when Huxley published his early scientific memoirs. In *The Oceanic Hydrozoa* the terms *ectoderm* and *endoderm*, meaning the outer and the inner layer respectively, are used. The names themselves are not his own, but were coined by George Allman in 1853 (70, p. 2; 589).

As MacBride pointed out in 1925, Huxley reached some bold conclusions, "comparing the outer layer or ectoderm of the hydrozoon polyp to the epidermis of a vertebrate animal, or rather of the vertebrate embryo, and the endoderm to the so-called mucous layer of the vertebrate embryo, which is applied to the yolk and draws nourishment from it" (499,

p. 735). In Huxley's view the endoderm in both vertebrates and invertebrates remains in an almost unaltered state during the life of the organism, while a far greater amount of change occurs in the ectoderm,
which gives origin to such structures as the nervous and sensory
systems.

As Huxley points out (3, p. 11), the study of the two layers which
constitute the organs of the Medusae is of paramount importance to an
understanding of homologies between structures. He follows two criteria in the discovery of homologies. The first states that two structures,
in order to be homologous, must undergo the same development in
similar parts of the body. Because it is often important to establish the
detail of that development, it is necessary to introduce intermediate
gradations: this is the second criterion.

One should always bear in mind that Huxley maintained throughout
his life that in animal structure it is possible to conceive a fundamental
unity of plan, which undergoes a series of variations represented by the
different animal forms. While such a view is obviously compatible with
the idea of evolution, it is equally obvious that it is not necessarily an
evolutionary view. I quote this central passage from the memoir:

> But in order to demonstrate that a real affinity exists among different classes
> of animals, it is not sufficient merely to point out that certain similarities and
> analogies exist among them; it must be shown that they are constructed upon
> the same anatomical type, that, in fact, their organs are homologous.
>
> Now the organs of two animals or families of animals are homologous when
> their structure is identical, or when the differences between them may be ac-
> counted for by the simple law of growth. When the organs differ considerably,
> their homology may be determined in two ways, either—1, by tracing back the
> course of development of the two until we arrive by similar stages at the same
> point; or, 2, by interpolating between the two a series of forms derived from
> other animals allied to both, the difference between each term of the series being
> such only as can be accounted for by the laws of growth. . . . Both methods may
> be made use of in investigating the homologies of the Medusae. [3, pp. 23–24]

These principles, together with the analysis of the Medusae, enable the
naturalist to establish the two criteria just enunciated:

> What has now been advanced will perhaps be deemed evidence sufficient to
> demonstrate—1st., that the organs of these various families are traceable back
> to the same point in the way of development; or 2nd.ly, when this cannot be
> done, that they are connected by natural gradations with organs which are so
> traceable, in which case, according to the principles advanced in 57, the various
> organs are homologous, and the families have a real affinity to one another and
> should form one group. [p. 27]

As E. S. Russell points out, Huxley's memoir is an interesting case of
the application of von Baer's germ-layer theory (879, p. 208), which

Rathke, another of Huxley's intellectual sources, had also adopted. Huxley writes:

A complete identity of structure connects the "foundation membranes" of the Medusae with the corresponding organs in the rest of the series; and it is curious to remark, that throughout, the outer and inner membranes appear to bear the same physiological relation to one another as do the serous and mucous layers of the germ; the outer becoming developed into the muscular system and giving rise to the organs of offence and defence; the inner, on the other hand, appearing to be more closely subservient to the purposes of nutrition and generation. [p. 24]

Huxley extends his researches to the whole of the Coelenterata, showing that they are made up of the two "foundation membranes" (cell layers, as we should call them today). The Coelenterata are a very varied group of animals, capable of organisation according to two different morphological types, the polyp and the medusa. Huxley is especially interested in the Siphonophores, of which he distinguishes two families, the Diphydae and the Physophoridae. Later, many other forms were added to the phylum Coelenterata, but what is really important—and herein lies Huxley's central contribution—is that with his "foundation membranes" he had provided scientists with a criterion on which to base the classification of the whole group, which had previously been assumed to be related to the Radiata (of which the starfish is a member).

That he was conscious of the importance of his discovery can be seen from a letter he wrote to his sister on 1 August 1849:

Now when we return from the north I hope to have collected materials for a much bigger paper. . . . If my present anticipations turn out correct, this paper will achieve one of the great ends of Zoology and Anatomy, viz. the reduction of two or three apparently widely separated and incongruous groups into modifications of the single type, every step of the reasoning being based upon anatomical facts. [472, vol. 1, p. 36]

This is one of Huxley's most important discoveries, and according to this letter sent by Allman to Mrs. Huxley one year after her bereavement, one that was insufficiently emphasised even in his own lifetime. Allman wants to stress

a fact which has been overlooked in all the notices I have seen, and which I regard as one of the greatest claims of his splendid work on the recognition of zoologists. I refer to his discovery that the body of the Medusae and of all other Coelenterata is essentially composed of two membranes, an outer and an inner, and his recognition of these as the homologies of the two primary germinal leaflets in the vertebrate embryo. Now this discovery stands at the very basis of a philosophical zoology and of a true conception of true affinities of animals. It is the ground on which Haeckel has founded his famous gastrea theory and without it Kowalewsky could never have announced his great discovery of the affinity of the Ascidians and Vertebrates. [*HP* 10.88–89]

Surprisingly enough, as M. P. Winsor points out (*581*), the term *Coelenterata* is not used by Huxley in his memoirs. The reason is that Frey and Leuckart had already proposed that name in the 1840s. Huxley, who was aware of this fact, said in a note he was preparing for the British Association in 1851:

It is curious enough that this has been done—for other reasons—by Messrs Frey and Leuckart in their invaluable "Beiträge". However my own *conclusions* may agree with those of these naturalists—I cannot think the physiological reasoning on which they base their proposed name for the class—Coelenterata—is correct—nor do I think that they have properly estimated the essential differences among its members. [*581*, p. 78; *HP* 37.12(35)]

This passage was not published, but only communicated verbally to the British Association. In his published material Huxley studiously avoided referring to Frey and Leuckart on this topic, and proposed for the new group the name *Nematophora*. In fact in 1850, he published "Notes on Medusae and Polypes": "The Hydroid and Sertularian Polypes, the Hydrostatic and ordinary Acalephae, and the Helianthoid Polyps form one large family which, from their invariable and peculiar 'thread-cell', I propose to call the 'Nematophora' " (*5*, p. 35). In one of his "Lectures on general natural history" of 1856, the term *Coelenterata* does appear, and the precedent of Frey and Leuckart is acknowledged (*47*, p. 563); but this does not disprove Winsor's point, since this is simply a report of a lecture, not something written by Huxley himself.

All this notwithstanding, Huxley's contribution to the knowledge of the Coelenterata is a very important one. Indeed, as Winsor points out, Huxley's claim that his grouping was based upon original grounds different from those of Frey and Leuckart is wholly justified (*581*, p. 79). Whereas Frey and Leuckart consider a standard acaleph and a standard polyp, and show, from anatomical data, that the two standard forms are homologous, Huxley detects resemblances between forms apparently completely different, such as siphonophores and hydroids. Huxley recognises the following similarities between the classes:

1. Body composed of two membranes out of which all the organs are modelled.
2. Thread cells universally (?) present.
3. Gemmiparous generation.
4. Sexual generation—spermatozoa and ova being formed in vase like external sacs. [*581*, p. 79; *HP* 34.38 (64)]

The Ascidians

Huxley's next important memoir is "Observations upon the Anatomy and Physiology of Salpa and Pyrosoma" (*7*) of 1851, in which he considers the famous zoological controversy which had arisen concerning the generation of "those strange gelatinous animals" (p. 38). This memoir provides us with further evidence that his method does not consist in extremely detailed descriptions of structures and functions. It consists again in studying a single case, the *Salpae* and their reproduction, and from it drawing general conclusions on the whole zoological group of the ascidians. Huxley is usually capable of finding the crux of the problem, from which he builds his case. For example, at the beginning of this memoir, he finds a satisfactory and unequivocal definition of dorsal and ventral side and of anterior and posterior extremity, a necessary premise for any description of the form in question, and one which, once the symmetry of the animal is described, is invaluable in the study of the invertebrates. (For example, one must first establish whether the symmetry is radiate or bilateral.) This method is common to all modern zoology and shows how Huxley tried to be clear and precise without being pedantic:

Throughout the present paper, that side on which the heart is placed will be considered as the dorsal side; that on which the ganglion and auditory vesicle are placed, as the ventral side. That extremity to which the mouth is turned will again be considered as the anterior extremity, the opposite as the posterior. Such a view of the case appears to be more harmonious with the determinations of corresponding parts in other animals than any other. In all the invertebrata the mouth end is always considered as the anterior, the heart side as the dorsal side. [p. 39; see also *HM* 121.94, a letter from Huxley to Milne-Edwards of 12 March 1857, on the same topic]

In his description of the structure of *Salpa* (pp. 39–53), Huxley claims to have detected a hitherto undescribed structure in the intestinal canal. Such an appendage consists

of a system of delicate, transparent, colourless tubes, with clear contents, arising by a single stem from the upper part of the stomachal caecum and thence ramifying over the surface of the intestine . . . on what may be called the rectum, that is the terminal portion of the intestine; it forms a sort of expansion of parallel anastomising vessels, which all terminate at the same distance from the anus anteriorly, and from the bend of the intestine posteriorly, either by uniting with one another or in small pyriform caeca. [p. 42]

He then recalls Milne-Edwards's description of the three tunics in the ascidians, which he considers with respect to the homologies of *Salpa*:

Authors speak of the greater or lesser adherence of the outer and inner sacs; and consider the "outer sac" of the ordinary Ascidian to be homologous with the outer tunic of the *Salpa*. The "inner sac", again, is with them homologous with the inner tunic of the *Salpa*. But it is not so; every Ascidian, as M. Milne-Edwards has clearly shown in *Clavelina*, consists of three tunics; an outer, the test; a middle, which is here called outer *tunic*; and an inner, the inner *tunic*.

The inner tunic of *Salpa* answers to the inner tunic of *Clavelina*, but its outer tunic answers to the test and the outer *tunic* together. [p. 59]

In a note, Huxley emphasises the importance of embryology: "This essential difference between the test and the two *tunics* of the Ascidians has its origin in the embryo. The tunics are formed by the ordinary process of development, while the test having a totally different chemical composition, is in a manner secreted round, and envelopes the whole embryo" (p. 59n).

A most interesting problem, discussed in this paper and also in the memoirs on the Coelenterata, is however the so-called alternation of generations. Goethe was not the only poet interested in science; in 1819, Adelbert von Chamisso, the author of *Peter Schlemil* and many enjoyable poems, published a scientific work asserting the alternation of generations in the *Salpae*. It was Chamisso's view that in the *Salpae* there occurs an alternation between a generation of budding, free-swimming forms and one of aggregate viviparous forms, and Huxley quotes his noteworthy statement from *Reise um die Erde*: "Es ist als gebäre die Raupe den Schmetterling und der Schmetterling hinwiederum die Raupe" (p. 64n). Chamisso himself regarded Eschscholtz as the original discoverer of the phenomenon. The sexual organs of the *Salpae* remained undiscovered until the 1840s, when they were described by Krohn and Steenstrup. In 1842, Steenstrup, a Danish zoologist, published a monograph (899) on the subject of the alternation of generations in what came to be called the Coelenterata, the Trematoda, and the Urochorda (see 902, vol. 3, pp. 456–65, p. 459).

For Huxley, Chamisso's view raises two major questions: "1st. Are the statements made by Chamisso correct? and 2nd.ly, if they be correct, how far is the "alternation theory" a just and sufficient generalization of the phenomenon?" (7, p. 38). Huxley considers the two "forms" of the *Salpae*, which he calls "*Salpa A*" and "*Salpa B*" (*S. solitaria* and *S. gregata* respectively, in Chamisso's terminology). After describing and comparing them (pp. 40–41), Huxley tries to draw some general conclusions about Chamisso's theory. First of all, he claims that part of Chamisso's theory is undoubtedly true: "*The solitary* Salpa (Salpa A) *produces the aggregate form* (Salpa B)" (p. 47), by gemmation, *Salpa B* being "*a bud of Salpa A*" (p. 49). It is also true that *Salpa B* produces *Salpa A*,

and the circulatory system of the foetus in this case is connected with that of the parent, *not immediately, but by means of a very distinct and well-developed placenta.*

While Chamisso's formula, then, expressed the truth with regard to the generation of the *Salpae*, it does not express the whole truth. [p. 49, 51]

It is very important to realise, Huxley continues, that although it may be true that *Salpa A* produces *Salpa B* and vice versa, the two processes are radically different: *Salpa A* produces *Salpa B* as a bud, while *Salpa B* produces *Salpa A* as an embryo (p. 51). Therefore Huxley claims that there is no *true* alternation of generations,

but there is an *alternation of true sexual generation with the altogether distinct process of gemmation.*

It would be irrelevant to discuss here the wide question of the "alternation of generations" in all its bearings; but the writer may be permitted to express his belief, founded upon many observations upon the Polyps, Acalephae, &c., that the phenomena classed under this name are always of the same nature as in the *Salpae*; that under no circumstances are the two forms alternately developed by *sexual generation*; but that wherever the so-called "alternation of generations" occurs it is *an alternation of generation with gemmation.* [p. 51]

On this topic, George Allman wrote to Huxley on 30 May 1852: "You have I think triumphantly demolished the whole system of Alternation of generation and its cousin Parthenogenesis" (*HP* 10.63). And now it is clear that the target of Huxley's attack was actually Richard Owen, rather than the harmless Chamisso. In *On Parthenogenesis* of 1849, Owen had accepted Chamisso's view (*835*, p. 22), praised Steenstrup's *Generationswechsel* (p. 34), and stated that the alternation of generations explained his own view of parthenogenesis, for example, in the aphids (p. 37). Darwin wrote to Huxley that he was very pleased by the way the latter had overturned Owen's views: "I fancy Owen thinks much of this doctrine of his; I never from the first believed it" (*HP* 5.58; 1857[?]).

The discussion of the alternation of generations leads to an even wider problem of zoology, that of animal individuality. The memoir described above is the first in which Huxley considers this problem. Edward Forbes treated the concepts of "individual" and "species" in "On the Supposed Analogy between the Life of an Individual and the Duration of a Species" (*690*) of 1852. The same year Huxley devoted a memoir to the question, in which he states: "The individual animal is the sum of the phenomena presented by a single life: in other words it is all those animal forms which proceed from a single egg taken together" (*16*, p. 150).

The problem of the apparent alternation of generations in the *Salpae* provides good material for a deep analysis of the biological concept of the individual. Neither *Salpa A* nor *Salpa B* is an individual, Huxley claims, using a similar zoological definition to that quoted above: "Not either of their forms, but both together, answer to the 'individual' among the higher animals" (*7*, p. 52). *Salpa A* and *Salpa B* are thus only parts of individuals; they should be regarded as "organs." But since Huxley realises that it would be unusual to apply the term *organ* to the completeness of organisation displayed by the two forms, he proposes for them the term *zoöid*, "bearing in mind always that while the distinction between zoöid and individual is real, and founded upon the surest zoological basis,—a fact of development,—that between zoöid and organ is purely conventional, and established for the sake of convenience merely" (ibid). The same concept could be applied to the "compound" animals, which would be seen "not [as] an aggregation of individuals into a common mass, but an individual which is developed into a greater or lesser number of zoöid forms, which . . . remain united" (p. 53). Similar views are expressed in "Remarks upon Appendicularia and Doliolum, two Genera of the Tunicata" (8); "Zoological Notes and Observations Made on Board H.M.S. Rattlesnake during the Years 1846–50" (9); and "Observations on the Genus Sagitta" (10).

In the first of these memoirs, Huxley claims on morphological grounds that the *Appendicularia* are a genus belonging to the Tunicata: "The whole organization of the creature, its wide respiratory sac, its nervous system, its endostyle, all lead to this view" (8, p. 73). The *Appendicularia*, because of the occurrence of only one aperture, the respiratory one, should be regarded as the lowest form of the Tunicata (p. 74). As far as *Doliolum* is concerned, its structure indicates to Huxley a position which is intermediate between *Salpa* and *Pyrosoma* (pp. 77–78). The third memoir is interesting for its remarks on the importance of distribution (10, p. 96)—a point influenced by Forbes—while the second is a survey of other discoveries in the field of invertebrate animals, such as "The Auditory Organs in the Crustacea" (9, pp. 82–85), "On the Anatomy of the Genus Tethya" (ibid.), and "Upon Thalassicolla, a New Zoophyte" (pp. 86–95).

The Echinoderms

Another field of zoological research in which Huxley's early work is of interest is that of the echinoderms. As early as 1835, Louis Agassiz made important observations upon this zoological group, with his "Prodrome d'une monographie des radiares ou échinodermes" (584). Agassiz was aware that some echinoderms, such as the sea urchin, depart from the radial symmetry of the members of Cuvier's embranchment Radiata, to which echinoderms, polyps, and acalephs belonged. He then individuated three "natural" orders of echinoderms: starfish, sea urchins, and holoturians.

While Agassiz was studying these animal forms, embryology was beginning to play a leading role in biological sciences. It was in 1845 that the great German biologist Johannes Müller described the metamorphosis of the echinoderm larva, called *pluteus* (see 581, ch. 5), into the adult form. The pluteus, which was not at first recognised as a larva, has a bilateral symmetry which during the process of metamorphosis changes into a radiate one.

In his "Report upon the Researches of Prof. Müller into the Anatomy and Development of the Echinoderms" (13) of 1851, Huxley points out that the larvae of the echinoderms resemble those of the annelids, in that they have a clear bilateral symmetry which in the adult becomes radiate (pp. 110–11). The process through which this phenomenon occurs can be regarded as "a sort of internal gemmation" (p. 111). The phenomenon can occur in two ways: "Either the new structure ultimately throws off more or less of the larva in which it was developed, or it unites with the larva to form the adult animal, no part being thrown off" (ibid.). We find, then, a further denial of the concept of the alternation of generations. In fact, Müller had pointed out that the development of the echinoderms was related to the alternation of generations; Carus had interpreted Müller's view as implying the alternation of generations in the echinoderms, but Müller disagreed with his colleague's interpretation (581, p. 113). Once more Huxley introduces his concept of the zoöid. In the echinoderms, he says, "the individual consists of two zooids—a larva-zooid and an Echinoderm-zooid, the latter of which is developed from the former by a process of internal gemmation" (13, p. 118). One can therefore detect two kinds of gemmation: an external one, such as in polyps and ascidians; and an internal one, such as in aphids and trematods, and also echinoderms (p. 119). This remark does not seem to have met with the approval of later scientists, who dropped Huxley's view unanimously.

The important point about Huxley's memoir is his reliance on embryological considerations; these establish a relationship between the echinoderms and the annelids. For Huxley, embryology proved that the echinoderms were not related to the Radiata, as the anatomical inspection of the adult form would suggest, but to the Annelida: "The Echinoderms and Entozoa then do not form properly any portion of a spherical Radiate Type but are rather modifications of the Annulose Type" (HP 37.12). All forms of echinoderm larva "can be reduced to one very simple hypothetical type; having an elongated form, traversed by a straight intestine, with the mouth at one extremity and the anus at the other, and girded by a circular ciliated fringe; just like the larvae of some Annelids" (13, p. 109).

When Huxley published his results on the echinoderms, Richard Owen was the leading morphologist in Britain; now, in the revised edition of his Lectures on . . . Invertebrate Animals of 1855 (832b), originally printed in 1843 (832a), Owen approached the problem of the classification of the radiates in a way that did not appeal to Huxley. In his previous edition, Owen had divided the Radiata into four classes, Polypi, Anthozoa, Enthozoa, and Infusoria (832a, p. 16). In 1855 Owen did not change the substance of his previous division; but now he stated that too little was known of the Radiata to justify statements about them as definite as those about the other subkingdoms (*832b*, p. 14). Then he introduced the subprovince Radiaria, divided into the classes of Echinodermata, Bryozoa, Anthozoa, Acalephae, and Hydrozoa. Owen's statements ignored Huxley's suggestion of the relation of the echinoderms to the annelids, although Huxley's report on Müller is quoted in his bibliography (*832b*, p. 658).

Huxley's reply was quick. In 1856 he rebuked Owen in a lecture whose report was later printed:

The efforts which have been made to improve the classification of the Radiata on this and the other side of the channel are, so far as I can observe, entirely ignored [by Owen]. It is my duty to express my belief that the general adoption of such a classification as this would be one of the most thoroughly retrograde steps ever taken since Zoology has been a science, and would impede to a most mischievous extent its advance in this country. [*47*, p. 484]

In this series of lectures of 1856 (*47*), Huxley proposes to abandon the subkingdom Radiata and to replace it with the two subkingdoms Coelenterata and Protozoa (p. 484). In the subkingdom Annulosa Huxley grouped the classes Articulata (insects, myriapods, spiders, and crustaceans—i.e., segmented Annulosa), Molluscoida (molluscs and brachio-

Table 1. Owen's Classification [*832b*, p. 16]

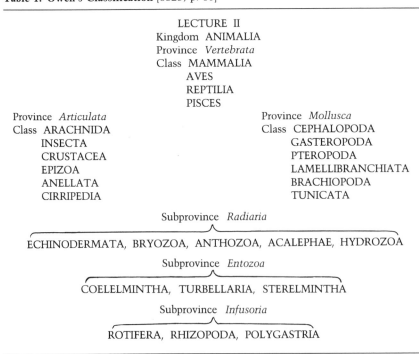

LECTURE II
Kingdom ANIMALIA
Province *Vertebrata*
Class MAMMALIA
      AVES
      REPTILIA
      PISCES

Province *Articulata*   Province *Mollusca*
Class ARACHNIDA   Class CEPHALOPODA
      INSECTA   GASTEROPODA
      CRUSTACEA   PTEROPODA
      EPIZOA   LAMELLIBRANCHIATA
      ANELLATA   BRACHIOPODA
      CIRRIPEDIA   TUNICATA

Subprovince *Radiaria*

ECHINODERMATA, BRYOZOA, ANTHOZOA, ACALEPHAE, HYDROZOA

Subprovince *Entozoa*

COELELMINTHA, TURBELLARIA, STERELMINTHA

Subprovince *Infusoria*

ROTIFERA, RHIZOPODA, POLYGASTRIA

Table 2. Huxley's Classification [47, p. 484]

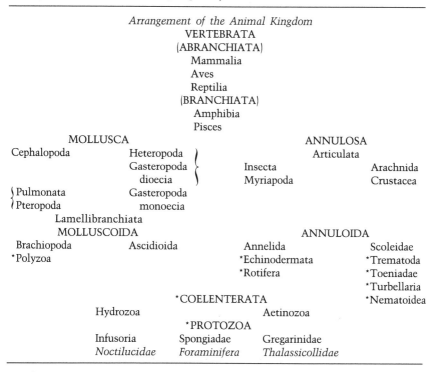

Arrangement of the Animal Kingdom

VERTEBRATA

(ABRANCHIATA)

Mammalia

Aves

Reptilia

(BRANCHIATA)

Amphibia

Pisces

MOLLUSCA		ANNULOSA	
Cephalopoda	Heteropoda ⎫	Articulata	
	Gasteropoda ⎬	Insecta	Arachnida
	dioecia ⎭	Myriapoda	Crustacea
⎰Pulmonata	Gasteropoda		
⎱Pteropoda	monoecia		
Lamellibranchiata			

MOLLUSCOIDA		ANNULOIDA	
Brachiopoda	Ascidioida	Annelida	Scoleidae
*Polyzoa		*Echinodermata	*Trematoda
		*Rotifera	*Toeniadae
			*Turbellaria
			*Nematoidea

*COELENTERATA

Hydrozoa		Aetinozoa

*PROTOZOA

Infusoria	Spongiadae	Gregarinidae
Noctilucidae	*Foraminifera*	*Thalassicollidae*

The groups marked * formed the "Radiata" of Cuvier.

pods), and Annuloida (unsegmented Annulosa, such as echinoderms, annelids, trematods, and rotifers) (pp. 462, 484, 537, 586, 635, etc.).

Theoretical Perspectives

God the Mathematician

We have seen from Huxley's early papers that he was primarily interested in data for what they could reveal about problems of general significance or theoretical importance. Throughout his life Huxley was preoccupied with the concept of the "order" of nature and with establishing the view that scientific investigation was the appropriate means of arriving at an understanding of that concept. He therefore rejected all intrusions of metaphysically or theologically inspired notions into the analysis of nature, opposing creationism and Platonism, and using traditional terminologies and techniques only after detaching them from whatever extrascientific basis their original introduction into science may have had. This empiricist bias is clear even in his early flirtation with MacLeay's "circular system."

[PLATE II]

Phil. Trans MDCCCXLIX *Plate* XXXVII

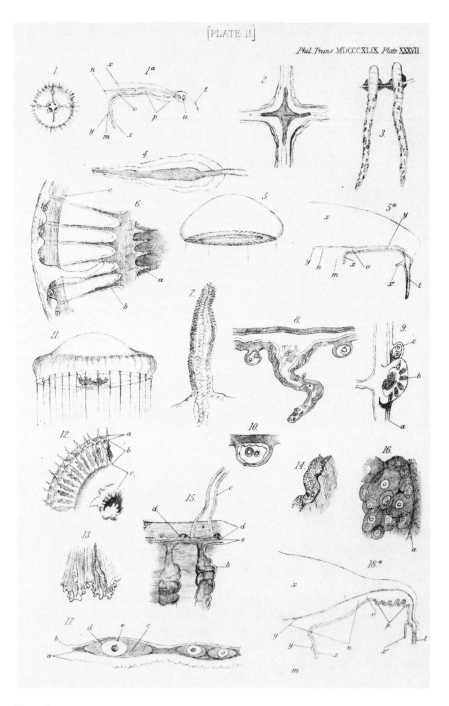

Figure 1

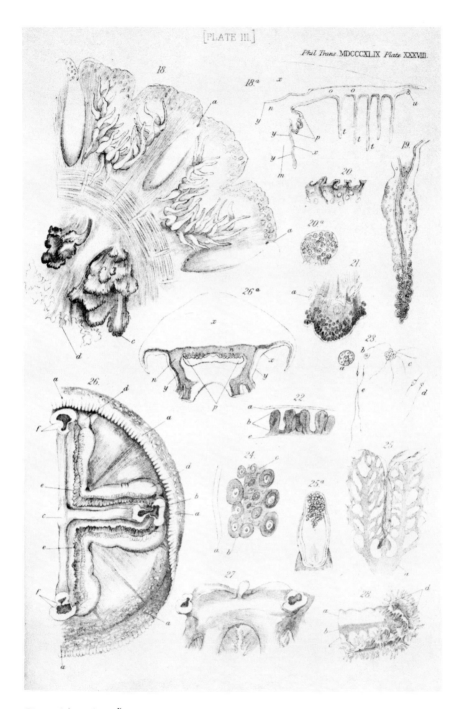

[PLATE III.]

Phil. Trans. MDCCCXLIX Plate XXXVIII.

Figure 1 (*continued*)

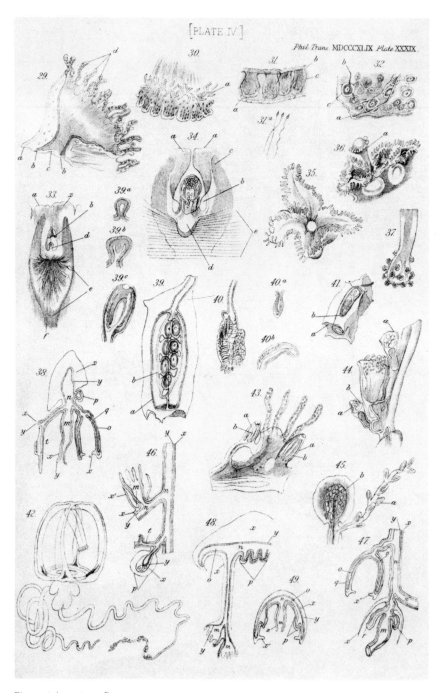

[PLATE. IV]

Phil. Trans. MDCCCXLIX. Plate XXXIX.

Figure 1 (*continued*)

DESCRIPTION OF THE PLATES.

PL. XXXVII. [Plate 2.]

Thaumantias —— ?

Fig. 1. Disc seen from above.
Fig. 1 *a*. Imaginary vertical section.
Fig. 2. Opening of the stomach into the canals seen from above.
Fig. 3. Marginal tentacles.
Fig. 4. Young generative organ.

Mesonema?

Fig. 5. Lateral view of the animal.
Fig. 5 *a*. Vertical section.
Fig. 6. View of a segment of the disc ; under surface.
    a. Buccal tentacles.
    b. Canals.
    c. Marginal membrane (20).
Fig. 7. A single buccal tentacle much magnified.
Fig. 8. A portion of the marginal canal with a tentacle and two marginal corpuscles.
Fig. 9. Portion of the marginal canal (*a*) with young tentacle (*b*), and a marginal vesicle containing two corpuscles, each enclosed within a delicate cell-wall.
Fig. 10. A marginal vesicle highly magnified ; the two corpuscles do not appear to have attained their full development, as they refract less, and the cell appears more opake.

Oceania —— ?

Fig. 11. Lateral view of the animal.
Fig. 11 *a*. Vertical section.
Fig. 12. Part of the under surface of the disc.
    a. Marginal membrane.
    b. Canals and generative organs.
    c. Common cavity.
Fig. 13. Part of the membrane surrounding the mouth.
Fig. 14. The edge of this much magnified.
Fig. 15. Part of the margin of the disc much enlarged.
    a. Marginal membrane.
    b. Canal and generative organs.
    c. Tentacles.
    d. Marginal corpuscles.
    e. Circular canal.
Fig. 16. Portion of the ovarium so folded as to have its inner membrane (*a*) outwards.
Fig. 17. Sectional view of the ovarium.
    a. Inner membrane.
    b. Outer membrane.
    c. Ovum.
    d. Germinal vesicle.
    e. Germinal spot.

PL. XXXVIII. [Plate 3.]

Phacellophora —— ?

Fig. 18. View of a segment of the under surface.
    a. Marginal vesicles.
    b. Tentacles in this individual very much shorter than usual.
    c. Ovary or testis.
    d. Buccal membrane.
Fig. 18 *a*. Vertical section.
Fig. 19. Tentacle.
Fig. 20. Portion of the buccal membrane.
Fig. 20 *a*. Round processes containing thread-cells scattered over its outer surface.
Fig. 21. Portion of the testis.
    a. Generative tentacles.

Figure 1 (*continued*)

Fig. 22. Sectional view of part of the testis.
  a. Outer membrane.
  b. Sperm-sacs.
  c. Inner membrane.
Fig. 23. Stages of development of the spermatozoa (45).
Fig. 24. Ovarium.
  a. Outer membrane.
  b. Ova.
  c. Inner membrane.
Fig. 25. Marginal vesicle from the under surface.
  a. Dilatation of the canal.
Fig. 25 a. Marginal vesicle and pedicle very much enlarged.

Rhizostoma mosaica.

Fig. 26. View of the under surface of the disc, the brachiferous plate being cut away.
  a. Marginal vesicles.
  b. Cut extremity of the suspending pillar of the brachiferous plate.
  c. Central crura.
  d. Lateral crura.
  e. Generative folds.
  f. Connecting membrane.
Fig. 26 a. Vertical section of the Rhizostoma.
Fig. 27. Side view of the brachiferous plate detached.

PL. XXXIX. [Plate 4.]

Rhizostoma mosaica.

Fig. 28. Extremity of one of the ultimate ramifications of the arms.
  a. Thick substance of the outer membrane.
  b. The central common canal.
  c. The lateral canals leading to the apertures.
  d. The fringes.
Fig. 29. Lateral view of one of the apertures much magnified.
  a. Thick outer membrane.
  b. Inner membrane.
  c. Lateral canal.
  d. Tentacles.
Fig. 30. Portion of the testis slightly magnified.
  a. Generative tentacles.
Fig. 31. Sectional view of testis much magnified.
  a. Outer membrane.
  b. Inner membrane.
  c. Sperm-sacs.
Fig. 31 a. Spermatozoa.
Fig. 32. Ovarium.
  a. Outer membrane.
  b. Inner membrane.
  c. Ova.
Fig. 33. Marginal vesicle, upper surface.
  a, b. Lobes connected by the arched membrane, f.
  c. Cæca of the canal f.
  d. Vesicle on its pedicle.
  e. Cordate depression.
Fig. 34. Marginal vesicle from below, much magnified.
  a a. Lobes.
  b. Inferior connecting membrane.
  c. Cæca.
  d. Elevation of the outer membrane.
  e. Muscular fibres.

Cephea ocellata.

Fig. 35. An aperture surrounded by its membrane.
Fig. 36. Portion of the extremity of an arm, with a young interbrachial tentacle (a).
Fig. 37. Extremity of one of the large interbrachial tentacles.

Figure 1 (*continued*)

Figure 1 (*continued*)

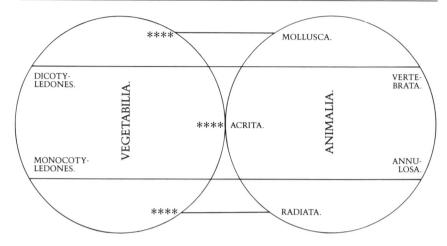

Figure 2.   General view of organised matter. [778, p. 212]

On its voyage, the *Rattlesnake* visited Sydney. Huxley's landings there had two noteworthy consequences: he met his future wife, and also encountered W. S. MacLeay, an entomologist who had emigrated to Australia. In *Horae Entomologicae* (778) of 1819, MacLeay had proposed a new system of classification, called "quinarian" or "circular." He aimed, he explained, to find connections between the structures of the animals and their manner of living; and that would entail a strict correlation between anatomy and physiology. He dreamt of founding a system which would combine the Cuverian zoological types and Leibnizian metaphysics with reminiscences of Plato in a united scheme of the whole of natural creation (895, p. 98). He thought that nature expressed a circular disposition, and that classification should take account of such a circularity. He therefore referred to a circular chain of beings and used circles for expressing the affinities detectable in the animal kingdom. Below is an example of his circular system (fig. 2).

My second example is his general classification of all animals, divided into five groups rather than Cuvier's traditional four (fig. 3). MacLeay's work shows the strong influence of the style of the *Naturphilosophie* and a strong Platonic bias. In fact, in the section which deals with the Annulosa, he proposed a table for them which has a particularly revealing footnote (fig. 4).

The number 5 in MacLeay's classification derives from notions of mathematical symmetry and harmony, rather than from zoological or empirical considerations. MacLeay claims that the series of affinities are parallel, and therefore that each series must have the same number of constituents, this number being five (581, p. 83). He was convinced

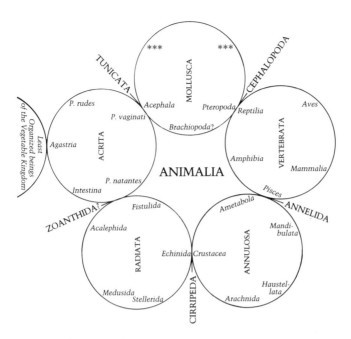

Figure 3. [778, p. 318]

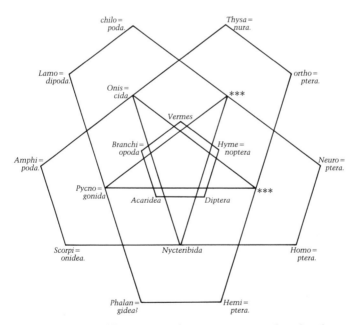

Figure 4. Nothing in natural history is, perhaps, more curious than that these analogies should be represented by a figure so strictly geometrical. One is almost tempted to believe that the science of the variation of animal structures may, in the end, come within the province of the mathematician. [778, p. 395]

that God was a mathematician, and that creation should therefore respect strictly mathematical rules. Huxley met MacLeay in 1848 (472, vol. 1, p. 41) and must have been deeply impressed by his senior colleague, for he communicated to Forbes in 1849: "I believe that there is a great law hidden in the "Circular system" if one could but get at it" (5, p. 34).

Huxley used MacLeay's system parsimoniously in his early papers; he cites MacLeay in respect of some personal favour and once as a scientific reference. In a report to the British Association of 1851, Huxley provides a scheme of the relations of the Radiata (fig. 5). Among Huxley's papers M. P. Winsor has discovered a much more detailed scheme that the scientist did not publish (fig. 6).

The fact that Huxley did not publish this scheme seems to me of some importance. Either he was not completely satisfied that MacLeay's system could be carried to such extremes, or he expected strong opposition from the scientific establishment, whom he was not inclined to displease. I have no hard evidence for either hypothesis. What is certain is that when he refers to MacLeay's system, Huxley does not seem greatly enchanted by his colleague's "mathematical rhapsody"; he seemed to have no great liking for its metaphysical basis. In fact, in a private note, he wrote: "The generalisations of the Circular System are for the most part true, but they are empirical, not ultimate laws" (HP 40.149).

MacLeay's system was extended by W. Swainson and revealed by L. Jenyns to the Philosophical Society of Cambridge in 1830 and 1831 (895, p. 98). Darwin was then in Cambridge engaged in collecting beetles and walking with Henslow—and doing other important things. We know that he took MacLeay's work very seriously, since in the Manuscript Room of Cambridge University Library some passages from *Horae Entomologicae* copied in 1838 by Darwin's valet, Covington, are preserved with notes made by Darwin himself (*Dar.* 71.128–38). In Darwin's catalogue of books, *Horae Entomologicae* is listed at no. 27 with the following comment: "MacLeay—Horae Entomologicae. On classification: very little, good sentence on analogy as distinct from affinity & on osculant group having few species" (*Dar.* 71.4).

Darwin is especially interested in the "osculant" groups, that is, those "occurring as it were at the point where the circles touch one another" (778, p. 37). Now, as we see from MacLeay's scheme (fig. 3), the cirripedes happened to be such an osculant group (778, p. 318). Darwin spent a long period of his scientific life working on the cirripedes (654; 655) and it is arguable that the study of these crustaceans had a considerable impact on his view of evolution (699, pp. 103–31).

Moreover, if we overlook the metaphysics and consider MacLeay's system from a purely technical point of view, we can see that his circles are to some extent compatible with Darwin's genealogical trees. In fact,

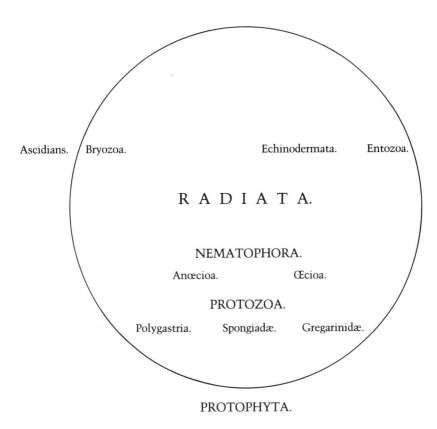

Ascidians. Bryozoa.   Echinodermata.   Entozoa.

R A D I A T A.

NEMATOPHORA.

Anœcioa.   Œcioa.

PROTOZOA.

Polygastria.   Spongiadæ.   Gregarinidæ.

PROTOPHYTA.

Figure 5.   [11, p. 80]

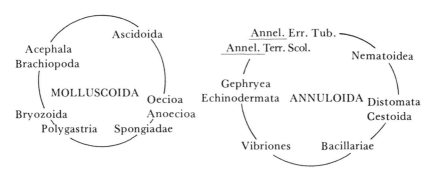

Ascidoida   Annel. Err. Tub.
Acephala   Annel. Terr. Scol.   Nematoidea
Brachiopoda
                                                     Gephryea
       MOLLUSCOIDA   Oecioa   Echinodermata ANNULOIDA Distomata
                               Anoecioa   Cestoida
Bryozoida
    Polygastria   Spongiadae
                                        Vibriones   Bacillariae

Figure 6.   [581, p. 94]

if we imagine cutting Darwin's tree through space rather than time, we obtain something like MacLeay's circles, in which the osculant groups represent the points of divergence in the tree.*

So far as Huxley is concerned, it is important to remark that he expressed sympathy for a system which later proved to be technically consistent with the Darwinian outlook, but rejected its metaphysics.

Von Baer and Embryology

In his early work in invertebrate morphology, Huxley came face to face with some fundamental theoretical problems relating closely to his search for "order" in nature—for some thread which would connect all the facts he had discovered and described and which would make sense of the affinities and relationships he had detected. Huxley's more mature solution to these theoretical problems was to adopt the concept of the "type." The problem of type and unity of plan had been very widely discussed by continental naturalists, and by Owen in Britain. As Rádl wrote:

Das Wort 'Plan' schwebte auf allen Lippen: Cuvier glaubte in der Tierwelt vier Pläne, Geoffroy einen einzigen gefunden zu haben, Goethe suchte einen einheitlichen Plan der Pflanzen, eine ideale Urpflanze, Decandolle gründete auf die "Symmetrie"-Lehre sein Pflanzensystem, Owen in England konstruierte ein schematisches Säugetier (Archetype wie er es nannte), Agassiz schreibt von einem Plane Gottes, der sich im Bau der Tiere verkörpert und ganz besonders waren es die deutschen Naturphilosophen, die sich in Erörterungen verloren über die Gedanken, welch zu ihnen aus der körperlichen Organisation der Tiere und der Pflanzen sprachen. [863, vol. 2, p. 22]

That Huxley used the concept of the type is in fact already clear from the analysis of the memoirs surveyed at the beginning of the chapter—but there are many ways of conceiving the type.

In *The Development of Darwin's Theory*, Dr. D. Ospovat puts forward a valuable analysis of trends in early nineteenth-century biology (823). Broadly speaking, Ospovat detects two different, conflicting ways of interpreting natural phenomena. On the one side stood the tradition of Cuvier, according to which there is no unity of type; his stress is on teleological adaptations. Whether the essence of Cuvier's view was teleology is arguable, but the point is that this is how the supporters of the rival view interpreted it. By the 1830s a number of British naturalists had repudiated what they saw as Cuvier's teleology. Referring instead to the works of the great embryologist K. E. von Baer, they began to develop an embryological understanding of the type concept.

---

*I am grateful to Dr. Sydney Smith, who drew my attention to this point.

Von Baer, Pander, and Rathke had underlined the importance of embryology to the understanding of nature. In 1825, Rathke discovered the gill slits of mammalian (866) and chick (865) embryos; the first volume of von Baer's masterly *Entwickelungsgeschichte der Thiere* was published in 1828 and the second in 1837 (596), and the *Schlussheft* appeared posthumously (864).

Von Baer's embryology is the nineteenth-century reply to the central problem of generation which had troubled previous groups of researchers, as J. Roger has shown with special reference to French research (869); moreover, the type concept came to be recognised as the major support for the notion of the "unity of plan." Von Baer lived in the period in which the *Naturphilosophie* was taking the German-speaking countries by storm (756). Yet the results of his enquiries are largely independent of any sympathy he may have had for the views of that highly speculative attitude to nature (796, pp. 64–65; 864, pp. 397–402): von Baer's research was based upon rigorous experiments.

Milne-Edwards was a convinced supporter of the use of embryology in classification; in a famous paper of 1844 (804a), which was partly translated into English four years later (804b), he claimed that, since embryos are more similar to each other than to the adult forms into which they grow, it is embryology which indicates the clearest features of the affinities we can discover:

Each animal experiences a variety of modifications, some which appertain to the particular species, while others are equally presented by a number, more or less large, of different animals; and the latter have a wider and wider scope, as they correspond chronologically to a more and more early part of the series of genetic phenomena. Moreover it is easy to show that it is the general tendency in nature to produce a correspondence between the primordial resemblances of animals under development, and the different degrees of zoological affinity exhibited when the species have completed their development. The modifications which are manifested successively in the constitution of the young, or germ, as it enlarges, determine successively its existence as a member of a particular order, class and family. I am far from believing in the identity of germs. But there is a resemblance, and this resemblance is close, as we approach the period of their origin. Hence it is that the embryogenic history of animals illustrates so fully and beautifully their natural relations. [804b, p. 71]

In his *Monographie des poissons du Vieux Rouge* (586) of 1844, Agassiz applied the results of embryology to palaeontology. He wanted to find the proper systematic place of the Devonian fish in order to demonstrate that the types, through the history of the earth; the animal classes, through the history of their families; and the embryos, through the stages of their development, go through the same phases, led by what he saw as the same "pensée créatrice." He believed that the fish of the Old Red Sandstone represented the embryological phase of the history of the fish type.

As Ospovat has shown (82£), von Baer's work was initially introduced to British audiences by Martin Barry, a Scottish physician who in 1836–37 published "On the Unity of Structure in the Animal Kingdom" (603), followed by W. B. Carpenter's *Principles of General and Comparative Physiology* of 1839 (639).

In 1853, Huxley translated the fundamental fifth *Scolium* of the *Entwickelungsgeschichte* into English. Huxley's translation appeared in *Scientific Memoirs,* a short-lived magazine initially edited by Richard Taylor, undersecretary of the Linnean Society, and later by Huxley, Tyndall, and Francis, which specialised in the memoirs of foreign scientists, with contributions by Becquerel, Carus, Ehrenberg, Berzelius, Gauss, Schleiden, Ohm, Liebig, Bunsen, J. Müller, Fresnel, Clausius, and Helmholtz (24).

Huxley explains in the short preface to his translation:

The present selections have therefore been made, and it is hoped that they embody all the important points of von Baer's doctrines. The translator will be more than gratified, if yet, during the lifetime of the venerable author, he should be the means of assisting to place in its proper position the reputation of one who had in the completest manner demonstrated the truth of the doctrine of Epigenesis three years before the delivery of Cuvier's *Leçons sur l'histoire des sciences naturelles* (in which he still advocates the Evolution theory); and who had long recognized development as the sole basis of zoological classification while in France Cuvier and Geoffroy St. Hilaire were embittering one another's lives with endless mere anatomical discussions and replications, and while in Germany the cautious study of nature was given up for the spinning of *Naturphilosophies* and other hypothetical cobwebs. [25, p. 176]

In von Baer's writings we can find many of the themes which deeply exercised Huxley. Animal forms must not be considered as uniserial developments from the lowest to the highest grade of "perfection"; embryology furnishes evidence that it is not true that the individual member of a group passes through stages characteristic of the lower animals. Eventually von Baer was able to formulate his famous law of development:

1. That the more general characteristics of a large group of animals appear earlier in their embryos than the more special characters. . . .
2. From the most general forms the less general are developed, and so on, until finally the most special arises. . . .
3. Every embryo of a given animal form, instead of passing through the other forms, rather becomes separated from them.

4. Fundamentally, therefore, the embryo of a higher form never resembles any other form, but only its embryo. [p. 214]

Von Baer recognised three stages in the process of embryological differentiation: primary, morphological, and histological, the latter being independent of cell theory and seen after the manner of Bichât. Basically, von Baer uses embryology to provide the criteria for his typology; all this is entirely accepted by Huxley.

Another of von Baer's main points was that fish and mammal start from a common point, thence diverging to follow distinct paths of development—the mammal therefore is not a "modified fish." Huxley was also prepared to follow von Baer here:

According to . . . the Theory of Progressive Development, the history of life, as a whole, in the past, is analogous to the history of each individual life in the present; and as the law of progress of every living creature now is from a less perfect to a more perfect, from a less complex to a more complex state—so the law of progress of living nature in the past was of the same nature; and the earlier forms of life were less complex, more embryonic than the later. In the general mind this theory finds ready acceptance, from the falling in with its popular notions, that one of the lower animals, e.g. a fish, is a higher one, e.g. a mammal, arrested in development; that it is, as it were, less trouble to make a fish than a mammal. [37, p. 301]

Huxley refers here to the views of J. F. Meckel, which both von Baer and he rejected. The idea of comparing the embryo of a higher animal with the adult forms of lower ones was widespread at the beginning of the nineteenth century, especially in the German-speaking countries. Between 1811 and 1821 Meckel enunciated the famous "law of parallelism":

The development of the individual organism obeys the same laws as the development of the whole animal series; that is to say, the higher animal, in its gradual evolution, essentially passes through the permanent organic stages which lie below it; a circumstance which allows us to assume a close analogy between the differences which exist between the diverse stages of development, and between each of the animal classes. [879, p. 93]

But Huxley points out "the extreme fallacy of this notion; the real law of development being, that the progress of a higher animal in development is not through the forms of the lower, but through forms which are common to both lower and higher: a fish, for instance, deviating as widely from the common Vertebrate plan as a mammal" (37, p. 304).

While supporting von Baer's concept of the embryological types, Huxley attacked the Cuvierian view of teleological adaptations in his 1856 lecture "On Natural History, as Knowledge, Discipline, and

Power" (46), entering into a controversy with Hugh Falconer, who defended Cuvier's viewpoint (445). Huxley emphasised that morphology demonstrates that the variety of living forms is modelled upon a very small number of plans or types (46, p. 306), as von Baer had proposed. He then attacked those who supported what he calls "utilitarian adaptations" (p. 307)—where "utilitarian" means purposive—including not only Cuvier but also Paley and the Natural Theologians. For them, Huxley argues, "the structure of living beings is, in the main, such as would result from the benevolent operation, under the conditions of the physical world, of an intelligence similar in kind, however superior in degree, to our own" (ibid.). But this is for Huxley patently false; natural history proves "that utilitarian adaptation to purpose is not the greatest principle worked out in nature, and that its value, even as an instrument of research, has been enormously overrated" (ibid.). This passage is of interest not only because it shows Huxley's rejection of Cuvier's (supposed) teleology, but also because it clearly declares Huxley's belief in the possibility of finding some "great principle" to account for the relationships detectable in nature. That great principle is of course von Baer's type concept; the lecture contains an incredible piece of Victorian rhetoric, whose meaning is simply that the harmony of nature can be understood only on the basis of von Baer's principle of the type:

Is it conceivable that the harmonious variation of a common plan which we find everywhere in nature serves any utilitarian purpose? that the innumerable varieties of antelopes, or frogs, of clupeoid fishes, of beetles, and bivalve mollusks, of polyzoa, of actinozoa, and hydrozoa, are adaptations to as many different kinds of life, and consequently varying physiological necessities? Such a supposition with regard to the three last, at any rate, would be absurd; the polyzoa, for instance, presenting a remarkable uniformity in mode of life and internal organization, while nothing can be more striking than the wonderful variety of their external shape and of the sculpture of their cells. If we turn to the vegetable world, we find in it one vast illustration of the same truth. Who has ever dreamed of finding an utilitarian purpose in the forms and colours of flowers, in the sculpture of pollen-grains, in the varied figures of the fronds of ferns? What "purpose" is served by the strange numerical relations of the parts of plants, the threes and fives of monocotyledons and dicotyledons? [p. 311]

Huxley not only championed von Baer's embryological type in his public statements, but also applied it in his actual scientific work, as all his memoirs concerning invertebrate morphology demonstrate. As he explained in 1856, it is the application of embryological results to the method of the type that the naturalist must follow in his enquiry:

For animals . . . like all living beings, not only *are*, but *become*; and it is within the limits of logical possibility, that the adult forms, anatomically similar, should be genetically different; that they should have arrived at a similar point by different roads. Before, then, we can affirm that two animals are constructed upon a common plan, or that two parts are homologous (which simply means that they are modifications of corresponding members of a common plan) we must be able to show that these parts or these animals, have passed through a corresponding series of developmental stages. It is the absence of this reference to development which is the vice of the ordinary works. [47, p. 432]

The two criteria for establishing homologies in the Medusae that we saw earlier are an example of the "embryological method," as E. S. Russell calls it (879). Huxley's researches on the molluscs provide further evidence. The most important memoir on this topic is "On the Morphology of the Cephalous Mollusca" (17) of 1853. It endeavours to give an account of certain general problems in the study of these animals, starting from their anatomical characteristics and introducing embryological considerations. We witness a further instance of Huxley's preference for commencing with a restricted question and moving to a problem of wider scope. In order to obtain a definite conception of the variety of molluscous forms, Huxley writes that he proposes

to set forth the structure of certain Heteropoda and Pteropoda; pelagic animals so transparent, that a perfect knowledge of the arrangement of their parts may be arrived at by simple inspection, without so much as interrupting a beat of their heart.

Afterwards I shall inquire how far the known laws of development account for these forms, and thence of what archetypal form they may be supposed to be modifications. [17, p. 153]

Huxley considers that the Heteropoda exhibit the furthest divergence in form from the cephalous mollusc (p. 170). He describes the organisation of the Heteropoda thus:

1. The intestine is bent dorsal, or towards the side on which the heart is placed. The visceral mass is situated below and behind the posterior portion of the alimentary canal; it may be called a postabdomen.
2. *Atlanta* is prosobranchiate; *Firoloïdes* is neither opistobranchiate nor prosobranchiate.
3. The foot consists of three parts, the propodium, mesopodium and metapodium in Atlanta; but of these the mesopodium disappears in *Firoloïdes*, and the metapodium becomes very rudimentary.
4. The auditory organs appear to be connected with the cephalic ganglia.
5. The animals are unisexual. [p. 164]

As far as the Pteropoda are concerned:

1. The intestine is bent towards the ventral side; the visceral mass is placed above, and in front of the anus; it may be called an abdomen.
2. Some Pteropoda are prosobranchiate, others intermediate, others opisttobranchiate.

3. The foot consists of four parts: three, the propodium, mesopodium, and metapodium, such as are found in the Heteropoda; and a fourth, the epipodium,
not found in the Heteropoda. All these parts (propodium?) may be distinguished in *Pneumodermon* and *Euribia*, while all but the epipodium and
metapodium have disappeared in *Cleodora*.
4. The auditory organs are connected with the pedal ganglia.
5. The Pteropoda are hermaphrodite. [p. 170]

Once these characteristics have been established, it is possible to identify the type of the whole group. The proper way to do this is by reference
to the development of the Heteropoda and Pteropoda (ibid.). Huxley
claims that, notwithstanding the lack of direct knowledge of the development of the two groups, the wide range of information in his possession on the development of other molluscs can virtually guarantee correct conclusions on these groups: "If from these data certain general
propositions can be established, it will, I think, be perfectly fair to make
these propositions the basis whence deductively to explain and account
for facts of organisation whose absolute genesis is not known" (pp.
170–71).

Now, a knowledge of the laws of development of a more general
group can throw light on a particular problem. Thus, the study of the
embryology of the molluscs enables scientists to detect two great modifications in their type:

the one characterised by the development of an *abdomen*, and a consequent
neural flexure of the intestine; the other marked by the development of a *post-
abdomen*, and a consequent *haemal* flexure of the intestine.

But these modifications of anatomical structure exactly correspond with
those which I have already demonstrated, upon anatomical grounds, to occur in
the Pteropoda and Heteropoda; and I trust I am not overstepping the bounds of
legitimate analogy in assuming that the anatomical fact of a neural flexure
indicates the embryological development of an abdomen; that of a haemal flexure, the development of a post-abdomen; and that therefore the Pteropoda fall
into the same category with the Cephalopoda and Pulmonata; the Heteropoda
into that of the Pectinibranchiata, Tectibranchiata, and Nudibranchiata. [p. 172]

Along these lines, it is finally possible to establish the type (here called
"archetype," following Owen) of the cephalous molluscs:

The Archetype of the Cephalous Mollusca then, it may be said, has a bilaterally
symmetrical head and body. The latter possesses on its neural surface a peculiar
locomotive appendage, the foot; which consists of three portions from before
backwards, viz., the propodium, the mesopodium and the metapodium, and
bears upon its lateral surface a peculiar expansion, the epipodium. [p. 177]

Again, it is embryology which provides the crucial evidence: "In the
Cephalous Mollusca *it is the haemal side of the body which is first*

developed. In the Articulata and Vertebrata it is the *neural side which first makes its appearance"* (ibid.).

Huxley's interpretation of von Baer's view of distinct types is a "radical" one: after pointing out that the type of the molluscs can be compared with those of the vertebrates and articulates, he states that "the differences between the three archetypes are so sharp and marked as to allow no real transition between them" (ibid.). Moreover:

> If, however, all Cephalous Mollusks, *i.e.*, all Cephalopoda, Gasteropoda and Lamellibranchiata, be only modifications by excess or defect of the parts of a definite archetype, then, I think, it follows as a necessary consequence that no anamorphism takes place in this group. There is no progression from a lower to a higher type, but merely a more or less complete evolution of one type.
>
> It may indeed be a matter of very grave consideration whether true anamorphosis ever occurs in the whole animal kingdom. If it do, then the doctrine that every natural group is organized after a definite archetype, a doctrine which seems to me as important for zoology as the theory of definite proportions for chemistry, must be given up. [p. 192]

Huxley's use here of the word *anamorphism* was quite recent in scientific literature as a synonym of anamorphosis (progression from a lower to a higher type). The word *evolution* is used in its purely embryological sense, that is, the enlargement and development of some parts during the life of the embryo. Here Huxley goes beyond von Baer; he in fact denies that there can be *any* transitions from one type to the other, modifications occurring *only* within the type. This implies that there is no continuity between the different types of animal organisation, a view Huxley was to retain after 1859 in respect of the vertebrate and invertebrate types. Von Baer had simply postulated the existence of four major types recognisable through their divergent modes of development. Huxley's view here approaches that of Cuvier, though as we have seen he opposed Cuvier's other central concept of "purposive adaptation." One might say that Huxley's view is a radical reinterpretation of Cuvier in the light of von Baer.

It is important to emphasise that in Huxley's mind the type concept has a purely empirical meaning, simply denoting a form which summarises and embodies the characteristics of all kinds of, say, molluscs—it is a general proposition. For Huxley the type is merely a convenient pattern; in this way he freed himself from any specific commitment to Platonic metaphysics. He explains his idea of the type (archetype) as follows:

> In using this term, I make no reference to any real or imaginary "ideas" upon which animal forms are modelled. All that I mean is the conception of a form embodying the most general propositions that can be affirmed respecting the

Cephalous Mollusca, standing in the same relation to them as the diagram to a geometrical theorem, and like it, at once imaginary and true. [pp. 176–7]

Thus, Huxley was committed to a basically Platonic concept without adhering to a properly Platonic philosophy. One might venture to say that here Huxley is either a bad Platonist or a bad empiricist—or both. Whatever one's opinion on this point may be, doubtless Huxley's lack of sympathy for the Platonic interpretation of the type helped him later to accept descent through *actual* modifications, but certainly, before joining the evolutionists, he found himself in an ambiguous and somewhat uncomfortable theoretical position.

Another major proponent of the type concept in Britain was of course Richard Owen; but there are clear differences in the manner in which he and Huxley presented the notion. Although they both agreed on the *use* of the type concept, they had different views of its *meaning*. Owen's major contribution to theoretical biology, *On the Nature of Limbs* (*834*), is entirely founded upon the Platonic interpretation of the type:

To what natural laws or secondary causes the orderly succession and progression of such organic phenomena may have been committed we are as yet ignorant. But if, without derogation of the Divine power, we may conceive the existence of such ministers, and personify them by the term "Nature", we learn from the past history of our globe that she has advanced with slow and stately steps guided by the archetypal light, amidst the wreck of worlds, from the first embodiment of the Vertebrate idea under its old Ichthyc vestment, until it became arrayed in the glorious garb of the Human form. [p. 86]

The different attitudes shown by the two scientists towards Platonism may help us to understand why Huxley was to sympathise with Darwin's interpretation of evolution, whereas Owen was to oppose it.

The concept of homology was one of Owen's major contributions to natural science. According to Mivart, writing in 1870, Owen's definition of homology had been "a close resemblance of parts as regards their relation to surrounding parts, to whatever cause that resemblance may be due, whether genetic or otherwise" (*806*, p. 115). But he goes on to say:

With regard to the question, What here is "covered by the term homology over and above homogeny?" . . . it may be replied that it is a complex correspondence between parts as to their relative positions, according to a certain line of thought, and independently of their mode of origin; in other words, conformity to type. This answer will, I know, be distasteful to some; but I contend that it is a very rational answer for all that. It is true that types have none but an ideal existence, that types, *as types*, are not real, objective entities; but that is . . . no reason for refusing to recognise their ideal existence and their objective realisation in individuals. [pp. 117–18]

The Platonic concept of types having an ideal existence separated from the contingent observed facts is here clearly stated and referred by Mivart to Owen (see also *810*). It is important to emphasise that, all things considered, Owen's view of the type is more consistent, albeit hopelessly "retrograde," than that held by Huxley, which however proved to be more adaptable to the trends of natural science after 1859.

Richard Owen: Villain of the Piece

Fair Play in Science

The relationship between Huxley and Owen went from bad to worse: and Owen, at least in the view that Huxley, Darwin, and their friends came to have of him, is the villain of the piece.

In fact, Richard Owen deserves serious consideration as one of the most, if not the most, influential naturalists in Britain in the years immediately prior to the publication of the *Origin of Species,* although he was not as good as he thought and, as E. S. Russell suggests (*879,* p. 102), most of his views were derivative. Although he was an outstanding anatomist—to whom we owe the first clear distinction between *analogy* and *homology* (*832a,* p. 374, p. 379), a distinction of fundamental importance in modern biology—his reputation both then and now was spoiled by the manner of his opposition to Darwin and his friends, in which personal pettiness overshadowed his scientific competence.

Owen's career before the 1850s was a brilliant series of scientific successes and public recognitions. He was established as the highest authority in most fields of natural science; but in the early 1850s he compromised his authority and reputation in a series of unfortunate controversies with the young Huxley and the scientific *nouvelle vague.* In all those controversies, Owen was shown to be wrong not only on general interpretations but even on matters of observational detail.

Huxley had at first a few coldly polite contacts with Owen. Owen wrote a couple of testimonials for Huxley for chairs to which the young scientist unsuccessfully applied. In one case Huxley had to badger him for a testimonial which he had promised but had delayed in writing (*HP* 23.247; 17 Nov. 1852). Owen's testimonial for a chair in Toronto is not especially enthusiastic:

I have much pleasure in bearing testimony to the high qualifications of Thomas Henry Huxley, Esq., F.R.S., for the duties of a Professorship of Natural History. During the Surveying Voyage of Captain Stanley, R.N., on the coasts of Australia and New Guinea, Mr. Huxley, one of the Medical Officers of the Survey, distinguished himself by the zeal and success with which he prosecuted his observations on the form, structure and habits of the rare animals of those seas; and the subsequent descriptions with which he has enriched the Transactions of the Royal and Linnean Society, attest his learning to be equal with his skill as an original observer. [HP 31.68 (72)]

Darwin's testimonial for the same chair is the standard polite statement we might expect from one Victorian gentleman who does not know much about another, so brief and vague that it could hardly have helped him either: "I have much pleasure in expressing my opinion from the high character of your published contributions to science, and from the course of your studies during your long voyage, that you are excellently qualified for a Professorship in Natural History" (HP 31.68 [70]). Indeed, Darwin admitted his ignorance of Huxley's work in a letter to Hooker: "You ask about Huxley: he has sent me his memoir [on the Cephalous Mollusca]. Thanks to you for it. I really do not know enough of outward form and anatomy of the mollusca to appreciate the paper" (Dar. 114.126; 7 March 1855). The testimonials provided by G. Allman, W. B. Carpenter, and especially Forbes reveal further how little Darwin yet knew about Huxley. Forbes was Huxley's first mentor, the man who had secured his election to the Royal Society at the early age of twenty-six. In his testimonial, Forbes writes that the researches conducted during the voyage of the *Rattlesnake* "have secured for their author a high place among the naturalists of Europe" (HP 31.68 [71]).

Only one letter (OP 15.496), in which Huxley informs Owen of Edward Forbes's death, is preserved in the Owen Papers at the British Museum (Natural History) of London. It is feared that the material suffered somewhat from the attentions of Owen's grandson, author of the rather unreliable *Life of Richard Owen* (846).

The irreparable personal breach between Huxley and Owen occurred in 1857, when Owen's name appeared in the Medical Directory as "Professor of Comparative Anatomy and Palaeontology" at the School of Mines, Huxley's post. Huxley indignantly wrote to John Churchill, the compiler of the directory:

In your valuable "Medical Directory" I observe at the name 'Owen, Richard' the title 'Professor of Comparative Anatomy and Palaeontology, Government School of Mines'.

Mr Owen holds no appointment whatever at the Govt. School of Mines, and as I am the Professor of General Natural History (which includes Comparative Anatomy and Palaeontology) in that Institution you will observe that the statement referred to is calculated to do me injury. You will therefore not think me unreasonable in requesting to know on what authority you ascribe to Mr Owen the office in question. A ready answer will oblige. [HP 12.194]

Churchill replied that the "authority" was Owen himself (*HP* 12.195).

It was relatively easy for Huxley to defeat Owen, thereby undermining his influence in the scientific circles of the time. Once Owen's reputation had been damaged, Huxley and his friends began to gain control of the British scientific world. His friendship with the prince consort notwithstanding, Owen spent the last years of his long life in progressive intellectual isolation. He maintained a measure of authority in scientific circles, and was approached throughout his life for scientific advice, but he never had a real disciple—not even Mivart. Even E. Hitchcock, an American palaeontologist who claimed in 1865 and 1866 to be a fervent disciple of Owen (*OP* 15.169, 173), admitted in 1885 that "my line of work is quite different from yours" (*OP* 15.174).

One controversy in particular between Owen and Huxley casts light on the personalities and motives of the two rivals. Owen had dealt with the structure of the Terebratulidae, which are inarticulate brachiopods. In "On the Anatomy of the Brachiopoda of Cuvier" (*829*) of 1835 and in *Lectures on the Comparative Anatomy and Physiology of the Invertebrate Animals* (*832a*) of 1843, Owen claims to be able to detect an anus in the Terebratulidae. In 1854 Huxley published "Contributions to the Anatomy of the Brachiopoda," in which he propounded a diametrically opposed view; in the following passage Huxley refers to *Rhynchonella psittacea* and *Waldheimia flavescens* (now called *Magellania flavescens* [*707*, p. 1406]), two species belonging to the Terebratulidae:

The result of my own repeated examinaton of *Rhynchonella psittacea* and of *Waldheimia flavescens* is—1. that the intestine does not terminate on the right side of the mantle as Professor Owen describes it, but in the middle line, as Mr. Hancock describes it in *Waldheimia*, while in *Rhynchonella* it inclines, after curving upwards, to the *left* side; and 2. that there is no anus at all, the intestine terminating in a rounded caecal extremity, which is straight and conical in *Waldheimia*, curved to the left side and enlarged in *Rhynchonella*. [*32*, p. 326]

In the same memoir, Huxley points out other mistakes in Owen's description of the circulatory system. The whole description of the ventricle seems to him incorrect, nor can he detect "the delicate membrane of the venous sinuses" to which Owen refers (p. 330). Huxley agrees instead with the results of the enquiries performed by the distinguished zoologist Albany Hancock, who wrote to him in April 1854: "I am glad to learn that you have arrived at similar conclusions to those I am inclined to adopt respecting two or three disputed points in the anatomy of Terebratula" (*HP* 17.271; see *721; 722*).

In the reprint of his *Lectures* of 1855, Owen reaffirmed his view of 1843, dismissing Huxley's arguments rather scornfully. In the Terebratulidae, he claimed:

the intestine is short, straight, and is continued downwards and a little back-wards, in a line with the pyloric part of the stomach to the interspace between the attachments of the adductores longi and cardinales to the ventral valve, where the minute vent opens into the pallial cavity. [*832b*, p. 493]

Mr. Huxley has been unable to find this vent, and describes the anal end of the intestine as imperforate. There may be blindness somewhere, but I think not at the termination of the intestine of *Terebratula*, any more than in *Orbicula* and *Lingula*. [p. 493n]

W. B. Carpenter drew Huxley's attention to this issue in a letter sent on 16 July 1855, which contains certain unpleasant remarks on Owen:

I do not want necessarily to spoil your happiness but after a consultation with Busk, I have determined to ask you—if you have seen Owen's new edition [of the *Lectures*]. If you have, I need say no more, as *you* will be the best judge of what your honour demands. If you have not, we think you ought immediately to have your attention directed to what this *facile princeps* says about you, in order that, if you wish to call him out, you may do so *at once*, rather than after the honey-moon is over, when you may have Mrs Huxley a disconsolate vidder, to say nothing of any other little consequence.

Putting aside many other little spitefulnesses he avers "There may be blind-ness somewhere, but not I think at the termination of the intestine of *Tere-bratula*".

Truly I think our friend is improving: I do not think he has ever said anything so smart before. Now I think the best proof you can give of your full possession of eyesight, will be to put a bullet into some fleshy part of your antagonist, without doing him mortal damage. If you are disposed to *go out*, I will be your second, unbellicose as I am.

But if you prefer a milder course, and would like to employ a spare hour or two during the honeymoon in giving him *tit for tat*, I shall be very well pleased to hand him to your tender mercies. Busk and I *roared* over his absurdities, which he had the face to put forward as a representation of the state of British Science in 1855. What *will* the Continentals think of this? [*HP* 12.78]

The reading of this letter prompts some reflections. First of all, it seems that Huxley and his friends were prepared to engage in inter-necine strife for scientific power in Britain. This group, including in the first rank John Tyndall and Joseph Hooker, were prepared, and indeed inclined, to attack Owen on any possible ground in order to discredit him. And as we have seen, Owen gave them many good opportunities.

Tyndall was the last to break with Owen, in 1877. He was a physicist and therefore had little to do with Owen; yet he represented Huxley's *alter ego* in his field. Huxley, Tyndall, and their friends can be cate-gorised as the scientific "Young Turks," ready to fight the aging sultan ruthlessly and relentlessly in the achievement of their goal—the re-placement of the old science, represented by Owen, with their own. But what new proposal for science could they advance? Albeit uneasy with most of Owen's theoretical assumptions, Huxley had nothing original with which to replace them. Throughout the fifties this awkwardness increased, following a series of discoveries and enquiries which repeatedly contradicted Owen. Yet the Young Turks were unable to provide a radically new approach to the understanding of living beings. The inevitable result was philosophical paralysis, an uncomfortable disease; in the long run it might have meant defeat, since scientists usually prefer bad theory to no theory at all. It is not surprising, therefore, that Huxley saluted with unconcealed enthusiasm Darwin's alternative comprehensive view of natural phenomena, published at the very end of the 1850s—a view whose details he could not even wholeheartedly endorse (see chapter 2). Had Darwin not published, Huxley would still have been regarded as one of the most accomplished zoologists in Europe, but Owen would probably have retained much of his power and influence, his errors and his disingenuousness notwithstanding.

Huxley, a self-made man, found the beginning of his career very hard and had to struggle to reach the top in Victorian scientific circles. Richard Owen, another self-made man, clearly saw in him a threat to his preeminent position. And that there was an element of careerism in the young Huxley, nobody can deny.

It is easy to make mistakes in zoology, as in most human activities, and to draw erroneous conclusions concerning structures. Any textbook of zoology shows that in the *Terebratula* affair, Huxley was right: *Waldheimia* and *Rhynchonella* have no anus (see *663; 664; 874*); on the other hand, articulate brachiopods, such as *Lingula*, do have an anus (see *707*, p. 1382n; *828*). But which of the contenders was right is of secondary importance. The real point is whether Owen was entitled to maintain his original stance in the face of Huxley's criticism, according to the knowledge of the time, or whether he dismissed Huxley's point out of hand, resting on the confidence of his own authority. Biologists at that time had to rely on optical microscopes, and the microtome was not yet in use. In such conditions it would be reasonable to suppose that it is easier not to see existing structures than to see nonexistent ones. Anybody conversant with zoology who disposes of some specimen of *Waldheimia* or *Rhynchonella* (rare and costly animals) could dissect it and observe it using an optical microscope. The disinterested observer would soon reach Huxley's conclusions. Owen obviously failed to take the criticism of his junior colleague seriously. He either lied or persisted in seeing what he wanted or expected to see.

Fair play in science, and the candid admission of one's mistakes, are of vital importance. Owen's reprehensible behaviour casts a shadow over his reputation visible even in a time less given to moral stricture than the Victorian age. Nor was this by any means the only example of intellectual cheating performed by this pillar of established science. We

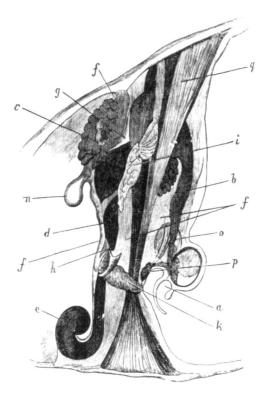

Figure 7. *Rhynchonella psittacea,* viewed in profile; the lobes of the mantle and the pedicle being omitted.
a. mouth; *b.* esophagus; *c.* stomach and liver; *d.* intestine; *e.* imperforate rectum; *f.* mesentery; *g.* gastro-parietal bands; *h.* ilio-parietal bands; *i.* superior "heart"; *k.* inferior "heart"; *l.* genital bands; *m.* openings of pallial sinuses; *n.* pyriform vesicle; *o.* sac at the base of the arm; *p.* ganglion; *q.* adductors. [32, p. 327]

have seen how he had advertised himself as holding a post which actually belonged to Huxley. Much later, in 1877, Sir William Flower complained to Huxley that Owen in his *Researches on the Fossil Remains of the Extinct Mammals of Australia* had reproduced certain plates he himself had published in the *Philosophical Transactions of the Royal Society* without acknowledgment; an unpardonable transgression. As Flower wrote, Owen's was "a gross discourtesy to the [Royal] Society. . . . I think the council should not pass it over in silence . . . a most dangerous precedent will be established" (*HP* 16.120 [121–22]).

The Vertebrate Skull

In 1854, following the death of E. Jamieson, Huxley's friend and mentor Edward Forbes moved from London to a professorial chair in Edinburgh, and Huxley had the chance to replace him at the School of Mines in

Jermyn Street. On 30 July 1854 Huxley wrote to his fiancée:

I was appointed yesterday to a post of £200 a year. It has all come in the strangest way. I told you how my friend Forbes had been suddenly called away to Edinburgh, and that I had suddenly taken his duties—sharp work it has been I can tell you these summer months, but it is over and done satisfactorily. Forbes got £500 a year, £200 for a double lectureship, £300 for another office. I took one of the lectureships, which would have given me £100 a year only, and another man was to have the second lectureship and the other office in question. It was so completely settled a week ago that I had written to the President of the Board of Trade who makes the appointment, accepting mine, and the other man had done the same. Happily for me, however, my new colleague was suddenly afflicted with a sort of moral colic, an absurd idea that he could not perform the duties of his office, and resigned it. The result is that a new man has been appointed to the office he left vacant, while the lectureship was offered to me. Of course I took it, and so in the course of a week I have seen my paid income doubled. [472, vol. 1, p. 118]

These fortunate circumstances had two effects on Huxley's life, one personal, the other professional: in 1855 he was able to marry his betrothed; and he was constrained to immerse himself in palaeontology, his declared lack of interest in that discipline notwithstanding (p. 143).

One of the early consequences of that move was that shortly before the publication of the *Origin of Species*, Huxley again crossed swords with Owen, this time in respect of the theory of the vertebrate skull. Owen considered the skull to be an expanded portion of the vertebral column; that is, the skull is only a series of expanded vertebrae, the brain being the anterior part of the nerve mass.

This theory had originally been formulated by Goethe as early as 1790, although he did not publish his data until 1803. It was Lorenz Oken who, after another publication in 1803 by Burdin, consolidated and extended the theory, in 1807. The theory of the vertebrate skull is a logical consequence of that tenet of the *Naturphilosophie* which asserts the repetition and multiplication of the parts within the organism (879, p. 94), just as the Meckel-Serres law derived from the other tenet, which asserts the existence of a parallel between the stages of individual development and the steps in the scale of beings. An interesting development of the theory was due to Carus who, in perfect Platonic fashion, took it as a good example of the "geometry of the skeleton" (879, p. 98). According to Carus, the sphere was the prototype of all organisms, while all other structures were formed through the operation of polar forces which divided and multiplied the sphere. As Russell explains:

In the course of development the sphere may change, by expansion into an egg-shaped body, or by contraction into a crystalline form, the changes due to expansion being typical of living things, those due to contraction being typical of dead. At the surface of the primitive living sphere is developed the protective *der-*

matoskeleton, which naturally takes the shape of a hollow sphere; round the digestive cavity which is formed in the living sphere is developed the *splanchnoskeleton*; round the nervous system (which is, as it were, the animal within the animal) is developed the *neuroskeleton*. All skeletal formations belong to one or other of these systems. [879, p. 98]

Carus's intention was to discover "rational" laws of nature far deeper than the empirically detectable laws.

There was no agreement among the supporters of the vertebral theory of the skull on how many vertebrae the skull consisted of: Oken thought there were four, Goethe six. To Owen, the vertebral theory of the skull was a corollary of his vertebral theory of the skeleton (833). In 1848 he described the vertebrate skeleton as consisting of a series of segments—the vertebrae. For him a vertebra was "one of those segments of the endo-skeleton which constitute the axis of the body, and the protecting canals of the nervous and vascular trunks" (833, p. 81).

Von Baer and J. Müller were supporters of the vertebral theory, and Rathke changed his mind from time to time; Karl Vogt made an all-out attack on it in 1842 (914). In his criticism Vogt used embryological arguments which in his opinion showed the inconsistency of the viewpoint he was opposing.

Huxley's paper of 1858 on this topic (64) is a synthesis of all the debates of the preceding years. Again, Huxley showed the effectiveness of his favourite "embryological method," which enables the scientist to trace back

skull and vertebral column to their earliest embryonic states and [to determine] the identity of parts by their developmental relations. . . . The study of the gradations of structure presented by a series of living beings may have the utmost value in suggesting homologies, but the study of development alone can finally demonstrate them. [64, p. 541]

The embryological method had been applied to the vertebral theory by Reichert, who in 1838 had obtained an embryonic type for the vertebrate skull based on three cranial vertebrae and their arches:

	Base	Sides	Top
First vertebra	Presphenoid	Orbitosphenoid	Frontals
Second vertebra	Basisphenoid	Alisphenoid	Parietals
Third vertebra	Basioccipital	Exoccipitals	Supraoccipitals

[879, p. 148] [867]

Huxley's approach to the question of the vertebrate skull follows Rathke's comparative embryology and compares the skulls of men, sheep, turtles, and carps. He shows that all skulls of the vertebrate animals are built upon a common plan and asks:

Are all vertebrate skulls constructed upon one and the same plan? . . . Is such a plan, supposing it to exist, identical with that of the vertebral column? But if propositions of this generality can be enunciated with regard to all bony vertebrate skulls, it is needless to seek for further evidence of their unity of plan. These propositions are the expression of that plan, and might, if one so pleased, be thrown into a diagrammatic form. There is no harm in calling such a convenient diagram the "Archetype" of the skull, but I prefer to avoid a word whose connotation is fundamentally opposed to the spirit of modern science. [p. 571]

The last sentence provides us with further evidence that Huxley was conscious of the theoretical difference between the empirical use of the type concept and its metaphysical interpretation, as in Owen's "Archetype."

As Vogt had proposed, Huxley believed that the study of the embryological development of the vertebrates shows that the vertebral theory of the skull is wrong:

Thus, I conceive, the study of the mode in which the skulls of vertebrate animals are developed, demonstrates the great truth which is foreshadowed by a careful and comprehensive examination of the gradations of form which they present in their adult state; namely that they are all constructed upon one plan, that they differ, indeed, in the extent to which this plan is modified, but that all these modifications are foreshadowed in the series of conditions through which the skull of any one of the higher *Vertebrata* passes.

But if these conclusions be correct, the first problem I proposed to you—are all vertebrate skulls constructed upon a common plan?—is solved affirmatively. . . . Is this plan the same as that of a spinal column? [p. 578]

The answer to this question is negative, and "it may be right to say, that there is a primitive identity of structure between the spinal or vertebral column and the skull; but it is no more true that the adult skull is a modified vertebral column, than it would be, to affirm that the vertebral column is a modified skull" (p. 585).

This memoir is one of the clearest Huxley ever wrote. It focuses on the essentials, the arguments it supports are carefully developed, and even though the target is Owen, the vehemence of the controversy is kept in the background, while the core of Huxley's attitude to morphology before 1859 is satisfactorily revealed—the development of the vertebrate cranium shows that "there is a general plan or primordial type which is manifested in the highest forms most clearly in their earliest development—an embryological archetype therefore" (*879*, p. 161). That was the grand truth taught by von Baer.

Huxley in the Fifties

An Overview

A review of the most important events and scientific encounters of Huxley's early career reveals some of the principal characteristics of his behaviour. His work in invertebrate morphology—in particular his contribution to the study of the coelenterates, and his clarification of the issues of the alternation of generations and animal individuality—shows from the start his interest in finding and analysing data of general consequence, an approach which ensured the significance of his early memoirs. His clashes with Owen reveal his willingness to do battle even with the mighty, when he was confident that his case was strong and clear enough. In terms of both scientific investigation and controversy, one of the ancillary results of his (enforced) move into vertebrate palaeontology, following his appointment of the School of Mines, was his contribution to the debates concerning the vertebrate skull.

Huxley was a "thinking man's" scientist, with a keen interest in—and firm views about—the philosophical context of the scientific endeavour: his obsession with theory expressing the "order of nature" (which doubtless partly motivated his enthusiasm for data of wide significance); and his insistence, in a context of creationist, mathematical, and Platonic scheme-building, on empirical method and theory, retaining only the empirical content or interpretation of notions of extrascientific provenance. These concerns clearly underlie his quest for a broad empirical principle to guide the investigation and understanding of organic phenomena; we have seen in that connection his adoption of the type concept and the embryological method, principally from von Baer.

A useful summary of his outlook in the fifties is provided by the *Explanatory Preface to the Catalogue of the Palaeontological Collection in the Museum of Practical Geology* (130; not in fact published until 1865). The second section of this work, entitled "Brief Exposition of Certain Principles of Natural History," delineates—with characteristic Huxleyan clarity—the essence of his theoretical positions.

He begins with the question of the principles underlying classification: "The most important of all the generalizations of natural history . . . is the law that all animals and plants, however infinitely various their forms may seem to be, are, in reality, constructed upon a very few plans" (p. 129). The evidence he adduces in support of this is purely anatomical; and he wishes to emphasise the strictly empirical nature of these "plans" as the basis of classification: "It is most important, however, not to form a wrong idea as to the real import of these "common plans." We must regard them simply as devices by which we render more clear and intelligible to our own minds the great truth that the

THE MAKING OF A ZOOLOGIST

parts of living bodies are associated together according to certain definite laws" (p. 131). By "law" is meant constant correlation. We may not
be able to account for these observed correlations; but their inex-
plicability does not vitiate their observable reliability as criteria of classification (p. 133). What emerges on this basis is a "natural classification" of groups and subvenient smaller divisions.

Having introduced the notion of the "type"—"In every group there is
some average form . . . around which the rest seem to arrange themselves. . . . Such a form is commonly called the *type* of the group" (p.
134)—he goes on to identify the five great plans or subkingdoms (Protozoa, Coelenterata, Vertebrata, Mollusca, Annulosa) by reference to
their "typical forms." Among the criteria by which the Vertebrata are
distinguished, Huxley includes embryological evidence:

In the development of the vertebrate embryo, a longitudinal groove appears in
the plate-like rudiment of the body . . . and plates grow up on each side of the
groove, eventually uniting together above, to form that spinal canal and skull
cavity, in which the central nervous system of the vertebrate animal is always
contained. [p. 137]

What follows is an analysis of the classes of the various subkingdoms,
again on the basis of a combination of their anatomical and embryological characters. But he wishes the import of the embryological evidence
to be clear:

There is a current impression that the lower animals correspond with the embryonic conditions of the higher. . . . This notion, however, is entirely incorrect. . . . [It] rests upon a misunderstanding of an undoubted fact, namely, that
there is a time in the development of each when all members of a subkingdom
resemble one another very closely. . . . Animals in their youngest condition
have, for a longer or shorter time, a similar form, from which each diverges to
take its special configuration. [p. 146]

Having thus encapsulated in a few pages the elements of the theoretical apparatus he had adopted, principally from von Baer, Huxley proceeds (pp. 146–57) to comment on the current understanding of distribution, inheritance, and the concept of species. In contrast to the
confidence of the opening pages of the work, his manner here reveals the
felt want of a general theory. His commentary applies some basic logical
considerations to the concept in question with his usual clarity, but
does not seem to be leading anywhere.

Thus, having suggested a relation between north-south distribution
and climate, he soon leaves east-west distribution hanging in the air as
"facts connected with distribution, the cause of which is by no means so
obvious" (p. 148); and goes on to lament the fact that current under-
standings of aquatic distribution do not permit scientists to determine

"at what depth living animals can no longer exist, nor even to trace the influence of depth in modifying their forms" (p. 149). His conclusions are:

> That all animals are adapted to the conditions in which they live is a truism, for if they were not so adapted, they would not live, but die; but the strange fact is, that we do not always find animals in those conditions for which they are adapted. . . .
>
> The commonest facts in distribution, therefore, teach us that it is never safe to apply conclusions based on the investigation of a limited area, however large, to the animal inhabitants of the rest of the world. . . . It is not understood why some genera are well nigh universal in their distribution, others limited in their area. [pp. 150–51]

He then proceeds to summarise the argument between those who believe "that all living beings were created as we find them" and those who believe "that all living things are the result of the gradual modification of one or more primitive forms" (p. 152). He bluntly attacks the intrusion of "passion and *odium theologicum*" into the dispute, and declares that "the assumption of creative acts being in reality nothing more than a grandiloquent way of expressing our ignorance of the real connexion of the phenomena and our incompetence to conceive their origination, every reduction in the number of such assumptions is a clear gain to science" (p. 153). He suggests that the two sides of the dispute may not even mean the same thing by "species," and commends his own favourite morphological concept, leaving the matter with the remark: "He who leans to the hypothesis of indefinite modifiability will tend to neglect, and he who inclines to that of the fixity of species will tend to exaggerate, minute differences" (p. 157) (the data not being such as to justify decision in one direction or the other).

This abandonment of the topic follows some rather peculiar remarks about inheritance, which presumably are intended to give the Lamarckian view some kind of benefit of the doubt. Having distinguished the forces acting on an individual into "intrinsic" (from the germ) and "extrinsic" (from the surrounding universe), he states that the "law of hereditary transmission" implies that "the operation of extrinsic forces on one generation may become in the next an intrinsic force" (p. 156). But he does not comment whether that "law," or that interpretation of it, should be accepted or rejected.

In summary, then, we see Huxley, after his forthright comments on the principles of classification, involved in these later pages in a delicate suspension of judgment. We should of course expect balance in a work intended as a general introduction to the theoretical context of a collection of specimens; but the manner of his handling of the issues other than classification also clearly reflects the absence of theoretical direction or insight afflicting this field at that time.

Huxley versus the Vestiges of Creation

Neutral as his comments on species in the *Explanatory Preface* were, there is no doubt that in the mid-fifties, Huxley was wholeheartedly opposed to the conception of the progression and transmutation of living forms. His reaction to the ideas of Lamarck and Chambers was fundamentally hostile.

The *Vestiges of Creation* was published anonymously in 1844 (*642a*) and went through eleven editions from then until 1860, when it was officially revealed that its author was the Scottish publisher and scientific amateur Robert Chambers. Many passages were rewritten, the most controversial and least defensible passages toned down to some extent, but in substance the work did not change very much over the period.

One should not mistake Chambers for a forerunner of Darwin. In fact, as Millhauser points out, Chambers was a follower of Buffon and Lamarck, and hoped to found the latter's speculations upon more solid bases (*802*); he was also a late product of the Scottish Enlightenment. He claimed that the sole purpose of his book was "improving the knowledge of mankind, and through that medium their happiness" (*642a*, p. 387). His means were consistent with the long-standing British tradition of "natural theology," whose most striking and influential examples were Paley's famous *Natural Theology* (*847*) and the *Bridgewater Treatises* (*620*). The basic tenets of the natural theologians were agreement between the results of theology, the study of God, and natural science, the study of God's creation. As Chambers wrote: "Thus we give, as is meet, a respectful reception to what is revealed through the medium of nature, at the same time that we fully reserve our reverence for all we have been accustomed to hold sacred, not one tittle of which it may ultimately be found necessary to alter" (*642a*, p. 390).

In some respects, natural theology was a Christian interpretation of Aristotle's concept of design. Whether one's belief is that intelligent design is constantly operating in nature, or that nature is under the operation of natural causes originally implanted by intelligent design (*821*, pp. 42–68), a Christian living in early nineteenth-century Britain believed that the world had been created by God, and was expected to believe in the existence of some sort of design in the universe. He might believe that God had created all natural groups separately, or he might believe, as Augustine proposed, that God had cast the "germs" of all creation and that all things which exist come to be what they are through a process. In other words, he believed that God has established certain laws which act upon beings, thus making and changing them throughout time. This was Chambers's view:

> How can we suppose an immediate exertion of this creative power at one time to produce zoophytes, another time to add a few marine mollusks, another to bring in one or two Crustacea, again to produce crustaceous fishes, again perfect fishes, and so on to the end? This would surely be to take a very mean view of the Creative power—to, in short, anthropomorphize it, or reduce it to some such character as that borne by ordinary proceedings of mankind. [642a, p. 151]

A priori design meant purposive adaptations, and we saw earlier that Huxley linked the views of the natural theologians to those of Cuvier (46).

In the eighteenth century, and in the nineteenth before Darwin, scientific orthodoxy was on the side of fixity, branding progression and transmutation as recurring forms of heresy. Chambers belonged to the tradition of natural theology, but he was a heretic insofar as he propounded progression: he belonged to the "liberal wing" of natural theology: "But may not the sacred text, on a liberal interpretation, or with the benefit of new light reflected from nature, or derived from learning, be shewn to be as much in harmony with the novelties of this volume as it has been with geology and natural philosophy" (p. 389)? In fact Chambers was attacked by such orthodox theologians as Samuel Bosanquet (618) as well as by the scientific establishment. Owen (621), Forbes, Miller, and Herschel (700) all rejected the arguments of the *Vestiges*; Sedgwick wrote a destructive review of it in the *Edinburgh Review* (885; see 675).

The starting point of the *Vestiges*, which commences with the treatment of cosmology, is that two laws control respectively the inorganic and organic worlds: in the former, the law of gravitation unifies all phenomena; in the latter that function is performed by the law of development. Chambers maintained that the fossils found in the geological strata showed a general progression from lower to higher type, through extinction and new appearances. In order to give support to his view of development, Chambers referred to the order of the geological succession of forms and to the embryological stages of animal development. He expressed his idea about the organic world thus:

> The idea, then, which I form of the progress of organic life upon the globe—and the hypothesis is applicable to all similar theatres of vital beings—*is that the simplest and most primitive type, under a law to which that of like-production is subordinate, gave birth to the type next above it, that this again produced the next higher, and so on, to the very highest,* the stages of advance being in all cases very small—namely from one species only to the other; so that the phenomenon has always been of a simple and modest character. [p. 223]

Huxley took the opportunity to express his dislike of Chambers's views in 1854, in his review of the tenth edition of the *Vestiges* for the *British and Foreign Medico-Chirurgical Review* (27). His language is downright abusive: Chambers's book is a "mass of pretentious nonsense" (p. 425). First of all, Huxley considers Chambers's conception of laws as causes; laws are entities intermediate between God, who has created the world, and the world itself (p. 427). He argues that, for the "Vestigiarian" (we must remember that the book was published anonymously), a law is simply the way the divine will operates and appears to men's eyes. We know the order in which natural phenomena are organised, and we call this a "law."

What then is this real proposition of the "Vestiges"? It is simply, exhibited in all its naked crudeness, the belief that *a law is an entity*—a Logos intermediate between the Creator and his works—which is entertained by the Vestigiarian in common with the great mass of those who, like himself, indulge in science at second-hand and dispense totally with logic. To use a phrase of M. Comte's—the mind of the Vestigiarian is in the metaphysic stage, and confounds its own abstractions with objective fact. [p. 427]

Chambers thought he was giving a scientific explanation of creation through the law of progressive development, but in Huxley's opinion:

If with the Progressionists, we conceive that this transmutation is from lower to a higher type; and that all the kinds of living beings which have ever existed upon the earth's surface, have originated in this way; the idea is a perfectly legitimate one, and must be admitted or rejected according to the evidence attainable, but, if fully proved, it would not be, in any intelligible sense, an *explanation* of creation; such "creation in the manner of natural law" would, in fact, simply be an orderly miracle. [p. 429]

In Huxley's opinion, progressionism was the basis of Chambers's unscientific enquiry. Progressionism was an attempt to explain creation not through separate acts of divine will but, as Gillespie suggests, as "an exertion of supreme power including in its fiat the simple fundamental laws which prescribed the course of descent taken by the forms of life from one species to the other" (*700*, p. 155). Huxley believes that progressionism is scientifically wrong: "Has the Progression theory any real foundation in the facts of palaeontology? We believe it has none" (27, p. 430).

Although Chambers is unable to provide evidence for his arguments and his statements are very often misleading or false (27, p. 437), Huxley notes that in the *Vestiges* one finds a notion, wholly independent of Chambers's tenets, which is of paramount scientific importance: "Such an idea, which took its origin in far other heads, [is] that the past may be interpreted by the present; and that the succession of phenomena in past times, took place in a manner analogous to that which occurs at the present day" (p. 429). As M. Bartholomew points out, we find here the direct influence upon Huxley of Sir Charles Lyell's geological views (*380*, p. 527). The nature of Lyell's influence is very important for an understanding of Huxley's attitude in this review of the *Vestiges*. Lyell strongly opposed progressionism (*774*). He denied that it is possible to know what the forms that lived during the deposition of the early rocks were like, and maintained that very often the earliest fossils appear more complex than the more recent ones. Huxley, following Lyell, maintains that both in plants (*27*, p. 430) and in animals (pp. 430–31) one finds many important examples of more highly organised but less modern fossil forms: "During the carboniferous epoch . . . the lycopodiaceae and equisetaceae . . . were much more highly organized plants than any of their present representatives" (ibid.).

Huxley concludes about Chambers's book: "Any man of science of ordinary judgment has considered and rejected the notions which the author of the "Vestiges" advances as great facts" (p. 439). However, when all is said and done, Chambers made the first thorough presentation of evolutionary theory in Britain, albeit in the rather unscholarly form of popular journalism (*802*, pp. 5, 21). It is interesting to note that Chambers concurred with MacLeay's system, with which Huxley was familiar, and propounded a saltative view of evolution (*802*, p. 106), just as Huxley himself was to do within a few years.

Darwin wrote to Huxley:

> I have just been reading your review of the *Vestiges*, and the way you handle a great Professor is really exquisite and inimitable. I have been extremely interested in other parts, and to my mind it is incomparably the best review I have read on the *Vestiges*; but I cannot think but that you are rather hard on the poor author. I must think that such a book, if it does no other good, spreads the taste for Natural Science.
>
> But I am perhaps no fair judge, for I am almost as unorthodox about species as the *Vestiges* itself, though I hope not quite so unphilosophical. How capitally you analyse his notion about law. I do not know when I have read a review which interested me so much. [*662*, vol. 1, p. 75]

But Darwin also wrote to Hooker:

> [Huxley's review] is exquisite & most clever, all about Owen—The review part strikes me as the best I have seen, on poor Vestiges. But I think he is too severe— you may say "birds of a feather flock together" & therefore I sympathise with the author. I fear (and for this I am very sorry) he makes mincemeat with Agassiz embryonic fish. [*Dar.* 114.124; 7 Sept. 1854]

Darwin had realised that, beyond the "Vestigiarian," the real targets of Huxley's attack were Agassiz and the scientific progressionists and, as ever, Owen, the eternal archenemy. Moreover, Darwin's judgment of the *Vestiges* is less negative than Huxley's. Amid Chambers's scientific "nonsense" and naive metaphysics, Darwin had recognised elements of truth. On the other hand, he objected to the details of the book and indeed the way it presented the case for evolution. A few pages of his copy of the sixth edition of the *Vestiges* of 1848, now preserved at Cambridge, are annotated by him. The passage below has a mark along its margin:

My proposition is that the several series of animated beings, from the simplest and oldest up to the highest and most recent, are the result, *first* of an *inherent* impulse in the forms of life to advance, in definite times, by generation, through grades of organization terminating in the highest dycotiledons and vertebrata, these grades being few in number, and generally marked by intervals of organic character which we find to be a practical difficulty in ascertaining affinities: second of another *inherent* impulse connected with the vital forces, tending in the course of generations, to modify organic structures in accordance with exter- nal circumstances, or food, the nature of the habitat, and the meteoric agencies, these being the "adaptations" of the natural theologian. [*642c*, p. 209]

Darwin underlined the word *inherent* in both instances, and noted in the margin: "quote to show differ[ence]"; "V. Whewells remarks against this." Several other annotations, especially of the "??!" kind, can be seen along the sentences that report Chambers's most blatant blunders. To the following passage Darwin's comment is: "Hence many turtles transformed!!"

The Chelonia present a sufficient variety of characters to have been the sole parentage of the Bird class; many being fierce and carnivorous, while others are vegetable feeders and of gentle character. [*642c*, p. 312]

This sentence a few pages later apparently inspired Darwin's mirth, for he notes: "!! oh": "Another swimming family composed of the Pelicans and Cormorants (*Pelicanidae*) gives rise to the Vultures, and thus is completed the raptorial stirp" (p. 319).

Huxley himself was bound to be dissatisfied with any theory that referred to creation—any kind of creation—as a means of understanding nature. As he recollected in 1887:

It seemed to me (as it does now) that "creation" in the ordinary sense of the word, is perfectly conceivable. . . . I had not then, and I have not now, the smallest *a priori* objection to raise to the account of the creation of animals and plants given in 'Paradise Lost' in which Milton so vividly embodies the natural sense of Genesis. Far be it from me to say it is untrue because it is impossible. I confine myself to what must be regarded as a modest and reasonable request for some particle of evidence that the existing species of animals and plants did originate in that way, as a condition of my belief in a statement which appears to me to be highly improbable. [*306*, pp. 187–88]

Interestingly, Huxley seems to conceive here of the possibility of two different attitudes to nature—his approach is related to his famous view of "Agnosticism" (320), which is regrettably outside the scope of this study (see 394; 395; 502; 467; 527). In what might be called his "metaphysical" attitude creation, and other concepts that cannot be empirically tested, can have a place in one's view of nature; in his "scientific" attitude concepts that cannot be empirically tested are simply outside the scope of the enquiry. The scientist must suspend judgment upon what can be neither proved nor disproved. Huxley's interest is of course primarily, but not solely, in the scientific attitude, and his opinion of creation as a supposedly scientific view is obviously a negative one. He finds a logical argument that enables him to reject it: "A phenomenon is explained when it is shown to be a case of some general law of Nature, but the supernatural interposition of the Creator can, by the nature of the case, exemplify no law, and if species have really arisen in this way, it is absurd to attempt to discuss their origin" (91, p. 57; written in 1860).

2
Winds of Change, 1859–1868

Die einfachsten Wahrheiten sind es gerade, auf die der Mensch immer erst am spätesten kommt.
—L. Feuerbach, *Zur Beurteilung der Schrift "Das Wesen d. Christenth"*

We saw in chapter 1 that Huxley's detailed self-introduction to the methods and theories of German science had led by the fifties to his adoption of the type concept as the solution to his quest for a principle expressing the harmony and order of nature. Huxley persists with this "pre-Darwinian" intellectual apparatus even in the 1860s. His continuous activity as a palaeontologist shows this in many (often short) notices and memoirs: we shall look in some detail at a connected series of more substantial works dating from 1859 to 1867 on fossil fish, amphibians, reptiles, and dinosaurs. (These years also saw the publication of *Man's Place in Nature* and related works. Given the substantial nature, reputation, and importance of that book, and the fact that it stands at the beginning of an involvement with various aspects of the subject of man spanning the sixties, seventies, and nineties in close relation to social and political questions as well as scientific ones, detailed consideration of those studies will be postponed until chapters 4 and 5.)

The fundamental subject matter in this chapter is a paradox. None of the above-mentioned works from this "middle period" prior to 1868 applies the notion of evolution. Yet this, as we shall see, is par excellence the period of Huxley's championship of Darwin (e.g., *83; 84; 88; 91; 123;* and the well-known but doubtless exaggerated contretemps with Wilberforce at Oxford in 1860).

1859 and After

Wallace's paper "On the Law Which Regulated the Introduction of New Species" (*926*) was published in 1855. It did not have a great impact on

Huxley, for he paid it little attention. In his unpublished material is a note on that article: it is undated, but the watermark indicates 1881 or later. Huxley regrets that "this remarkable paper should have attracted so much less attention than it deserved," given that it should have had a "decisive influence on the course of biological speculation" (HP 41.57).

Much the same fate awaited the joint Darwin–Wallace paper of 1858 (660). Nonetheless, during this period Huxley's apparent hostility to the notions of "modification" and "transmutation" was beginning to moderate; so much so that by 25 June 1859 he could write to Lyell: "I think transmutation may take place without transition" (472, vol. 1, p. 185). In the same month Huxley delivered a lecture entitled "On the Persistent Types of Life," in which he stated: "That hypothesis which supposes the species of living beings living at any time to be the result of the gradual modification of pre-existing species—a hypothesis which . . . [is] unproven and sadly damaged by some of its supporters, is yet the only one to which physiology lends any countenance" (72, p. 92). But "supporters" here still refers to Chambers and Lamarck rather than Wallace or Darwin.

In fact Huxley had been aware for some while that Darwin was working on a major project; indeed, Darwin had consulted him on specific points of embryology. On 5 July 1857, Darwin sent a copy of folios 41–44 of chapter 7 of his projected work to Huxley. Darwin wanted Huxley's opinion of "Brullé's law" which he thought might be relevant to Milne-Edwards's embryologically based classification. This is Darwin's letter:

Will you be so kind as to read the enclosed pages as you said you would, and consider the little point therein referred to. I have not thought it worth troubling you with how far and in what way the case concerns my work, the point being how far there is any truth in MM Brullé and Barneoud. My plan of work is just to compare partial generalisations of various authors and see how far they corroborate each other. Especially I want your opinion how far you think I am right in bringing in Milne Edwards' view of classification. I was long ago much struck with the principle referred to: but I could then see no rational explanation why affinities should go with the *more or less early* branching off from a common embryonic form. But if MM Brullé and Barneoud are right, it seems to me we get some light on Milne Edwards' views of classification; and this particularly interests me. I wish I could anyhow test M. Brullé's doctrine; as in the Vertebrates the head consists of greatly altered Vertebrae, according to this rule, in an early part of the development of a Vertebrate animal, the head ought to have arrived more nearly to its perfect state, than a dorsal or cervical vertebra to its perfect state. How is this? I have been reading Goodsir, but have found no light on my particular point. The paper impresses me with a high idea of his judgment and knowledge, though, of course, I can form no independent judgment of the truth of his doctrines. But by Jove it would require a wonderful amount of evidence to make one believe that the head of an elephant or tapir had more vertebrae in it than the head of a Horse or Ox. Many thanks for your last lecture. How curious the development of *Mysis!* [898, pp. 275–76]

Auguste Brullé (1809–1873) (669a) was a French zoologist, and assistant naturalist to the chair of entomology at the Musée d'Histoire Naturelle de Paris, where he came to know Milne-Edwards. In 1859 he went to Dijon as professor of zoology and comparative anatomy, after which he progressively disappeared from the scientific scene (his last publication seems to date from 1856). He was known in scientific circles for the "law" according to which the more one animal part departs from the archetype, the earlier it develops in the embryo. Thus, if one compares the same functional system in different animal groups, the *more* the organs in question are developed, the *earlier* they appear in the embryo. An example of this is given by the comparison of the circulatory systems of the vertebrates and the annelids. In general, therefore, the "law" proposes that the more widely two animals differ from each other, the earlier the resemblance of their embryos ceases.

In Darwin's opinion, this view was clearly relevant to Milne-Edwards's view of classification, since it would provide an embryological basis for classification; and furthermore it therefore appeared to Darwin to have positive implications for the validation of the principle of natural selection. As Darwin wrote in the draft chapter 7 of 1856:

> Indeed the main basis of all affinities, so strongly insisted on by Milne Edwards in this paper and elsewhere, seems to hang on the same principle,— namely that the more widely two animals differ from each other, the earlier does their embryonic resemblance cease; thus a fish on the one hand, & mammals together with birds on the other hand branch off from the common embryonic form at a very early period, whereas mammals and birds being more closely related to each other than to fish, diverge from each other at a later period. This seems to accord with M. Brullé's principle that the more each part is changed from the common archetype the earlier it is developed; for as a fish differs in nearly all its organization from a mammal, more than a bird differs from a mammal, the fish as a whole would have to be differentiated at an earlier period than a bird. [898, pp. 303]

Huxley's reply referred to the methods of von Baer and Rathke (see chapter 1); devastated Brullé; claimed that Brullé's and Milne-Edwards's views were independent; and disagreed somewhat with Darwin's interpretation of Milne-Edwards:

> With regard to Milne Edwards' views—I do not think they at all involve or bear out Brullé's. Milne Edwards says nothing as far as I am aware about the relative time of appearance of more or less complex organs—I should not understand Milne Edwards' doctrine as you put it, in the paragraph I have marked: he

seems to me to say that, not the *most highly complex*, but the most *characteristic* organs are the first developed—Thus the chorda dorsalis of vertebrates—a structure characteristic of the group but which is & remains excessively simple, is one of the earliest developed—the animal body is built up like a House—where the Judicious builder begins with putting together the simpler rafters—according to Brullé's notion of Nature's operation he would begin with the cornices, cupboards, & grand piano.

It is quite true that "the more widely two animals differ from one another the earlier does their embryonic resemblance cease" but you must remember that the differentation which takes place is the result not so much of the development of new parts as of the *modification of parts already existing and common to both of the divergent types.*—

I should be quite inclined to believe that a more complex part requires a longer time for its development than a simpler one; but it does not at all follow that it should appear *relatively* earlier than the simple part. The Brain, I doubt not, requires a longer time for its development than the spinal cord. Nevertheless they both appear together as a continuous whole, the Brain continuing to change after the spinal cord has attained its perfect form. The period at which an organ appears therefore, seems to me not to furnish the least indication as to the time which is required for the organ to become perfect.

You see my verdict would be that Brullé's doctrine is quite unsupported—nay is contradicted by development—so far as animals are concerned—& I suspect a Botanist would give you the same opinion with regard to plants. [pp. 276–78]

Huxley copied down and marked the following passage from Brullé's memoir in which the major points of the latter's doctrine are expounded:

En suivant, comme on l'a fait dans ces derniers temps les phases du développement des Crustacés, on voit que les pièces de la bouche et des antennes se manifestent avant les pattes; celles-ci ne se montrent que par suite des développements ultérieurs—2) De leur côté, les antennes sont encore fort peu développées que les pièces de la bouche le sont déjà plus; enfin c'est lorsque les appendices buccaux ont revêtu la forme qu'ils doivent conserver que les pattes commencent à paraître. Il en résulte donc cette conséquence remarquable [*sic*], *que les appendices se montrent d'autant plus tôt que leur structure doit être plus complexe.* On trouve, en outre, dans ces développements divers une nouvelle preuve de l'analogie des appendices. Ainsi les pattes n'ont pas de transformation à subir elles ne se montrent que quand les autres appendices ont déjà revêtu la forme des mâchoires ou d'antennes. 3) Donc dans un animal articulé *les appendices se montrent d'autant plus tard qu'ils ont moins de transformations à subir*: c'est le complément de la loi précédente. On peut par conséquent juger du degré d'importance et de complication d'un appendice par l'époque même à laquelle il commence à se manifester. [*624; 898*, p. 278]

In response to Huxley's complete condemnation of Brullé, Darwin noted:

There is only one point in which I cannot follow you.—*Supposing* Barneouds I do not say Brullé's remark were true & universal, i.e., that the petal which has to undergo the greatest am't of development or modification begins to change the soonest from the simple & common embryonic form of the petals; then I cannot but think it wd throw light on Milne Edwards' proposition that the wider apart (more different) the classes of animals, the sooner do they diverge from the common embryonic plan.—which common embryonic plan, may be compared to the *similar* petals in the early bud.—The several petals in *one* flower being compared to the distinct, but similar embryos of the different classes.—I see in my abstract that M. Edwards speaks of the most perfect & important organs being first developed & I shd have thought that the char[acteristic] organs wd be developed. [*898*, p. 279]

Moreover, Darwin wrote at the top of folio 41: "Do not copy this Heading or pages" (*898*, p. 303n), while folio 45 was entitled "40 to 45," which meant that folios 41–44 were to be deleted.

Despite such detailed correspondence, Huxley did not know exactly what Darwin was up to. We saw from his lecture of June 1859 that Huxley was increasingly willing to entertain "modification" or "transmutation" as an account of the observed zoological facts, but the basic question remained unanswered. If species transmute, *How do they do it?* Chambers and Lamarck had failed to supply an adequate answer. Huxley wrote in 1860 that before the publication of the *Origin of Species*:

However much the few, who thought deeply on the question of species, might be repelled by the generally received dogmas, they saw no way of escaping from them save by the adoption of suppositions so little justified by experiment or by observation as to be at least equally distasteful.

The choice lay between absurdities and a middle condition of uneasy scepticism; which last, however unpleasant and unsatisfactory, was obviously the only justifiable state of mind under the circumstances. [*91*, pp. 69–70]

Huxley's Enthusiasm

In 1859 Darwin's *Origin of Species* was published. It seemed to be the answer Huxley required:

The Darwinian hypothesis has the merit of being eminently simple and comprehensible in principle, and its essential positions may be stated in a very few words: all species have been produced by the development of varieties from common stocks; by the conversion of these, first into permanent races and then into new species, by the process of *natural selection*, which process is essentially identical with that artificial selection by which man has originated the races of domestic animals—the *struggle for existence* taking the place of man, and exerting, in the case of natural selection, that selective action which he performs in artificial selection. [*91*, p. 71]

One aspect of this passage is worth emphasising at once: Huxley exaggerates Darwin's reference to the resemblance between natural and artificial selection. Huxley speaks of their "essentially identical" action, whereas Darwin actually refers to artificial selection only as an analogy to the operation of natural selection. I return to this point in the next section.

Huxley claims that Darwin's theory provided what he was seeking: a plausible causative account of the major biological phenomena, which both Lamarck and the *Vestiges of Creation* had completely failed to supply. As he recalled in 1887:

A hypothesis respecting the origin of known organic forms, which assumed the operation of no causes but such as could be proved to be actually at work [given in the *Origin of Species*] . . . provided us with the working hypothesis we sought. . . . In 1857, I had no answer ready, and I do not think that any one else had. A year later [in fact two years later!] we reproached ourselves with dullness for being perplexed by such an enquiry. My reflection, when I first made myself master of the central idea of the "Origin" was, "How extremely stupid not to have thought of that." [*306*, p. 197]

The thesis of the *Origin of Species* is evolution through natural selection. The superiority of Darwin's hypothesis over its rivals was that it gave a plausible reason for what occurs in nature. Darwin postulates not only evolution itself, but its causes. On this point, in a letter to Lyell, Huxley is clear:

I will look at Lamarck again. But I doubt if I shall improve my estimate of [him]. The notion of common descent was not his—still less that of modification by variation—and he was as far as De Maillet from seeing his way to any *vera causa* by which varieties might be intensified into species.

If Darwin is right—about natural selection—the discovery of this vera causa sets him to my mind in a different region altogether from all his predecessors—and I should no more call his doctrine a modification of Lamarck's than I should call the Newtonian theory of the celestial motions a modification of the Ptolemaic system. Ptolemy imagined a mode of explaining these motions. Newton proved their necessity from the laws and a force demonstrably in operation. If he is only right Darwin will I think take his place with such men as Harvey, and even if he is wrong his sobriety and accuracy of thought will put him on a far different level from Lamarck. I want to make this clear to people. [*HP* 30.41; 17 Aug. 1862]

Darwin's doctrine is a working hypothesis which enables scientists to unify such biological facts as variability and adaptedness, facts which had been observed individually, but not hitherto expressed in a comprehensive form.

In October 1859, Darwin wrote to Huxley: "I shall be *intensely* curious to hear what effect the book produces on you. . . . I am very far from expecting to convert you to many of my heresies; but if, on the whole, you and two or three others think I am on the right road, I shall not care what the mob of naturalists think" (*661*, vol. 2, pp. 172–73). Huxley replied on 23 November, just before the actual publication of the *Origin of Species*, hailing Darwin's view "as a true cause for the production of species" (*472*, vol. 1, p. 188). Darwin replied two days later: "Like a good Catholic who has received the extreme unction, I can now sing 'nunc dimittis'. I should have been more than contented with one quarter of what you have said. . . . My dear Huxley, I thank you cordially for your letter" (*661*, vol. 2, p. 232–33).

Apart from the *"vera causa"* reason for supporting Darwin's view, there was another, equally important, consideration: Huxley's persistent quest for principles expressing the order of nature. As he wrote in 1876:

> It has taken long ages of toilsome and often fruitless labour to enable man to look steadily at the shifting scenes of the phantasmagoria of Nature, to notice what is fixed among her fluctuations, and what is regular among her apparent irregularities; and it is only comparatively lately, within the last few centuries, that the conception of a universal order and of a definite course of things, which we term the course of Nature, has emerged.
>
> But once originated, the conception of the constancy of the order of Nature has become the dominant idea of modern thought. To any person who is familiar with the facts upon which that conception is based, and is competent to estimate their significance, it has ceased to be conceivable that chance should have any place in the universe, or that events should depend upon any but the natural sequence of cause and effect . . . and, as we have excluded chance from a place in the universe, so we ignore, even as a possibility, the notion of any interference with the order of Nature. Whatever may be men's speculative doctrine, it is quite certain that every intelligent person guides his life and risks his fortune upon the belief that the order of Nature is constant, and that the chain of causation is never broken. [*229*, pp. 47–48]

Now, Darwin's doctrine happens to be a hypothesis of the order of nature, which

> assumes that the present state of things has had but a limited duration; but it supposes that this state of things has been evolved by a natural process from an antecedent state, and that from another, and so on; and, on this hypothesis, the attempt to assign any limit to the series of past changes is, usually, given up. [p. 50]

During the process of change postulated by the hypothesis of evolution there is

> no point at which we could say: "This is a natural process", and: "This is not a natural process"; but that the whole might be compared to that wonderful

operation of development which may be seen going on every day under our eyes, in virtue of which there arises, out of the semi-fluid comparatively homogeneous substance which we call an egg, the complicated organisation of one of the higher animals. [p. 55]

Thus, Darwin's view was an empirically based hypothesis of the order of nature, which also proposed a natural mechanism for "modification"; as such, it could hardly fail to meet Huxley's approval. It was "the flash of light, which to a man who has lost himself in a dark night, suddenly reveals a road which, whether it takes him straight home or not, certainly goes his way" (306, p. 197).

Huxley's "Philosophical" Reservation

The preceding section might suggest that Huxley was a wholehearted supporter of Darwin's view. But in fact Huxley was never entirely confident about the notion of natural selection, which he rightly considered the centrepiece of Darwin's doctrine. E. Poulton adapts the words of Mercutio in commenting on Huxley's opinion of natural selection: "It may not be 'so deep as a well, nor so wide as a church door,' to contain the whole explanation of evolution, 'but 'tis enough 'twill serve' " (861, p. 12).

Huxley expressed his reservations from the very beginning. The *Times* of 26 December 1859 published a review of the *Origin of Species.* It was anonymous, but it was soon known that it had been written by Huxley. The review was later reprinted in Huxley's *Collected Essays:* its title was "The Darwinian Hypothesis" (83). The following year Huxley wrote another article, for the *Westminster Review,* entitled "The Origin of Species," also reprinted in *Darwiniana,* the second volume of his *Collected Essays* (91; 342). In "The Darwinian Hypothesis" he writes:

That this most ingenious hypothesis enables us to give a reason for many apparent anomalies in the distribution of living beings in time and space, and that it is not contradicted by the main phenomena of life and organization appears to us to be unquestionable; and, so far, it must be admitted to have an immense advantage over any of its predecessors. But it is quite another matter to affirm absolutely either the truth or falsehood of Mr. Darwin's views at the present stage of the enquiry. Goethe has an excellent aphorism defining that state of mind which he calls "Thätige Skepsis"—active doubt. It is doubt which so loves truth that it neither dares rest in doubting, nor extinguish itself by unjustified belief: and we commend this state of mind to students of species, with respect to Mr. Darwin's or any other hypothesis, as to their origin. The combined investigations of another twenty years may, perhaps, enable naturalists to say whether the modifying causes and the selective power, which Mr. Darwin has satisfactorily shown to exist in Nature, are competent to produce all the effects he ascribes to them; or whether, on the other hand, he has been led to over-estimate the value of the principle of natural selection, as greatly as Lamarck over-estimated his *vera causa* of modification by exercise. [*83*, pp. 19–20]

In his 1860 essay "The Origin of Species," Huxley states his doubts more succinctly. "Is there such a thing as natural selection?" he asks. The answer is that it is probable, but not yet definitively proved. However, it is a useful model of an otherwise obscure process. The following passage throws much light on Huxley's approach:

> There is no fault to be found with Mr. Darwin's method, then; but it is another question whether he has fulfilled all the conditions imposed by that method. Is it satisfactorily proved, in fact, that species may be originated by natural selection? that there is such a thing as natural selection? that none of the phenomena exhibited by species are inconsistent with the origin of species in this way? If these questions can be answered in the affirmative, Mr. Darwin's view steps out of the rank of hypotheses into those of proved theories; but, so long as the evidence at present adduced falls short of enforcing that affirmation, so long, to our minds, must the new doctrine be content to remain among the former—an extremely valuable, and in the highest degree probable, doctrine, indeed the only extant hypothesis which is worth anything in a scientific point of view; but still a hypothesis, and not yet the theory of species.
>
> After much consideration, and with assuredly no bias against Mr. Darwin's views, it is our clear conviction that, as the evidence stands, it is not absolutely proven that a group of animals, having all the characters exhibited by species in Nature, has ever been originated by selection, whether artificial or natural. Groups having the morphological character of species—distinct and permanent races in fact—have been so produced over and over again; *but there is no positive evidence, at present, that any group of animals has, by variation and selective breeding, given rise to another group which was, even in the least degree, infertile with the first.* Mr. Darwin is perfectly aware of this weak point, and brings forward a multitude of ingenious and important arguments to diminish the force of the objection. [*91*, pp. 73–75; italics added]

The solution to Darwin's problems, Huxley thinks, might come from decisive experiments which "conducted by a skilful physiologist, would very probably obtain the desired production of mutually more-or-less infertile breeds from a common stock, in a comparatively few years; but still, as the case stands at present, this 'little rift within the lute' is not to be disguised or overlooked" (p. 75).

These passages reveal explicitly Huxley's adherence to a criterion of "experimental proof" by which theories proper are distinguishable from provisional or working hypotheses. The italicised passage above further underscores the connection of this concern with his overreading of Darwin's analogy between natural and artificial selection. The elements of Huxley's argument are therefore clear enough. Darwin's view, despite being the best available, is a hypothesis and not the theory of species, because natural selection has not been "proved experimentally." And this critique of Darwin's view is justified especially by the proposition that, if we can demand experimental proof of artificial selection, and natural and artificial selection are "essentially identical," then it is proper to demand experimental proof of natural selection itself. (For problems relating to the testing of natural selection, see 749; 765; and 931.)

Darwin did not accept this approach. Prior to the actual publication of the *Origin of Species,* he wrote to Huxley:

You speak of finding a flaw in my hypothesis, and this shows you do not understand its nature. It is a mere rag of a hypothesis with as many flaws and holes as sound parts. My question is whether the rag is worth anything? I think by careful treatment I can carry in it my fruit to market for a short distance over a gentle road; but I fear that you will give the poor rag such a devil of a shake that it will fall all to atoms; and a poor rag is better than nothing to carry one's fruit to market in. So do not be too ferocious. [*HP* 5.65]

And, more clearly, he wrote to Hooker:

I quite agree with what you say of Lieutenant Hutton's review [735; see also 731] (who he is I know not); it struck me as very original. He is one of the very few who see that the change of species cannot be directly proved, and that the doctrine must sink or swim according as it groups and explains phenomena. It is really curious how few judge it in this way, which is clearly the right way. [661, vol. 2, p. 362; 23 April 1861]

For Darwin it is not the hypothesis itself which is to be tested directly; but if its consequences are not in accordance with those facts which the hypothesis should account for, the hypothesis is to be abandoned, as M. T. Ghiselin argues in his important book, *The Triumph of the Darwinian Method* (699). Now, Darwin's position, as Sir Gavin de Beer suggests, was that

if species are the result of evolution by natural selection, then such facts as uniformity of plan of structure, resemblances between embryos, abortive organs, classification of groups within larger groups, and continuity of distribution of species geographically in space and geologically in time would be expected to occur, and they do occur. [668, pp. 161–62]

This quotation from *The Variation of Animals and Plants under Domestication* of 1868 should make Darwin's opinion clear:

The principle of natural selection may be looked at as a mere hypothesis, but rendered in some degree probable by what we positively know of the variability of organic beings in a state of nature—by what we positively know of the struggle for existence, and the consequent almost inevitable preservation of favourable variations—and from the analogical formation of domestic races. *Now this hypothesis may be tested—and this seems to me the only fair and legitimate manner of considering the whole question—by trying whether it explains several large and independent classes of facts;* such as the geological succession of organic beings, their distribution in past and present times, and their mutual affinities and homologies. *If the principle of natural selection does explain these and other large bodies of facts, it ought to be received.* [657, vol. 1, p. 9; italics added]

What is basically at issue here between Darwin and Huxley is their philosophies of science. It is, to put it perhaps crudely, a question of whether it is to be evaluated on an "absolute" or a "relative" basis: that is, whether a theory can be isolated and individually assessed in a context of truth or falsity provided by directly observed or experimentally ascertained fact; or, on the other hand, can be evaluated only in relation to its precursors, rivals, and potential successors which provide criteria of evaluation which themselves undergo modification in the light of changing theory. Huxley's theory and practice of science is close to the former approach. If you believe that knowledge, in the strict Cartesian sense, is available, and also that empirical methods are a means of access to it, then you are bound to believe that a theory can—indeed *must*—have an absolute value, which it is the task of experimentation to discover. Hence Huxley's frequent use of his notion of "experimental *proof*," whose result is the extraction of pieces of knowledge.

The second, relative approach, outlined above, would see the extraction of "pieces of knowledge" as a secondary, even illusory, objective. Instead, its central concern is with the comparative capacity of a scientific theory to exhibit and account for connections among phenomena, and the use of a theory of relatively superior power in that respect to direct further investigation of the phenomena in question until something better is proposed. The existence of a mechanism can be postulated, the phenomena classified appropriately; then one can see how far the resulting structure will go in comparison with other theories advanced towards an understanding of the phenomena in question. Darwin's scientific presentation, it seems to me, accords more closely with this approach than with the first, absolute approach. We can now understand, for example, why Darwin was not unduly worried by Huxley's criticisms, while Mivart's criticism that natural selection was unable to account for several natural phenomena (808) provoked a whole chapter in reply, in the sixth edition of the *Origin of Species* (656b, pp. 168–204).

In fact Darwin once almost lost his temper in his arguments with Huxley on sterility, as the rather brusque tone of this letter shows:

I did not understand what you required about sterility; assuredly the facts given do not go nearly so far. We differ so much that it is no use arguing. To get the degree of sterility you expect in recently formed varieties seems to me simply hopeless. It seems to me almost like those naturalists who declare they will never believe that one species turns into another till they see every stage in the process. [662, vol. 1, p. 225; 28 Dec. 1862]

Huxley, then, can be viewed as following the traditional British empiricism of the epistemological analysis of sensory experience, while Darwin can be seen to some degree as a forerunner of pragmatism. This discussion therefore has some bearing on the intellectual relationship between Darwin and the British empiricists. D. Hull has argued that, contrary to what scholars thought a few years ago (see for instance 680), both idealists and empiricists opposed Darwin's doctrine (731, p. 68; other relevant works are 625; 725; 798; 876; 877; 906; 934).

After an early Romantic phase (443; 527; 554), Huxley became an empiricist and openly declared the accordance between his way of looking at science and the views expressed by John Stuart Mill. In 1863 he declared: "Those who wish to study fully the doctrine of which I have endeavoured to give you some rough-and-ready illustrations, must read Mr. John Stuart Mill's System of Logic" (111, p. 376n). It seems to me that the difference of approach I have described between Darwin's and Huxley's views of science means that an orthodox nineteenth-century empiricist could not wholeheartedly accept Darwin's theory unless he were prepared to give up his belief in the "absolute" evaluation of theory through decisive experiments—which Huxley was not. On the other hand, Hull overstates his point when he claims that empiricists were "opposed" to Darwinism: it is one thing to oppose, as Whewell did (even forbidding the placing of a copy of the Origin of Species in the library of Trinity College, Cambridge, of which he was Master), and another to qualify one's approval, as Mill (798, People's Edition, 1884, p. 328) and Huxley did. After all, Darwin never denied the importance of induction in his research, and Mill did underline the hypothetico-deductive aspects of the scientific method. We can perhaps agree with Julian Huxley that by "Darwinism" is implied "that blend of induction and deduction which Darwin was the first to apply to the study of evolution" (742, p. 13). Moreover, Darwin and the "orthodox" empiricists shared the same conception of causation as invariable succession; all Darwin's work emphasised that there is no such thing as a metaphysical "first cause" or entity external to natural phenomena which can be invoked in their explanation. Mill said, "When in the course of this enquiry I speak of the cause of any phenomenon I do not mean a cause which is not a phenomenon; I make no research into the ultimate or ontological cause of anything" (798, 9th edn, 1875, vol. 1, p. 376). The celebrated final passage in the Origin of Species [656a, pp. 489–90] propounds exactly the same idea. Darwin also declares: "I mean by Nature only the aggregate action and product of many natural laws; and by laws the sequence of events as ascertained by us" (*852*, p. 165).

And finally, for both "orthodox" empiricists like Huxley and "unorthodox" ones like Darwin, the Darwinian evolutionary view *is* empirically accessible—in clear contrast to an empirically inaccessible theory such as Mivart's concept of an "internal force" (*808*).

Saltative Evolution

In 1894 Huxley wrote to William Bateson:

> I have put off thanking you for the volume *On Variation* [*607*] which you have been so good as to send me in the hope that I should be able to look into it before doing so.
>
> But as I find that impossible, beyond a hasty glance, at present, I must content myself by saying how glad I am to see from that glance that we are getting back from the region of speculation into that of fact again. . . .
>
> I see that you are inclined to advocate the possibility of considerable "Saltus" on the part of Dame Nature in her variations. I always took the same view, much to Mr. Darwin's disgust, and we used often to debate it.
>
> If you should come across my article in the *Westminster* (1860), you will find a paragraph on that question near the end. [*472*, vol. 2, p. 394]

Huxley's "The Origin of Species" in *Darwiniana* (*91*) reports two remarkable cases. The first concerns a ram (Ancon sheep) which was born with very short legs and a long body, in contrast to its parents, which had longer legs and shorter bodies. The second concerns a Maltese boy, Gratio Kelleia, born with twelve fingers and twelve toes, from normal ten-fingered and ten-toed parents, an incident first reported by Bonnet and Réaumur (*869*, p. 719; both examples are also mentioned in the *Vestiges*).

> Two circumstances are well worthy of remark in both cases. In each, the variety appears to have arisen in full force, and, as it were, *per saltum*; a wide and definite difference appearing, at once, between the Ancon ram and ordinary sheep; between the six-fingered and six-toed Gratio Kelleia and ordinary men. . . . The variations arose spontaneously. [*91*, pp. 35–36]

Huxley suggests that the greatest number of variations probably arise in this spontaneous way. In the case of the Ancon sheep we find "a remarkable and well-established instance . . . of a very distinct race being established *per saltum*" (p. 39). Later he remarks:

> One of the most valuable and suggestive parts of Mr. Darwin's work is that in which he proves, that the frequent absence of transitions is a necessary consequence of his doctrine, and that the stock whence two or more species have sprung, need in no respect be intermediate between these species. If any two species have arisen from a common stock in the same way as the carrier and

pouter, say, have arisen from the rock-pigeon, then the common stock of these two species need be no more intermediate between the two than the rock-pigeon is between the carrier and pouter. Clearly appreciate the force of this analogy, and all the arguments against the origin of species by selection, based on the absence of transitional forms, fall to the ground. And Mr. Darwin's position might, we think, have been even stronger than it is if he had not embarrassed himself with the aphorism "*Natura non facit saltum*", which turns up so often in his pages. We believe, as we have seen above, that Nature does make jumps now and then, and a recognition of the fact is of no small importance in disposing of many minor objections to the doctrine of transmutation. [pp. 76–77]

Here is another point of disagreement, a major one, between Huxley and Darwin. Huxley wrote to Darwin on 23 November 1859:

The only objections that have occurred to me are—1st, That you have loaded yourself with an unnecessary difficulty in adopting *Natura non facit saltum* so unreservedly; and 2nd, It is not clear to me why, if continual physical conditions are of so little moment as you suppose, variation should occur at all. [*472*, vol. 1, p. 189]

Hooker wrote to Darwin in 1862: "Huxley is rather disposed to think you have overlooked 'Saltus' " (*744*, vol. 2, p. 38). Darwin replied to this comment in a few lines at the end of a letter to Hooker on 18 March 1862: "I am not shaken about '*saltus*'. I did not write without going pretty carefully into all the cases of normal structure in animals resembling monstrosities which appear *per saltus*" (*662*, vol. 1, p. 198). So we see that Darwin rather discounts Huxley's criticism, confining *saltus* to monstrosities.

Throughout his life Huxley inclined towards a saltative conception of change in life forms. In 1859, a few months before the *Origin of Species* appeared, he noted:

Suppose that external conditions acting on Species A, give rise to a new species B. . . .
I know of no evidence to shew that the interval between the two species must *necessarily* be bridged over by a series of forms, each of which shall occupy, as it were, a fraction of the distance between A and B. . . . In an organic compound having a precise & definite composition—you may effect all sorts of transmutations by substituting an atom of one element for an atom of another element—You may in this way produce a vast series of modifications—but each modification is definite in its composition & there are no transitional or intermediate stages between one definite compound and another. I have a sort of notion that similar laws of definite combinations rule over modifications of organic bodies. [*395*, p. 44]

This approach is in total accord with that of his early works.

Huxley's proposal of evolution *per saltum* is linked with the difficult and oft-debated problem of "blending-inheritance." To quote P. J.

Vorzimmer: "The term *blending-inheritance* refers to the view (erroneous as it turned out) of inheritance as a fusion of both paternal and maternal elements in the offspring in an inseparable mixture which results in the external features appearing to be midway between the two" (*917*, p. 99). Blending-inheritance was the leading conception of inheritance in Darwin's time. Darwin wanted to bring his own views into line with contemporary genetic knowledge.

Fleeming Jenkin's argument that blending-inheritance and natural selection could not be reconciled (*746*) greatly intrigued Darwin. If blending-inheritance occurs and variations are as slight as Darwin maintains, then advantageous variations will be lost within a few generations, and natural selection is fundamentally impotent: it cannot induce permanent change. Jenkin's sarcastic comment is known: "A highly favoured white cannot blanch a nation of negroes" (*746*, p. 291). Francis Bowen, an American professor of philosophy, expressed this viewpoint quite clearly:

Variations, if slight, are seldom transmitted by inheritance. . . . Variations, if great, either die out by sterility as monsters, or are rapidly effaced by crossing the breed. . . . The very act of crossing the varieties tends, by splitting the difference, to diminish the distance between them. Under domestication, indeed, the varieties will be kept apart; but in the wild state, Nature has no means of preventing them from pairing. They will interbreed if not prevented and will thereby kill out instead of multiplying their variations. [*917*, pp. 111–12]

Though not directly arguing against Jenkin or Bowen, Huxley tries to mollify their kind of criticism. He refers to the phenomena of "prepotency" and "reversion" and also to saltations, the latter, in his opinion, increasing the efficiency of natural selection in producing new forms. The notions of prepotency and reversion were known to all Victorian scientists as exceptions to blending-inheritance. *Prepotency* denotes the persistence of a character despite blending, and thus prefigures the Mendelian concept of "dominance." *Reversion* occurs in the resurgence of a certain ancestral characteristic which had apparently been lost in the process of blending. Huxley points out that in many cases proper blending-inheritance does not occur, but we observe a sort of prepotency of some character which has suddenly arisen in the offspring. Evolution is therefore no longer bound to minute variations, and natural selection can truly operate on advantageous variations:

Once in existence, many varieties obey the fundamental law of reproduction that like tends to produce like; and their offspring exemplify it by tending to exhibit the same deviation from the parental stock as themselves. Indeed, there seems to be, in many instances, a prepotent influence about a newly-arisen variety which gives it what one may call an unfair advantage over the normal descendants from the same stock. [*91*, p. 37]

In other words, Huxley thinks that there are some factors, the laws of which are unknown to him, which can overcome the (supposed) blending process of heredity. This would not meet the approval of Jenkin, who also opposed saltation: "It is impossible that any sports or accidental variation in a single individual, however favourable to life, should be preserved and transmitted by natural selection" (746, p. 291).

Huxley's opinions on heredity are in fact the closest contemporary anticipation of modern mutationist views of evolution (917, p. 113). As J. A. Thompson wrote, "Huxley foresaw part of the truth that there is in the mutation theory; he had a glimpse of *Natura saltatrix*" (567, p. 717).

Reptiles, Fish, Birds—Some Fundamental Contributions

We have seen Huxley coming to terms with the publication of the *Origin of Species*. We have also had some indication of his willingness to speak out in defence of the scientific importance of the work of others, and of the serious consideration of which he was capable in criticism. The memoirs reviewed below bear witness to his sound knowledge of the past and present work of other researchers, the thoroughness of his own observation, and the consequent detailed and emphatic documentation of his conclusions, all basic factors in the high quality of his scientific contributions. My other purpose in this section is to illustrate in some measure the absence from Huxley's work until the late sixties of anything resembling an "evolutionary approach."

Stagonolepis

Huxley's colleague at the School of Mines was J. W. Salter, an entomologist and palaeontologist of considerable repute. His collaboration was of great help to Huxley, who had hitherto done no original palaeontological work (79; 881).

In February 1859 Huxley made his first major contribution to reptilian palaeontology with his memoir on *Stagonolepis robertsoni*, a form from the Elgin Triassic formation. The story of this fossil and its interpretation provides good evidence of Huxley's alertness to what was going on in scientific research contemporary with his controversies on behalf of Darwin.

The systematic position of *Stagonolepis* had been problematic since the early 1840s when Patrick Duff (673) had sent a specimen in his possession to Goodsir, Rhind, Hugh Miller, Thomas Stevenson, and other leading British palaeontologists, none of whom was able to determine to which class it belonged. Duff then lent it to Robertson, who drew some sketches of the mysterious animal, which he sent to Louis Agassiz, the acknowledged authority in the field. It is extremely hard to classify an animal on the basis of sketches, however accurate. Agassiz thought that it was a fish, and named it in honour of Robertson. In the *Monographie*, Agassiz proposed that *Stagonolepis* was close to *Glyptopomus*, a Devonian fish (*586*, p. 139). In 1852 (*619*) L. Brickenden described the footprints of a reptile in the Old Red Sandstone of Elgin (County Maory); Alexander Young discovered the remains of the animal which reached Mantell and received full description: it was called *Telerpeton* (*782*). Young also discovered marks of *Stagonolepis* in the very same slabs of Devonian strata which contained the footprints of *Telerpeton*, but no traces of other animals of the same complexity were found there. Although Brickenden called *Stagonolepis* a fish (*619*) suspicions that it might be a reptile increased in the late 1850s: in 1858 Murchison referred to it as a reptilian remain (*814*, pp. 435–39), and the following year G. Gordon, describing *Telerpeton* and *Stagonolepis*, questioned whether the latter was a reptile rather than a fish (*703*, p. 46). By then Lyell had also communicated to Huxley his doubts about the piscine nature of *Stagonolepis* (*73*).

Huxley collected all the material available on *Stagonolepis* and more emphatically than anyone else before him supported the view that it was a reptile, principally on the basis of the nature of its dermal armour (*73*, p. 103). He shows here one of his major characteristics. He carefully detects which way the wind is blowing, finds as much evidence as possible, then supports his cause to its logical limit—so forcefully on occasion that one who reads only his memoirs might think that he is propounding his own original ideas. Gordon, Murchison, and Lyell had suggested that *Stagonolepis* was likely to be a reptile; Huxley made a point of demonstrating to the whole scientific world that it *was* a reptile. His behaviour in respect to Darwinism is similar. Darwin elaborated a theory; Huxley backed it, and made Darwin's point more emphatically than anyone else in Britain.

As the *Stagonolepis* memoir predates the *Origin of Species* by a few months, Huxley's considerations in reaching his conclusion are purely "traditional," in that his argument rests solely on the survey of structural affinities. But we might not so readily expect what the following pages demonstrate—namely, that Huxley's approach and arguments do not appear to change even after Darwin's publication.

Fish and Amphibians

A significant memoir of Huxley's "middle period" is "Preliminary Essay upon the Systematic Arrangement of the Fishes of the Devonian Epoch" of 1861 (*96*). Like most of Huxley's memoirs it displays to the full his interest in finding facts relevant to the understanding of some general biological problem, rather than in merely describing (*576*). A similar attitude is displayed in his work in invertebrate morphology, as we saw in chapter 1. This memoir summarises the results obtained in more than thirty years' search for a credible classification of fossil fish.

Huxley was keenly aware of this history, which began, as Christian Pander remarked in 1860 (848), when I. R. Murchison provided the first description of the Devonian fish in Britain, in 1827 (811). (Although, strictly speaking, they have different meanings, "Old Red Sandstone" and "Devonian" will be used here as synonyms, as they were in the nineteenth century.) The following year he and Adam Sedgwick wrote what was to be a great classic in the interpretation of geological strata and their palaeontological significance: "On the Structure and Relations of the Deposits Contained between the Primary Rocks and the Oolitic Series in the North of Scotland" (815). Here the authors presented the first complete description of the order of the Red Sandstone and superposed masses, which they showed to consist of three parts, Lower Sandstone and Conglomerates, Central Caithness Flagstone, and, overlying, Red Sandstones of Dunnett Head and Orkney Island (813). Numerous fossil fish were discovered during that period, and their interpretation posed an intriguing problem.

Between 1833 and 1844 the great Swiss zoologist Louis Agassiz wrote two reference works on the classification of the fossil fish then known: *Recherches sur les poissons fossiles* (585) and *Monographie des poissons du Vieux Rouge ou système dévonien (Old Red Sandstone) des îles Britanniques et de Russie* (586). According to Agassiz, fish exhibit three palaeontological epochs. During the first, from the Silurian to the Trias, ganoids with the vertebral column prolonged to the upper lobe of the tail inhabited the seas; in the second, the Jurassic, we find ganoids with nonprolonged tails; in the third, from the Cretaceous to the present day, placoids, ctenoids, and cycloids constitute almost the entire fish population (783, vol. 1, pp. 212–16; 713; 857).

The importance of Agassiz's works was immediately recognised by his colleagues. Hugh Miller remarked that while Cuvier had named 92 species of fossil fish (651), Agassiz had brought their number to about 1300 (801, p. 60). In the *Recherches* Agassiz devised the ordo Ganoidei and divided it into six families: lepidoids, sauroids, pycnodonts (all individuated by him), scleroderms, gymnodonts, and lopobranchs (already described by Cuvier) (585, vol. 2, pp. 1–2). According to Agassiz the structure of the scales was the essential character of the ordo:

Le caractère essentiel des Ganoïdes est tiré de leurs écailles qui sont toujours formées de deux substances différentes et bien distinctes, savoir de lames osseuses superposées comme celles de toutes les écailles des poissons ordinaires, et d'émail qui recouvre la partie de l'écaille qui est visible à l'extérieur. La forme des écailles est généralement rhomboïdale; cependant il existe de nombreuses variations dans leur disposition. (585, vol. 2, p. x)

Some interesting Devonian fish were discovered shortly before the appearance in 1844 of Agassiz's second work on the subject: Sir Philip G. Egerton described *Gyrolepis* and *Osteolepis* in his "Catalogue of Fossil Fish" of 1836 (*676*, pp. 368, 370). In 1841 Hugh Miller gave an account of *Glyptolepis*—a form inspected by Agassiz himself—and remarked that "the most characteristic parts of the creature are the scales. They are of great size compared with the size of the animal" (*801*, pp. 105–6).

Lady Gordon Cumming described a large number of Devonian fish and sent her descriptions to other geologists (see *586*, p. vii). Once again it was Agassiz who made the major contribution to the necessary taxonomic reconsiderations, with his masterly *Monographie* of 1844. As we saw in chapter 1, Agassiz's intentions were as much theoretical as practical, but regardless even of his theory of the correspondence between the embryonic stages of living fish and the appearance of fossil forms, his became the major reference work. Now Agassiz recognised four families of Devonian fish—cephalaspids, acanthods, dipterian sauroids, and coelacanths—as belonging to the ordo Ganoidei, and one family, plagiostoms, belonging to the ordo Placoids (*586*, p. xxvi). *Glyptolepis, Bothriolepis, Asterolepis, Psammosteus,* and *Dendrodus* belong to the celacanths; *Pteryditys, Coccosteus, Cherlyophorus,* and *Cephalaspis* are genera of the cephalaspids; *Dipterus, Diplopterus, Osteolepis,* and *Glytopomus* belong to the sauroids; while the acanthods include *Cheirolepis* and others. Agassiz had defined the cephalaspids thus: "Ganoïdes hétérocerques, sans vertèbres, ayant la tête et la partie antérieure du tronc couvertes des plaques osseuses" (*586*, p. 5). In 1848 F. M'Coy criticised Agassiz's classification and proposed a new family:

I provisionally propose to establish a distinct family under the [name Placodermi], to include those Ganoid fish of the palaeozoic rocks having the head and body encased in a series of odd or central, and of subsymmetrical or lateral, bony, variously tubercolated plates of large size. It might probably include all the genera described by Agassiz in his "Monog. du Syst. Dévon.", under the title *Cephalaspides*, except *Cephalaspis*, to which that family name might be retained, the other genera having no obvious affinity with it; in addition to these, the present group will conveniently embrace the genera *Bothriolepis, Asterolepis* and *Psammosteus*, which, although widely separated from the former by Agassiz and placed by him in his family of Coelacanths, are so obviously and closely allied to some of them (e.g. *Chelyophorus, Coccosteus,* &c.),that they cannot be separated either by general appearance or any points of structure with which we are acquainted; while they differ, on the other hand, from the other Coelacanthi by the body not being covered by imbricating scales. [*776a*, p. 6]

Egerton disagreed with M'Coy's new classification:

I cannot however allow a charge to be brought against my friend Professor Agassiz, in his absence, of having grouped together genera under the title

Cephalaspides, having no obvious affinity with the genus *Cephalaspis*, and having *widely separated* genera *so obviously and closely allied to some of them, that they cannot be separated either by general appearance or any points of structure*, without claiming that in justice to Agassiz, his opinion on this subject may be accorded in your pages the same publicity which Mr. M'Coy's observations have already received. [*677*, p. 189]

In his reply, M'Coy claimed that he had not detected affinities actually overlooked by Agassiz, but had simply emphasised some results entirely consistent with the Swiss naturalist's researches (*776b*).

In the same period Johannes Müller dealt with the systematics of the Ganoidei, which he considered from the viewpoint of his main field of enquiry, physiology (*816a, b, c*). He referred to Agassiz's classification in the *Recherches* and, while he agreed that *Polypterus* and *Lepisosteus* could be ranked among the Ganoidei, he expressed doubts about the other families established by Agassiz. In Müller's opinion the crucial characteristic of the Ganoidei was their possession of a muscular tunic in the arterial trunk constituted of transversely striated fibres, as in ventricle and auricle, which could be observed to pulsate like a true heart, as in the Selachii and the frogs; the inspection of skin, scales, and fins was therefore basically irrelevant (*816c*, p. 518).

In 1860 Pander, following the comparative anatomical method of Agassiz, showed that in *Glyptolepis* the principal jugular plates are separated by a small jugular plate, and that there are two plates which meet in the midline behind the jugular plates and resemble those to be found under the pectoral arch of *Polypterus*; moreover, the sculpture of the scales of *Glyptolepis* is peculiar to this form and therefore very important for discriminating it from other forms (*848*). Pander's most important innovation was the introduction of the family dendrodonts, so called from the peculiar "tree-like" structure of their teeth, described by Owen in his *Odontography* (*830*), and which Agassiz had shown to occur in several genera of Ganoidei.

Huxley was familiar with this history of different approaches, classifications, criticisms, and amendments, and able to assess their relative importance. In his memoir, he quotes M'Coy and Egerton, refers to Miller and only indirectly—perhaps surprisingly—to Müller, while his main references are to Agassiz and Pander, as the most important attempted classifications on which he wishes to improve.

Huxley disagrees with Pander about the dendrodonts, because he thinks that the character used to define them is in fact strongly marked in other fish. He tries instead to reform the classification proposed by Agassiz in 1844. He starts from the single problem of the systematic position of *Glyptolemus* (*593*; *594*), a genus of Devonian fish allied to *Glyptolepis*, and from there reaches conclusions of much wider scope.

The analysis of *Glyptolemus* demonstrates that it is a typical member of the ganoids, and presents some common characters with five other genera, *Glyptopomus, Gyroptychius, Holoptychius, Platygnathus,* and *Glyptolepis;* these common characters are:

—Two dorsals, acutely lobate paired fins (ventrals of *Glyptolepis*); principal and lateral jugular plates, and no branchiostergal rays; more or fewer large teeth with grooved bases, and consequently folded dentine; sculptured scales and cranial bones—among which last are to be noted three occipital plates—large, distinct parietals, and equally distinct frontals. [96, pp. 430–31]

Huxley therefore proposes to group these six genera into a family of the subordo Crossopterigidae, ordo Ganoidei, the Glyptodipterini, divided into two subfamilies, the rhombiferous Glyptodipterini, containing *Glyptolemus, Glyptopomus,* and *Gyroptychius,* with diphycercal tails and mostly rhomboidal scales, and the cycliferous Glyptodipterini, containing the other three, with heterocercal tails and cycloid scales. Huxley also wants to underline a clear distinction between *Polypterus* and the other members of the subordo Crossopterigidae, such as *Osteolepis* and *Diplopterus;* so he establishes the family Polypterini to contain *Polypterus:*

Thus both ends of the Crossopterigian series appear, if I may use the expression, to be cut off from the modern representatives of the suborder; *Polypterus* being separated from those members of its suborder with which it has the closest zoological relations, by a prodigious gulf of time, and from the fossil allies which are nearest to it in time, by deficient zoological affinities. [pp. 445–46]

Polypterus is in fact the only surviving member of its family, which flourished in the Devonian epoch (p. 421). Huxley's final classification is as follows:

Ordo Ganoidei
Subordo I —Amiadae
Subordo II —Lepidosteidae
Subordo III—Crossopterigidae
    Fam. 1. Polypterini
        Dorsal fin very long, multifid; scales rhomboidal
        Polypterus
    Fam. 2. Saurodipterini
        Dorsal fins two; scales rhomboidal, smooth; fins subacutely lobate
        Diplopterus, Osteolepis, Megalichtys
    Fam. 3. Glyptodipterini
        Dorsal fins two; scales rhomboidal or cycloidal, sculptured; pectoral fins
        acutely lobate; dentition dendrodont
      Sub-Fam. A. with rhomboidal scales
        Glyptolemus, Glyptopomus, Gyropthychius

(*continued*)

Sub-Fam. B. with cycloidal scales
Holoptychius, Glyptolepis, Platygnathus [*Rhizodus, Dendrodus, Cricodus, Lammodus*]
Fam. 4. Ctenodipterini
Dorsal fins two; scales cycloidal; pectorals and ventrals acutely lobate; dentition ctenodont
Dipterus [*Ceratodus?, Trisichopterus?*]
Fam. 5. Phaneropleurini
Dorsal fin single, very long, not subdivided, supported by many interspinous bones; scales thin, cycloidal; teeth conical; ventral fins very long, acutely lobate
Phaneropleuron
Fam. 6. Coelacanthini
Dorsal fins two, each supported by a single interspinous bone; scales cycloidal; paired fins obtusely lobate; air bladder ossified
Coelacanthus, Undina, Macropoma
Subordo IV—Chondrosteidae
Subordo V —Acanthodidae   [96, pp. 442–44]

This classification—a very important contribution indeed to the understanding of fish—is entirely traditional insofar as it is purely anatomical and does not refer to either the fact or the possibility of evolution. The state of knowledge when Huxley wrote this memoir was hardly sufficient for a survey to introduce phylogenetic arguments; yet the complete absence of evolution indicates that in the early 1860s Huxley was not prepared to see the problems of practical zoology—in this case of comparative anatomy—in an evolutionary light.

One may surmise that the observation of the Devonian fish might have engaged Huxley because Müller's comments about the structure and physiology of the heart (816) implied a resemblance between them and amphibians, into whose comparative anatomy he had started to enquire about two years before the publication of his memoir on the fossil fish. Huxley interested himself in the labyrinthodonts, early amphibians described by Owen (831). In 1859 Huxley published "On Dasyceps Bucklandi (Labyrinthodon Bucklandi, Lloyd)" (80; 767), on a specimen which he thought to be distinct from any known labyrinthodont (80, p. 268), and "On a Fragment of a Lower Jaw of a Large Labyrinthodont from Cubbington" (81), in which he suggested that labyrinthodonts were likely to have had a form similar to that of salamanders and newts (p. 270).

He reconsidered these amphibians in 1862 in "On New Labyrinthodonts from the Edinburgh Coal-Field" (105). This memoir deals with specimens shown to Huxley by Allman in Scotland, and describes for the first time an animal which Huxley proposes to call *Polidogaster pisciformis* (105, pp. 533–34). The name emphasises the resemblance between this early amphibian and fish, and gives a hint that by then

Huxley was approaching the theme which was to absorb him within a few years: the discovery of transitional forms between large groups (especially classes) of animals.

In 1863 Huxley described *Anthracosaurus* (*114*). A few years later some vertebrate fossils were found in Bengal, among them remains of labyrinthodonts, which Huxley described in a lengthy memoir of 1865 (*128*). The characteristics of many species of labyrinthodonts are reported in "On a Collection of Fossil Vertebrata, from the Jarrow Colliery, County of Kilkenny" (*136*), read in 1866. None of these works deploys the idea of evolution; but we shall see below how Huxley began from the mid-sixties onwards to develop a specific interest in transitional forms which was to lead to his espousal of evolutionism in his own research.

Dinosaurs and Birds

The two memoirs I shall briefly consider are "On Some Remains of Large Dinosaurian Reptiles from the Stormberg Mountains, South Africa" (*137*) of 1866 (published 1867); and "On the Classification of Birds; and on the Taxonomic Value of the Modifications of Certain of the Cranial Bones Observable in That Class" (*144*) of 1867.

The first of these concerns a box of fossils sent to Murchison by a Mr. Brown, which Huxley declares to contain "certain large reptilian bones, to which a very considerable interest attaches" (*137*, p. 198). Of the approximately fifty numbered items he singles out a pair of femora as being among the most important; the description of the more complete leads him to the conclusion that there is "no doubt as to the Dinosaurian affinities of the animal to which it belonged" (p. 199). Huxley then proceeds to delineate the ten principal differences between Megalosaurian and Iguanodont femora which he has detected from the study of the most complete specimens available; and this leads him to the conclusion that the specimen in question approaches *Megalosaurus* rather than *Iguanodon* in most respects, departing from *Megalosaurus* in the proportional size and form of its trochanters and in its much heavier proportions (pp. 200–201). He christens the animal *Euskelesaurus* (since "it may fitly be said to have 'good legs' " [p. 201]) *Brownii* (after its discoverer).

Only three other items are described in any detail. Item no. 1 is found to correspond closely with the distal end of the femur of *Iguanodon*; but Huxley is more intrigued by the other two:

No. 3 is a very interesting fossil, comprising nearly seven inches of the distal ends of a right tibia and fibula, with an astragalus in undisturbed position, though much mutilated. The width of the conjoined ends of the tibia and fibula is 7.8 inches, six inches being occupied by the tibia alone. The antero-posterior diameter of the tibia is 4.5 inches. The posterior surface presents a wide longitudinal groove; while the anterior appears somewhat trilobed, from the presence of two superficial longitudinal depressions. The astragalus is much damaged, but presents a general resemblance to that bone in Crocodilia and *Scelidosaurus,* its proximal end exhibiting a concave surface, and its distal a convex pulley.

No. 47 is the proximal end of a tibia, which answers very well to the foregoing in size. It is remarkable for the great size of its *cnemial* process, the inferior edge of which (so far as it is preserved) is rounded and concave, like the *procnemial* process in the Flamingo and Albatros. These leg-bones would answer very well to the femur of *Euskelesaurus.* [pp. 201–02]

So Huxley finds himself with a set of specimens, in his opinion belonging to the same animal, which present both reptilian and ornithic characteristics. This may be presumed to mark the beginning of his intensive interest in fossil forms, which was shortly to lead to his explicit espousal and application of the notion of evolution in his own research; though neither the considerations advanced here nor the notions deployed in his next major memoir "On the Classification of Birds" gives any overt hint in that direction, being solely of the same "traditional" structural nature as we have observed throughout the middle period.

"On the Classification of Birds" is curious in one respect, however. The bulk of the memoir (*144,* pp. 241–92) is exactly what the title would imply—a lengthy and detailed exposition of an entirely traditional character regarding the classification of birds extinct and extant. But the memoir begins with a few paragraphs (pp. 238–41), substantially irrelevant to the concerns of the rest of the work, in which the typological proximity of the birds and the reptiles is asserted and defended—the structural evidence on which his imminent evolutionary analysis of the matter will partly depend. Thus:

> The members of the class *Aves* so nearly approach the *Reptilia* in all the essential and fundamental points of their structure, that the phrase "Birds are greatly modified Reptiles" would hardly be an exaggerated expression of the closeness of their resemblance.
>
> In perfect strictness, no doubt, it is true that Birds are no more modified Reptiles than Reptiles are modified Birds, the reptilian and ornithic types being both, in reality, somewhat different superstructures raised upon one and the same ground-plan. [p. 238]

He then proceeds to defend his proposal to group birds and reptiles together as a single group of the Vertebrata, to be called Sauropsida, by enunciating fourteen structural, embryological, and physiological characteristics which distinguish both birds and reptiles from mammals; then elaborates his grounds for maintaining their separation as classes within the group (the question of feathers, and of the structures of the anterior vertebrae, the ribs, the sternum, and the ischia). But in commenting on the tarsal bones, he notes the possibility that their features in the reptile *Compsognathus* may render their features in birds merely "characteristic" of that class rather than "diagnostic" (p. 241). Then he notes: "Birds have hot blood, a muscular valve in the right ventricle, a single aortic arch, and remarkably modified respiratory organs; but it is, to say the least, highly probable that the Pterosauria, if not the Dinosauria, shared some of these characteristics with them" (p. 241); the grounds for this possibility being physiological (see again below). These points were to be further cited and elaborated in his work from 1868 onwards; but here they are merely noted as points affecting the discrimination of the reptilian and avian types.

The rest of the memoir sets forth comprehensively the considerations, "wholly based upon osteological characters" (p. 292), in virtue of which Huxley proposes to divide the birds into the Saururae (comprising only *Archaeopteryx*), Ratitae (the nonflying birds, whose present distribution indicates that they are "in all probability . . . but the waifs and strays of what was once a very large and important group" [p. 244]) and Carinatae (all other extant birds), and their various suborders, arguing for the importance of palatal structures in respect of the subdivisions of the Carinatae.

"On the Classification of Birds" is Huxley's last major "pre-evolutionary" memoir; but even so, any suggestion that the memoir presages his move to "evolutionism" can only be made through hindsight—there are no overt hints. The mere presence of an oddly irrelevant introduction to the work is not much to go on. Taken together with his great interest in the transitional characteristics of *Euskelesaurus* and his involvement in the same period with *Archaeopteryx*, on which he presented a paper in January 1868 (*149*), the appearance of a careful and systematic increase of knowledge in the area of the dinosaur-bird transition is inescapable. This appearance is reinforced by the fact that the points made are repeated as evidence of evolution in later works (see chapter 3). But the present works consist entirely of the kind of material and argument which had characterised Huxley's work from the moment of his adoption of the embryological type concept and the beginning of his work in vertebrate palaeontology; and the question whether in reality he knew where he was going between 1865 and 1868 is undecidable for want of any other evidence.

Haeckel and *Descendenztheorie*

In his memoir of 1868, "On the Animals Which Are Most Nearly Intermediate between Birds and Reptiles" (*146*), Huxley applies for the first time a notion of evolution in the exposition of his own scientific research. It is therefore of crucial significance to us here. The next chapter, which is specifically concerned with Huxley's application of "evolutionism" from 1868 onwards, examines the scientific details of the memoir. What is of importance here is its conceptual and historical context, for it is my contention that it was the work of Ernst Haeckel which finally led Huxley to incorporate the notion of evolution explicitly into his scientific memoirs.

The memoir opens with a dramatic assertion of the principle of evolution: "Those who hold the doctrine of Evolution (and I am one of them) conceive that there are grounds for believing that the world, with all that is in it and on it, did not come into existence in the condition in which we now see it, nor in anything approaching that condition" (146, p. 303). But it quickly becomes apparent that the memoir is not to be an exemplification of the views of Darwin per se. The doctrine of evolution is in fact first referred to in Spencer's *System of Philosophy* as "the only complete and systematic statement of the doctrine with which I am acquainted" (p. 303n), and Huxley speaks of those who "favour the general doctrine without giving an absolute assent to its particular applications" (p. 303). Those applications are, for example, the nebular, uniformitarian, and Darwinian hypotheses in astronomy, geology, and biology respectively: "For many of the objections which are brought against these various hypotheses affect them only, and even if they be valid, leave the general doctrine of Evolution untouched" (p. 304).

Huxley then identifies an issue which he believes to "strike at the heart of the whole doctrine of Evolution": animals and plants in general fall into clearly distinct groupings.

And out of this fact arises the very pertinent objection,—How is it, if all animals have proceeded by gradual modification from a common stock, that these great gaps exist?
We, who believe in Evolution, reply, that these gaps were once non-existent; that the connecting forms existed in previous epochs of the world's history, but that they have died out. [p. 304]

He therefore moves the focus of his argument squarely into the interpretation of the palaeontological record, where the question of observing and demonstrating the operation of natural selective processes cannot of course arise. Instead he is going to testify to the plausibility of genealogy or descent as an evolutionary understanding of fossil data. His decision here parallels the production of Haeckel's *Descendenztheorie* in 1866 (see 716). There is a small and curious piece of terminological evidence in the memoir also pointing in the direction of positive Haeckelian influence: Huxley's use of the term *phylum* (146, p. 312). Darwin's term for the description of relationships of descent was *genealogy*, while *The Oxford English Dictionary* refers *phylogeny* and its cognates specifically to "Haeckel, 1866."

Biographical detail and the correspondence between Huxley and Haeckel are perhaps more indicative of the relationship than the memoir itself. Haeckel's *Generelle Morphologie der Organismen* (716) appeared in 1866, and the two scientists met in London the same year. Huxley was "deeply interested" in his "daring endeavour," Haeckel claims (461, p. 466), which, he grandiloquently asserts, was

the first endeavour to base the general outlines of organic morphology on the theory of descent as it had been revived by Charles Darwin. . . . For in that work I had tried to carry into direct effect that theory, and had given the first sketch of organic pedigrees, the exhibition of which had, by the newly-founded theory of descent, been made the special task of Phylogenetic Systematology. [Ibid.]

Since Huxley's memoir on the dinosaurs dates from February 1868, he appears to have taken some time to assimilate his colleague's views, though as we have seen his work in 1866–67 on dinosaurs and birds shows him expanding his knowledge of data in the areas relevant to the evolutionary statement of 1868 (a process which continued subsequently—see chapter 3). Huxley wrote to Haeckel on 21 January 1868:

In scientific work the main thing about which I am engaged is a revision of the Dinosauria—with an eye to the Descendenz Theorie! The road from Reptiles to Birds is by way of Dinosauria to the Ratitae—the Bird 'phylum' was Struthious, and wings grew out of rudimentary fore-limbs. You see that among other things I have been reading Ernst Haeckel's Morphologie. [571, p. 15]

So the direct pretext was provided by Haeckel. But the problem is to find out why Haeckel was more successful than Darwin in convincing Huxley. First of all it is essential to point out that Haeckel's theory of descent was based upon the interpretation of von Baer's embryological results in the light of the idea of evolution. For Haeckel, ontogeny was the short and rapid recapitulation of phylogeny; during its development the individual repeats the major changes in form evolved by its ancestors during their natural history (705). Haeckel expresses the essence of his thought in the following florid passage from the *Generelle Morphologie*:

Phylogeny, or the palaeontological development of blood-related forms which leads to the establishment of genuses, orders, families and all the other categories of the organic world, is a physiological process which, like all other physiological functions of organisms, proceeds of absolute necessity by mechanistic means.

These means are the atomic and molecular motions which piece organic matter together, and the limitless variegation evidently achieved in the process of phylogenetic development expresses a similar limitless variegation first in

the concatenation of organic matter and then in the subtle compounds of which
the active plasma of the constituent plastides of all organisms is composed. The
phylogenetic or palaeontological development of the main trunk and its diverse
subordinate categories is therefore neither the premeditated purposeful result of
a creative intelligence nor yet the outcome of some mysterious vital force of
nature, but rather the simple and necessary operation of that familiar physical
and chemical process identified by physiology as the operative mechanism in
the development of organic matter. [716, vol. 2, p. 365]

The mechanistic conception of biology emphasised by Haeckel is, as
we have seen, a matter close to Huxley's heart, underlying his conception of the type, his major theoretical weapon. And here Haeckel sub-
sumes those conceptions under phylogenetic principles.

We have observed in all Huxley's work to 1868 a consistent application of von Baer's general approach. Its success consisted of its capacity
to reveal the "pattern" of nature: if you want to understand nature, you
must compare the different types of organisation with the different
levels of development proper of the types. Now, if you replace the modifications of the type by actual historical genealogical connections, you
have preserved your existing picture of the pattern of nature—and you
have created the *Descendenztheorie.*

W. Coleman has shown that this is exactly what was done by Carl
Gegenbaur (645), Haeckel's friend and colleague at Jena (913). Coleman
emphasises that in the 1870 reprint (696b) of his *Grundzüge der vergleichenden Anatomie,* originally written in 1859 (696a) and published
a few months before the *Origin of Species,* Gegenbaur replaced the
relationships between the types with genealogical connections. Gegenbaur wrote in 1870:

The theory allowed what previously had been designated as *Bauplan* or *Typus* to
appear as the sum of the structural elements of animal organisation which are
propagated by means of inheritance, while modifications of the structures are
explained as being adaptations. . . . From the standpoint of descent theory the
'relatedness' of organisms loses its figurative meaning. Whenever we encounter
through the use of precise comparison demonstrable agreement in structural
organisation, this indicates common ancestry founded on inheritance. [696b, p.
19; quoted from 645, p. 162]

As Oscar Schmitt put it in 1872, the new trend of zoology was to base
classification upon the genealogical expression of the types (645, p. 169).
Chapter 3 will confirm Huxley's complete participation in that "new
trend."

We therefore see that Huxley's scientific career was intimately enmeshed with those of his German contemporaries, in respect to both the
notion of the type and the notion of evolution. The first importance of

Haeckel, then, is that he was a member of that community of thought, one of the heirs of the Baerian theoretical tradition.

His other significance is that he was also one of the heirs of the Baerian methodological tradition, again in common with Huxley. It is at this point that we can begin to unravel the paradox which I stated to be the underlying subject matter of this chapter. In the first section we saw Huxley's qualified endorsement of Darwin's "hypothesis"; but in the next we saw the conspicuous absence of influence of that hypothesis on Huxley's own research. Paul Farber (684)* has recently underlined the simultaneous but separate development of the natural-historical and the laboratory-based approaches to biology in the nineteenth century, reminding us of the "tension" between the two sides (pp. 151–52). Further, Allen (588) has stressed that that tension between what he terms the "naturalists" and the "experimentalists" persisted well into this century. Darwin's *Origin of Species* can correctly be counted as "the major intellectual monument of nineteenth-century natural history" (Farber, 684, p. 151). But it neither directly addressed the questions exercising the experimentalists nor directly lends itself to investigation tion by their methods or within their theoretical paradigms.

For example, experimentalists found evolutionary questions tiresome and basically unanswerable by the traditional methods of descriptive morphology; at the same time naturalists found problems of genetic transmission virtually irrelevant to the broader issues of phylogeny and evolution. [Allen, 588, p. 179]

It follows that, while clearly Darwin rehabilitated the idea of evolution as such in the eyes of science, the research of laboratory enthusiasts or workers like Huxley is not the right place to look for evidence of the impact of Darwin's natural-selective theory on the scientific community. The key, as far as the experimentalists were concerned, was rather the realisation that the idea of descent could be placed in the driving seat of an essentially Baerian typology (see 434).

The apparent inconsistency of Huxley's behaviour in the middle period can therefore be resolved into the wider "tension" between the two principal schools of nineteenth-century biological thinking; it appears especially paradoxical only because he to a degree kept a foot in each camp. His behaviour is in fact a perfect exemplification of the accuracy of the broader picture drawn by both Farber and Allen. Huxley's endorsement of evolution in his work from 1868 cannot however be seen as any kind of synthesis of these two aspects—the evolutionism is that of the experimentalists, the physiologists and morphologists, and not an importation of the naturalist natural-selective conception into that tradition.

* I am grateful to Paul Farber for sending me a copy of his article.

These points also deepen our understanding of the context of Huxley's quarrel with Darwin over the scientific status of natural selection. The experimentalists were inclined to regard "theory in evolutionary study as 'speculation'" (588, pp. 182–83). Huxley at times shared something of this attitude: in a footnote to the publication of 1865 of his pre-1859 "Explanatory Preface" (130) he wrote: "It should be noted that these pages were written before the appearance of Mr. Darwin's book on the "Origin of Species"—a work which has effected a revolution in biological speculation" (p. 157n). Fundamentally, therefore, his disagreement with Darwin concerned what could finally count as "good science"—which is why I chose to call it a "philosophical" reservation.

3

The Dinosaur Connection: Palaeontology and the Evidence for Evolution

There are animals so near of kin to both birds and beasts, that they are in the middle between both; amphibious animals link the terrestrial and aquatic together.

—J. Locke, *An Essay Concerning Human Understanding*, book 3, chapter 6, section 12

The Vertebrates

Birds and Dinosaurs

There is an air of pulling rabbits out of a hat about Huxley's memoir "On the Animals Which Are Most Nearly Intermediate between Birds and Reptiles" (*146*). Having asserted the principle of evolution, and complained about the frequent absence of "missing links" to support that principle effectively, he unveils one such link with considerable dramatic flourish. "In short, if I cannot produce the complete title-deeds of the doctrine of animal Evolution, I am able to show a considerable piece of parchment belonging to them" (p. 305).

Huxley then points out the main differences between birds and reptiles (pp. 305–06), showing that existing birds differ widely from existing reptiles. Among the birds, we have to distinguish between the Ratitae, the nonflying birds, such as the ostrich, rhea, emu, *Apterix*, and *Dinornis*, and all other birds, the Carinatae. The Ratitae seem closer to the reptiles than any other extant birds; however, their resemblance to reptiles is not sufficient for them to fill the gap (p. 306). One must therefore refer to fossil forms, and solve the problem by answering two questions:

1. Are any fossil Birds more reptilian than any of those now living?
2. Are any fossil Reptiles more bird-like than living Reptiles? And I shall en-

deavour to show that both these questions must be answered in the affirmative. [p. 307]

Huxley now recalls the circumstances of *Archaeopterix lithographica*, whose discovery has captured the imagination of the scientists of two centuries. In 1861 a feather of this creature was found by Hermann von Meyer (*797*), and in the same year Haeberlein discovered its skeleton. Richard Owen was able to study the remains, which had been bought by the British Museum: for once Huxley and Owen agreed, both detecting the ornithic characteristics of *Archaeopterix*. Andreas Wagner, the noted Munich palaeontologist, tried to demonstrate that *Archaeopterix* provided no evidence for the evolutionary hypothesis (*924*). *Archaeopterix* is still the oldest known bird, and Huxley considered it to be closer to reptiles in structure than any modern bird (*146*, p. 308).

Archaeopterix therefore provides the affirmative answer to Huxley's first question. As to question 2, Huxley does not propose an important transitional role for pterodactyls, which, he claims,

approach birds as much as Bats, among Mammals, may be said to do so. They are a sort of reptilian Bats rather than links between Reptiles and Birds, and it is precisely in those organs which, in birds, are the most characteristically ornithic, the manus and the pes, that they depart most widely from the ornithic type.

Clearly, then, the passage from Reptiles to Birds is not from the flying Reptile to the flying Bird. [pp. 308–9]

In Huxley's view, the extinct reptiles which we must regard as the connecting forms are the dinosaurs. The study of the dinosaurs had been greatly advanced by the discoveries made in the 1830s by von Meyer. In England it was, not surprisingly, Owen who became an authority in the field. It was Owen who coined the name *dinosaurs* ("terrible lizards"). Owen saw the dinosaurs as huge, cold-blooded, and mentally torpid lizardlike animals (*831*).

Dinosaurs became fashionable in the 1850s, when under Owen's supervision B. W. Hawkins reconstructed several life-size models of these vast creatures, which were assembled on a special "Dinosaur Island" at the Great Exhibition, and later moved to the Crystal Palace. In 1854 a dinner was held inside the model of *Iguanodon* for thirty-four guests, Owen himself sitting in its head (*670*, pp. 119–21).

For Huxley, *Iguanodon* is a good example of a dinosaurian genus provided with many characteristics common to reptiles and birds. Certain facts concerning the anatomy of *Iguanodon* suggest that

this vast reptile, and perhaps others of its family, must have walked, temporarily or permanently, upon its hind legs.

However this may be, there can be no doubt that the hind quarters of the *Dinosauria* wonderfully approached those of birds in their general structure, and therefore that these extinct Reptiles were more closely allied to birds than any which now live. [*146*, p. 311]

In "Further Evidence on the Affinity between the Dinosaurian Reptiles and Birds" (*176*), Huxley points to such "ornithic affinities of the *Dinosauria*" as the structure of the pelvis, considered in *Megalosaurus, Iguanodon,* and *Hypsiliphodon* (*176*, p. 480), and the distal end of the tibia and astragalus. The pubis of *Hypsiliphodon,* Huxley claims, constitutes an "unmistakable transition" between reptiles and birds (p. 482).

But another fossil is still closer to being the missing link between reptiles and birds: *Compsognathus longipes* (*146*, p. 311), according to Huxley the most birdlike of all the dinosaurs. It is a creature about two feet long, something like a chicken, and was described for the first time

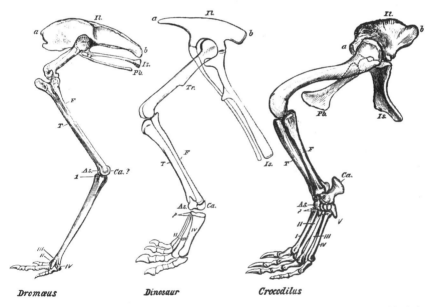

Dromæus   *Dinosaur*   *Crocodilus*

Figure 8.   The pelvis and hind limb of an emu (*dromous*) and a crocodile (*crocodilus*), for comparison with the diagrammatic restoration of the corresponding parts in an iguanodontoid dinosaurian. The bones of the bird are in their natural position; in the dinosaur it may be a question whether the metatarsus was so much raised; in the crocodile the foot would naturally be flat upon the ground, and the thigh turned out nearly at right angles to the body. The letters have the same signification throughout; *Il*, ilium; *a, b*, its anterior and posterior extremities; *Is*, ischium, *Pb*, pubis; *Tr*, trochanter of the femur of the dinosaur; *T*, tibia; *F*, fibula; *As*, astragalus; *Ca*, Calcaneum; I, the distal division of the tarsus; I, II, III, IV, V, the digits. [*196*, p. 483] by Andreas Wagner (923). Its modern taxonomic position can be referred to during the following discussion:

Order Saurischia
Suborder Theropoda
Infraorder Coelurosauria
Family Procompsognathidae
Genus & Species *Compsognathus longipes*, late Jurassic, Europe (827, p. 181)

Writing about this creature, Huxley maintains:

Notwithstanding its small size (it was not much more than two feet in length), this reptile must, I think, be placed among, or close to, the *Dinosauria*: but it is still more bird-like than any of the animals which are ordinarily included in that group. . . . It is impossible to look at the conformation of this strange reptile and to doubt that it hopped and walked, in an erect or semi-erect position, after the manner of a bird, to which its long neck, slight head and small anterior limbs must have given it an extraordinary resemblance. [146, pp. 311–12]

Huxley was not completely sure whether *Compsognathus* was a true dinosaur, and in 1869 he pointed out that its features suggest that it should be placed in a related but separate group. He proposed the order Ornithoscelida, to include Dinosauria and Compsognatha. In Dinosauria the cervical vetebrae are short and the femur is as long as, or longer than, the tibia; in Compsognatha the cervical vertebrae are long, the femur shorter than the tibia (167, pp. 491–92). In any case we must refer to dinosaurlike forms if we wish to understand the origin of birds. Major evidence is provided by the mode of walking:

It is certain that Compsognathus must have walked on its hind legs.
The question, then, naturally arises, did the gigantic Dinosauria, such as Iguanodon and Megalosaurus, have the same mode of progression? This seems, at first sight, hard to believe, but there is considerable reason for thinking that it may have been the case. [235, p. 182]

From palaeontological evidence, we may therefore conclude that towards the beginning of the Mesozoic there were semi-erect animals, possibly endothermic, with two ornithic feet. Such bipeds were either reptiles or birds or, more probably, both (146, p. 312). Finally, "there is nothing very wild or illegitimate in the hypothesis that the *phylum* of the class *Aves* has its root in the Dinosaurian reptiles" (ibid.). All this is obviously strong evidence for the evolutionary view, and thus:

The facts of Palaeontology, so far as Birds and Reptiles are concerned, are not opposed to the doctrine of Evolution, but, on the contrary, are quite such as that doctrine would lead us to expect; for they enable us to form a conception of the manner in which Birds may have evolved from Reptiles, and therefore justify us in maintaining the superiority of that hypothesis, that birds have been so origi-nated, to all hypotheses which are devoid of an equivalent basis of fact. [p. 313]

In "On the Classification of the Dinosauria, with Observations on the Dinosauria of the Trias" (167), Huxley's point is that Owen was mistaken in thinking that the dinosaurs were closer to the mammals than to the birds (pp. 488–89), since von Meyer's analysis of the group had clearly shown their affinities with the class Aves (p. 489). On such an assumption, and on the grounds of a grouping obtained after a few years' study, Huxley proposes a classification of the dinosaurs, the

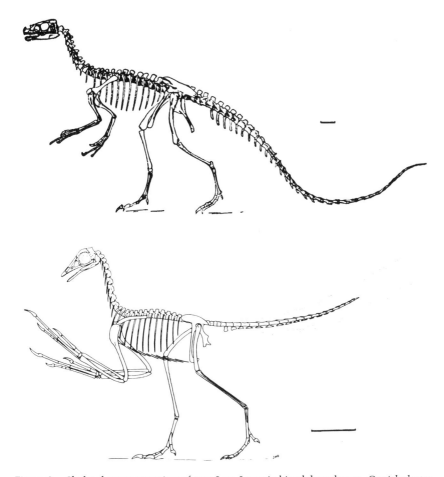

Figure 9.   Skeletal reconstruction of two Late Jurassic bipedal predators; *Ornitholestes hermanni* (above), a coelurosaurian dinosaur from the Morrison Formation (Kim-meridgian age) of North America, and *Archaeopteryx lithographica* (below) from the Solenhofen Limestone (Kimmeridgian age) of Europe. [827, p. 170]

theme of which is to show once more the affinities of those ancient reptilian forms with the birds.

Huxley's view of the dinosaurs as the ancestors of the birds was shared by some of his most illustrious contemporaries. In a letter sent to Huxley which was later published (856), John Phillips claimed agreement with the views propounded by his colleague. In 1871 E. D. Cope published his "Synopsis of the Extinct Batrachia and Reptilia of North America" (647; see also 646), wherein he pointed out that many structural characters supported the view of a close relationship between dinosaurs and birds. These were the major modifications of the dinosaurs departing from the reptilian type to approach the birds (Cope's reference is to *Laelaps*). The position of the ilium becomes transverse from its original vertical position; the acetabulum is thus thrown upwards and forwards; the great size and the inferior and posterior position of the other pelvic elements transfer the weight of the viscera posteriorly; as a consequence, a longer series of sacral vertebrae derives from the lumbar ones and the body of the animal is supported by strong hind limbs, more nearly beneath the centre of gravity than in other types of reptiles. The structure of the hind limbs also approaches the birds (647). On the other hand, Cope disagreed with Huxley in that he thought *Iguanodon* was a quadrupedal dinosaur rather than an erect one (647, p. 16). Huxley's views were shared by Gegenbaur (697), and also by O. C. Marsh, although he thought that the dinosaurs should be classified as a subclass (789); Dollo (671; 672), W. M. Parker (849), M. Fürbringer (695), and (not surprisingly) Andreas Wagner opposed them. Fürbringer's criticism was especially serious; he claimed that the anatomical similarities which the supporters of the rival theory had detected were simply convergent adaptations, and as such of no evolutionary significance (695). He proposed a monophyletic origin for the birds and thought that the ancestor of the birds must have been a common sauropsid form to be placed between the Dinosauria, the Lacertilia, and the Crocodilia.

Early in the twentieth century, E. R. Lankester again proposed *Iguanodon* as the most likely ancestor of the birds (757, p. 202). But later, after the influential works of Broom (622) and especially Heilmann, Huxley's opinion was abandoned. G. Heilmann, a Danish zoologist, published in 1926 a masterly work, written in English, entitled *The Origin of Birds* (724). In this book he agrees with Huxley so far as *Archaeopterix* is concerned, and in the first part he seems sympathetic to the possibility that coelurosaurian theropods, to which *Compsognathus* belongs, are the ancestors of the birds; but he goes on to claim that the coelurosaurian theropods cannot be such forms, since they are not primitive enough. In fact they have no clavicles, Heilmann explains, while such a structure occurs both in birds and in the pseudosuchians, ancestors of the theropods:

It would seem to be a rather obvious conclusion that it is amongst the Coelurosaurs that we have to look for the bird-ancestor. And yet, this would be too rash, for the very fact that the clavicles are wanting would in itself be sufficient to prove that these saurians could not possibly be the ancestors of the birds. . . . A bird-ancestor could not be without clavicles. [p. 182]

Today, a group of palaeontologists led by Professor John Ostrom of Yale University propounds a view which is in fact a revival of Huxley's. Ostrom rightly claims that the real problem lies in finding the ancestor of *Archaeopterix*, which is still the oldest known bird (827). Heilmann's argument, he points out, resting entirely on the absence of clavicles in theropods, is not tenable, since (1) theropods with clavicles have been discovered (e.g., *Velociraptor mongoliensis*); (2) the argument is merely negative and therefore inconclusive; and (3) the clavicles are membranous bones rather than endochondral, and may have been present unossified in some theropods, therefore failing to be preserved in the fossil specimens available to us (825, p. 75). Ostrom points to an impressive series of resemblances between the features of coelurosaurian theropods and *Archaeopterix*:

(a) Vertebral column:	(1) Thoracic vertebrae pleurocoelus (and probably amphicoelus)
	(2) Ten cervical vertebrae and 12 to 15? thoracics
(b) Fore limb:	(3) Manus reduced to digits I, II, and III
	(4) Phalangeal proportion of the fingers
	(5) Proportions of the three metacarpals
	(6) Carpus of two or three elements including a lunate radiale
	(7) Proportions of humerus to radius and ulna
	(8) Morphology of the humerus
(c) Pectoral arch:	(9) Very narrow, strap-like scapula
	(10) Subrectangular coracoid fused to scapula
(d) Hind limb:	(11) Pes with four digits, V being lost
	(12) Phalangeal proportions
	(13) Reversed allux
	(14) Metatarsal proportions
	(15) Mesotarsal joint
	(16) Well-developed ascending process of the astragalus
	(17) Hind limb proportions
	(18) Morphology of the femur
(e) Pelvis:	(19) Shape of the ilium

(20) Shape of the pubis, with a distal expansion and a
long symphysis
(21) Open acetabulum [*824*, p. 136]

His conclusion is:

All available evidence indicates that the immediate ancestor of *Archaeopterix*
was a small coelurosaurian dinosaur and that the phylogeny of avian ancestry
was:
Pseudosuchia—Coelurosauria—*Archaeopterix*—higher birds. [*827*, p. 174]

The general features of *Archaeopterix* are more dinosaurian than avian
or pseudosuchian (*825*, p. 73); * the ornithic characteristic of *Archaeop-*
terix is the presence of a furcula (and, of course, of feathers). Ostrom
concludes:

The critical question, however, is: Is it more probable that *Archaeopterix*
acquired the large number of derived "theropod" characters by convergence or
in parallel at the same time that these same features were being acquired by
some coelurosaurian theropods—presumably from a common ancestor? Or is it
more likely that these many derived characters are common to some small
theropods and *Archaeopterix* because *Archaeopterix* evolved directly from such
a theropod? There is absolutely no question in my mind that the last explanation is far more probable.
    The fact that so many traits occurred almost simultaneously in both groups
is strong prima facie evidence of a direct evolutionary relationship between
theropods and *Archaeopterix*. [*825*, pp. 74–75]

On the other hand, it seems that *Compsognathus* can be excluded as the
ancestor of the birds, as Ostrom has shown in his monograph on this
small creature, which was not even feathered. *Compsognathus* is, according to Ostrom, a dead-end theropod line (*827*, p. 115).
    A question relevant to this view concerns the blood circulation of the
dinosaurs. Reptiles are ectotherms, birds are endotherms: in imprecise
lay terms, reptiles are cold-blooded, birds warm-blooded. Now, if we
maintain that there is a derivative link between birds and dinosaurs,
good evidence for that view would be that the latter, or some of them,
were warm-blooded. Huxley had no means of proving that the warm-
bloodedness of the dinosaurs was more than a mere possibility, and the
inference of function from structure is in any case a complicated matter
(*873*). In "On the Classification of Birds" he points out, as we have seen,
that pterosaurs, "if not Dinosaurs," were probably endotherms, given
the amount of work required to sustain aerial motion and (probably)
erect posture respectively (*144*, p. 241). The electron microscope and

---

* I am grateful to Professor Ostrom for sending me a copy of this paper.

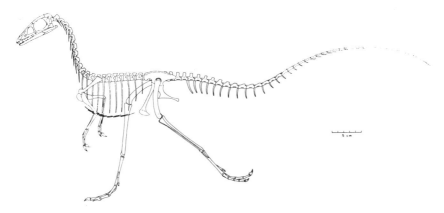

Figure 10. Skeletal reconstruction of *Compsognathus longipes*. The distal parts of the tail are hypothetical, as is the exact form of the ilium and the posterior part of the skull. Notice the large size of the head, the long hands, and the great length of the foot and metatarsus. [826]

other innovations have provided evidence which would have pleased Huxley.

In the bones of warm-blooded animals, the cells have a distinct oval shape and a large number of blood vessels is detectable; such structures are connected to the more highly specialised and complex metabolism of the warm-blooded animals, such as birds and mammals, and do not occur in the ectothermic ones, such as the reptiles. Dr. A. de Ricqlès in Paris (609;* 670) has for some years been observing slices of dinosaur bone by means of the electron microscope, and has reached the conclusion that the cellular structure of the bones of dinosaurs resembles that of the known warm-blooded animals.

Of course, we can know neither the structure of the soft parts nor the physiology of extinct animals. Nonetheless, bearing in mind the principle of the relationship between function and structure, we can make deductions concerning the probable physiology if we know the structure of the hard parts. Furthermore, as Ostrom repeats, "the evidence indicates that erect posture and locomotion are not possible without high metabolism and high uniform temperature" (670, p. 60).

Relying, perhaps too confidently, on the much-debated evidence available, R. T. Bakker and P. M. Galton claim that dinosaurs and birds should be placed together in a new class of vertebrates, the Dinosauria.

---

*I am grateful to the BBC for sending me the script of their programme "The Hot-Blooded Dinosaurs."

Such a class would contain three subclasses, Saurischia, Aves, and Ornithischia (599, p. 171). Ostrom's views have been criticised by A. D. Walker (925), who claims that the analysis of the evolution of the pelvis shows that birds cannot derive from dinosaurs, and that there is a close relationship between birds and crocodiles; birds are more likely, on this view, to have originated from quadrupedal, arboreal ancestors from the late Triassic to mid-Jurassic. I am not prepared to take sides here. From a historical point of view what is important is that we have evidence that Huxley is among the forerunners of an important palaeontological hypothesis, and one of the founders of the study of avian phylogeny.

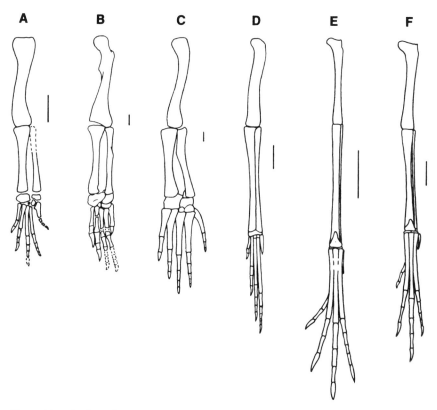

Figure 11. Outline drawings of the left hindlimb skeleton of *Archaeopteryx* (E) contrasted with those of various pseudosuchians (A–D) and that of a small theropod (F). All figures are views of the anterior aspect with femora drawn to the same length in order to minimize differences due to size. A, *Euparkeria*; B, *Riojasuchus*; C, *Ticinosuchus*; D, *Lagerpeton*; E, *Archaeopteryx*; F, *Compsognathus*. [827, 154]

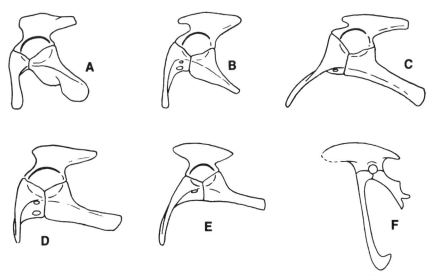

Figure 12.   Thecodontian pelves compared with that of Archaeopteryx (F). All figures are of left pelves in lateral view, but not to the same scale. A, *Erythrosuchus* (a protero-suchian); B, *Stagonolepis* (an aetosaur); C, *Ticinosuchus* (a pseudosuchian); D, *Euparkeria* (a pseudosuchian); E, *Ornithosuchus* (a pseudosuchian); F, *Archaeopteryx* (as reconstructed from all five skeletal specimens). [*827*, p. 155]

Crocodiles

In his memoir of 1859 on *Stagonolepis,* Huxley had mentioned another fossil, *Hyperodapedon gordoni* (*73,* p. 118), to which ten years later he was to devote a whole memoir (*160*). There Huxley explained that from 1866 onwards he had had the chance to reconsider the palaeontological questions presented by *Stagonolepis* and *Hyperodapedon.* In 1866 G. Gordon had sent him several specimens of structures belonging to *Hyperodapedon* (*160,* p. 376). One interesting fragment enabled Huxley to distinguish the teeth and jaws of *Hyperodapedon* from those of other reptiles. Later he was to receive other fragments of *Hyperodapedon* from India (p. 377). These specimens indicated that *Hyperodapedon* was more widespread than had been supposed, and especially that there were good reasons to think that Murchison was wrong in considering *Hyperodapedon* a fossil of Devonian origin. Huxley thus sided with Lyell in his controversy with Murchison on this fossil. According to Lyell, *Hyperodapedon* was from the Triassic; according to Huxley, the presence of a specimen of this fossil in the sandstone of Triassic age in Warwickshire was important evidence supporting him. Moreover, the importance of this fossil lies in its having a unique arrangement of the palato-maxillary apparatus and in its wide distribution. Huxley claims that it was a purely terrestrial animal:

> The question of the terrestrial habit of *Hyperodapedon* assumes a great importance when the wide distribution of the genus is taken into consideration. It has now been discovered in the North of Scotland, in the centre of England, and in central India; and if it were, as I doubt not it was, a terrestrial or semi-terrestrial animal, that alone indicates the existence of a very extended mass of dry land in the Northern hemisphere during the period in which it lived. And the proof of the existence of continental land in the Northern hemisphere acquires increased interest when we consider the evidence which shows what period this was.
>
> The cardinal fact in that evidence is the occurrence of *Hyperodapedon* in the Coton-End Quarry in Warwickshire, as proved by Dr. Lloyd's specimen. It has never been doubted, I believe, that the Sandstone in which this quarry is excavated is of Triassic age. It has yielded Labyrinthodonts and Thecodont Saurians; and its stratigraphical position is such that the only question which can possibly arise is, whether it is Triassic or Permian. [p. 385]

Remains of the reptilian forms had been found in India, South Africa, England, and Würtenberg. Now,

> all these four faunae are connected by reptilian genera, which are respectively common to two of them; thus the British and the Indian by *Hyperodapedon*, the Indian and the African by Dicynodon: the British and the German by *Labyrinthodone* (which according to von Meyer occurs in Germany). The Labyrinthodonts and Crocodiliform reptiles are common to all four. [p. 387]

From this survey of distribution, Huxley begins to form a clear mental picture of the relations among the various forms of reptiles. Distribution is a major aspect of the evolutionary view of biology. New Zealand, for example, still houses *Sphenodon* and representatives of the giant birds Dinornithidae, seeming thus to indicate the survival of ancient forms up to the present day. *Sphenodon* aptly exemplifies what Huxley called "persistent types." *Sphenodon,* also called *Hatteria* (p. 384), is nowadays often called a "living fossil" because it is the one reptile which retains approximately the same organisation as that of fossil reptiles, as Huxley points out.

Although the term *living fossil* is obviously anomalous, the concept of "persistent types" is important, and Huxley devoted a memoir to it in 1859 entitled "On the Persistent Types of Animal Life" (72). There he stated:

Certain well marked forms of living beings have existed through enormous epochs, surviving not only the change of physical conditions, but persisting comparatively unaltered, while other forms of life have appeared and disappeared. Such forms may be termed "persistent types" of life; and examples of them are abundant enough in both the animal and the vegetable worlds. [p. 91]

The importance to evolution of such persistent types is great, once the concept of transmutation has been accepted, for they exemplify forms resembling the presumed ancestors of many other living forms, and therefore provide useful indications of the probable appearance of the organisation of ancestral forms. *Hatteria* is a striking example of ancestral reptilian form.

In the memoirs on *Stagonolepis* and *Hyperodapedon*, Huxley prepares the ground for a general evolutionary survey of the Crocodilia, which is one of his most important contributions to evolutionary science. This work, "On Stagonolepis Robertsoni, and on the Evolution of the Crocodilia" (222), appeared in 1875. Here Huxley considers the differences and affinities of *Stagonolepis* and *Belodon*, the most closely allied form to *Stagonolepis*, discovered in Würtenberg by von Meyer, and the relations of these forms to the crocodiles (pp. 68–70).

Huxley was convinced that *Belodon* was allied to the crocodiles, though other scientists differed—Cope (647, pp. 56–61), for example, classified it in Owen's subordo Thecodontia, stating that here

we have a singularly generalized group, combining characters of lizards, crocodiles and Sauropterygians. The neural arch of the vertebrae united by suture and the slightly biconcave centrum, resemble the last two, so also the abdominal ribs. The limbs are rather crocodilian, the position of the nares, Plesiosaurian. The clavicle is lacertilian, while the three vertebrae of the sacrum and the femur are between those and the dinosauria.

The most important characters distinguishing these animals from the Sauropterygia are the presence of an elongated sacrum and the more ambulatory form of limbs. [p. 56]

Huxley considered Cope's evidence inconclusive (222, p. 69n), and continued to see *Belodon* as important evidence of the evolutionary relationships of the crocodiles. As a result of the analysis of their comparative anatomy, Huxley proposed three suborders of the ordo Crocodilia: Parasuchia, Mesosuchia, and Eusuchia (p. 71). The characteristics of the base of the cranium and their influence on the position of the nostrils were taken as the criteria of comparison. On the relationship between *Hatteria* and the Crocodilia, Huxley assumed that the former was little modified and the latter greatly modified from a common ancestral form which he assigned to the Palaeozoic (p. 83).

In Parasuchia, which include *Belodon* and *Stagonolepis*, "neither the palatine nor the pterygoid bones are produced into osseous plates which prolong the nasal passage and give rise to secondary posterior nares.

Consequently the nasal chambers communicate with the mouth by apertures situated beneath the anterior part of the skull" (p. 71).

The palatine bones of Mesosuchia "are produced into osseous plates, which prolong the nasal passages and give rise to secondary posterior nares, which are situated beneath the middle of the skull. The pterygoid bones take no share in the formation of secondary posterior nares" (ibid.).

The subordo Eusuchia includes the modern crocodiles ("the most Crocodilian of Crocodiles" [p. 73]): "Both the palatine and pterygoid bones are produced into osseous plates, which prolong the nasal passages backwards, and give rise to secondary posterior nares, situated beneath the hinder part of the skull" (p. 72).

Mesosuchia are to be considered as intermediate between Parasuchia and Eusuchia (p. 73). Parasuchia, especially *Hyperodapedon* and *Sphenodon*, resemble the Lacertilia (lizards). There are no great differences between Mesosuchia and Eusuchia, while Parasuchia are remote in their organisation from the former. Morphologically, the three suborders form a more or less continuous series, with a larger gap between Parasuchia and Mesosuchia and a smaller one between Mesosuchia and Eususchia, but the modifications necessary to connect the various groups are very simple, and of the same order: "The kind of change which would convert a Parasuchian Crocodile into a Mesosuchian, would, if continued, convert a Mesosuchian into a Eusuchian" (p. 74). This is for Huxley a decisive step towards an evolutionary interpretation of the crocodilian forms. If palaeontological evidence can be found to show that structurally more primitive forms are *temporally* more ancient than the more complex, this will be good evidence of the occurrence of evolution:

Hence, if there is any valid historical foundation for the doctrine of evolution the *Eusuchia* ought to have developed from the *Mesosuchia*, and these from the *Parasuchia*; and if this process of evolution has taken place under such conditions that the skeletons of the *Crocodilia* which have been subject thereto have been preserved, geological evidence should show that the *Parasuchia* have preceded the *Mesosuchia*, and the *Mesosuchia* the *Eusuchia* in order of time.

Now, this is exactly what the geological evidence does prove. [Ibid.]

All the modifications which the crocodilian form has undergone are evidence for the theory of evolution: "The case of the crocodiles is . . . cogent evidence of the actual occurrence of evolution" (p. 76).

Huxley was deeply involved, even before 1859, with the problem of the gaps between the various reptilian forms. A report of a paper of 1858 is preserved in his private papers under the title "On a New Species of *Plesiosaurus* from Street, Near Glastonbury: With Remarks on the

Structure of the Atlas and Axis Vertebrae, and of the Cranium, in That Genus." It is a comparison between *Plesiosaurus etheridgi* and *Teleosaurus*, treating the structure of a portion of the cranium of the former. He concludes that "teleologically, such an arrangement appears not very comprehensible. . . . In many respects the *Teleosauria* bridge over the gap between the long-necked *Enaliosauria* and the existing *Crocodilia*—a conclusion not without interest when the relations in time of the two orders are considered" (*HM*, vol. 95, pp. 1–2; also 63).

Huxley's survey of the Crocodilia is an early and interesting case of a survey of the evolution of groups above the level of species (see 868), a kind of evolution which is still somewhat controversial (709) and which, of course, can be established only if the palaeontological record is adequate.

Huxley continued his study of the Crocodilia in 1877, with "The Crocodilian Remains Found in the Elgin Sandstones, with Remarks on the Ichnites of Cummingstone" (240), one of his longest scientific memoirs. We find here the most complete description of *Stagonolepis* (pp. 188–225), the form which had first attracted Huxley to the study of the reptiles. *Stagonolepis* must have resembled a modern cayman, he concludes, but with rather gavial-like elongated skull (p. 225). Huxley has no doubt that *Stagonolepis* and *Belodon* constitute a suborder of the Crocodilia, viz. Parasuchia (p. 227). The temporal distribution of the crocodilian suborders is:

1. The *Parasuchia*, in the Trias and perhaps earlier (215–190 million years ago)
2. The *Mesosuchia*, in the Middle Mesozoic rocks from the *Upper Lias* to the Wealden (c. 150 million years ago)
3. The *Eusuchia*, in the later Mesozoic rocks and in the Tertiaries from the *Later Cretaceous* to the Recent Epoch (from 100 million years ago)

In other words, the order of occurrence of the three divisions of the *Crocodilia* in time, coincides with the order in which they depart from the Lacertilian type, and put on special crocodilian characters; and thus, palaeontological fact is in precise accordance with the needs of the theory of Evolution. The evidence in favour of the gradual development of existing from ancient *Crocodilia*, is in fact as cogent, though not so complete, as that by which the origin of the horse from a three-toed ancestor has been demonstrated. [p. 231]

Huxley reconsidered *Hyperodapedon* for the last time in his 1887 memoir, "Further Observations upon Hyperodapedon Gordoni" (300). This consists of a comparison between *Hyperodapedon* and *Sphenodon*; a discussion of *Rynchosaurus* is included. Huxley concludes that the three forms constitute the Lacertilian Sphenodontinae, comprehending the two families of Rynchosauridae and Sphenodontinae (pp. 654–55).

Mammals

Huxley's contributions to mammalian palaeontology are numerically rather few, his main concern being to express with his usual clarity the current thought of his fellow scientists. His early works on mammalian palaeontology are "On a New Species of Macrauchenia (M. boliviensis)" (a camelid) of 1861 (*94*), and "On the Osteology of the Genus Glyptodon" of 1863 (*122*); these memoirs were defined by Sir Arthur Smith Woodward as "models of exposition" (*551*, p. 729), but they do not seem to be much more than that.

Huxley delivered three presidential addresses to the Geological Society.* The following extract, from the 1870 address, is one of his clearest and most detailed descriptions of how, in his opinion, evolution occurs in animal forms in the light of palaeontological evidence. The reasoning accords closely with his analysis of the crocodiles.

Every fossil which takes an intermediate place between forms of life already known, may be said, so far as it is intermediate, to be evidence in favour of evolution, inasmuch as it shows a possible road by which evolution may have taken place. But the mere discovery of such a form does not, in itself, prove that evolution took place by and through it, nor does it constitute more than presumptive evidence in favour of evolution in general. Suppose A, B, C to be three forms, of which B is intermediate in structure between A and C. Then the doctrine of evolution offers four possible alternatives. A may have become C by way of B; or C may have become A by way of B; or A and C may be independent modifications of B; or A and C may be independent modifications of some unknown D. . . . But if it can be shown that A, B and C exhibit successive stages in the degree of modification, or specialization, of the same type, and if, further, it can be proved, that they occur in successively newer deposits, A being in the oldest, and C in the newest, then the intermediate character B has quite another importance, and I should accept it, without hesitation, as a link in the genealogy of C. I should consider the burden of proof to be thrown upon anyone who denied C to have been derived from A by way of B, or in some closely analogous fashion; for it is always probable that one may not hit upon the exact line of filiation, and, in dealing with fossils, may mistake uncles and nephews for fathers and sons. [*177*, pp. 529–30]

It is therefore possible to speak of two kinds of types: *intercalary*, which are intermediate between two others, but without genetic relationship, and *linear*, in which such a relationship can be established (p. 530).

---

*The first address was delivered in 1862, when Huxley, not yet president, stood in for the then incumbent (*104*). In that address he proposed to replace the term *contemporaneity* with *homotaxis*, the latter being better in expressing similarity of order and excluding the notion of time. In his second address (*163*) in 1869, he endeavoured to reply to Lord Kelvin's claim that the age of the earth was not sufficient to allow the time required for the slow process of evolution by natural selection (*748*). A complete and satisfactory reconstruction of this episode can be found in *628; 629; 887*; see also *854; 878*.

For Huxley, a characteristic example of linearity is the evolution of the Equidae (pp. 532–33). It is possible (p. 534) to draw the lineage of the modern horse from *Anchitherium* in the Miocene to *Equus* through *Hipparion* (which corresponds to B in the quoted passage). The same method can be applied backwards to earlier times. The process by which *Anchitherium* became *Equus* is one of specialisation, Huxley points out, one of the major principles of the evolution of large groups.

A number of studies on the horses, their systematic position, and their genealogy were performed by other palaeontologists in the same period. Especially active in the field were the Americans Cope and Marsh (648; 785; 786; 788). In 1874 Marsh applied to American horses the same principles Huxley had used four years earlier for European horses, and quoted Huxley (788, p. 292). In 1882, Cope obtained a genealogy of the order Peryssodactila to which horses belong:

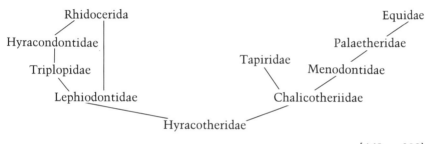

[648, p. 380]

The "linear" view of the genetic derivation of form which Huxley and Cope propose is called *orthogenesis.* It is important to note that all these studies emphasised the aspect of descent and made the principle of natural selection almost unnecessary to the evolutionary survey. As Rensch wrote: "The increasing number of orthogenetic lines of descent discovered towards the end of the last century by palaeontologists such as Gaudry, Cope and others, presented an ever-increasing amount of material apparently rendering impossible any interpretation by principles of selection" (868, p. 57). The presidential address of 1870 shows that Huxley, who as we have seen was not completely confident about natural selection, was one of those palaeontologists who, by emphasising orthogenesis, contributed to making descent rather than natural selection the focus of the evolutionary view.

Huxley's major memoir on mammals is "On the Application of the Laws of Evolution to the Arrangement of the Vertebrata and More Particularly of the Mammalia" (267). In Huxley's opinion there is evidence for the evolution of the Equidae, commencing from forms in the Tertiary epoch which differed least from the general type of structure of the higher mammals, to forms most widely departing from that type, through a series of forms displaying intermediate characters (p. 457). For example, the most ancient ancestors of the horse known to palaeontologists had four digits in the fore foot and three in the hind foot; the modern horse has only one complete digit in each foot, the others being mere rudiments. The intermediate Equidae should therefore exhibit intermediate characters (ibid.). Huxley suggests that the evolution of the Equidae, like that of all groups above the species level, consists in a progressive specialisation of forms from an original generalised stock. In the Equidae it is possible to detect from the Eocene period a threefold process of modification:

1. There has been excess of development of some parts in relation to others.
2. Certain parts have undergone complete or partial suppression.
3. Certain parts, which were originally distinct, have coalesced. [p. 458]

These three processes constitute what Huxley calls a "threefold law of evolution" where "law" means a general statement summarising certain observational facts concerning the passage from the Eocene *Eohippus* to the present *Equus*.

This law of evolution of the ancestral horses is identical to that which describes the development of any animal form from the moment in which the characters of the group to which the animal belongs are detectable in the embryo:

After a mammalian embryo, for example, has taken on its general mammalian characters, its further progress towards its specific form is effected by the excessive growth of one part in relation to another, by the arrest of growth or the suppression of parts already formed, and by the coalescence of parts primarily distinct. [Ibid.]

This passage shows its connection with Haeckel's interpretation of von Baer's embryology. The "coincidence" between the law of individual development and the law of ancestral development is a very useful one, since the law of individual development helps the otherwise doubtful palaeontologist in his enquiry into the ancestral development of large animal groups (ibid.). The application of this method implies that *Eohippus* must have been preceded in the Mesozoic by equine forms with five digits and other primordial characteristics. For example, this ancestral form must have had a "lower" form of brain (and here Huxley quotes Marsh [787] and Lartet). It had been demonstrated that such is the case in the older forms of all mammalian groups. It is worth remarking that "since the existing Horse has a diffuse allantoic placentation, the primary form could not have presented a higher, and may have possessed a lower, condition of the various modes by which the foetus derives nourishment from the parent among the vertebrated animals" (267, p. 459). Such a form would closely resemble an insectivore, according to Huxley. This does not mean that the *present* insectivores are the ancestors of present mammals, since they are also the result of a series of evolutionary modifications of primordial forms.

The case of the Equidae is only one example of what happens in mammalian evolution: more modern, specialised forms such as carnivores, artiodactyls, and perissodactyls are connected with less-developed forms, which all resemble the insectivores very closely (p. 460). In producing a classification of animals that takes account of the many palaeontological resemblances discovered between 1859 and 1880, Huxley argues, we must consider the morphological resemblances and differences between the animal forms. They fall under three headings:

(1) those of adult individuals; (2) those of successive stages of embryological development or individual evolution; (3) those of successive stages of the evolution of the species, or ancestral evolution. . . .

Hence, in attempting to classify the Mammalia, we must take into account not only their adult and embryogenetic characters, but their morphological, in so far as *the several groups represent different stages of evolution.* [p. 460; italics added]

If evolution does occur, Huxley argues, it is worth maintaining the concept of a *scala animantium*, after expurgating from it the metaphysical implications inherent in Bonnet's formulation of the concept, and taking it as a simple reference point for an evolutionary classification (p. 461); as for the type, Huxley is here convinced that it is possible to use a metaphysical concept without reference to its metaphysics.

We can thus have a "natural classification," in which each mammalian group is arranged according to its place in the scale of evolution of the mammalian type. And the position of a species on such a scale is to be decided according to the application of the "laws of evolution":

That is to say, those groups which approach the non-mammalian Vertebrata most closely, present least inequality of development, least suppression and least coalescence of the fundamental parts of the type, must belong to earlier stages of evolution; while those which exhibit the contrary characters must appertain to later stages. [p. 461]

If this be so, the monotremes are the earliest stage of mammalian development (ibid.); but again we must not suppose that the monotremes themselves are the ancestors of all mammals. They too are modifications, as Haeckel suggests, of the original mammalian type. It is therefore necessary to postulate the existence of a group representing the lowest stage of mammalian organisation, of which the present monotremes are the only known members: Huxley proposes the name of Prototheria (pp. 462–63). Next in the scale come the Marsupialia, which are intermediate between the Prototheria and the higher mammals; and if we now apply considerations similar to those applied to the mono-tremes, we can determine the position of the Metatheria (pp. 463–64). Finally we have forms in which "we have the mammalian type in a higher state of evolution than that presented by the Prototheria and the Metatheria. Hence we may term forms which have reached this stage the *Eutheria*" (p. 467). In the process here described, the insectivores play a key role:

Given the common plan of the Insectivora and of the Rodentia, and granting that the modifications of the structures of the limbs, of the brain, and of the alimentary and reproductive viscera which occur among them may exist and accumulate elsewhere, and the derivation of all the *Eutheria* from animals which, except for their simpler placentation, would be Insectivores, is a simple deduction from the law of evolution. [Ibid.]

This time Huxley does not hesitate to postulate the occurrence of a group of animals which would fill the palaeontological gaps in the "sub-mammalian" stage of evolution. He proposes, in perfect Haeckelian fashion, the name Hypotheria: "I do not doubt that when we have a fuller knowledge of the terrestrial Vertebrata of the later Palaeozoic epochs, forms belonging to this stage will be found among them" (p. 468).

In 1879, in a memoir entitled "On the characteristics of the pelvis in the Mammalia, and the conclusions respecting the origin of mammals which may be based on them" (*258*), Huxley had proposed that the mammals were connected with the amphibians by unknown premammalian forms, and not by any forms of the Sauropsida (p. 354). The general scheme of vertebrate classification obtained by applying to all the vertebrates the rules of the mammalian law of evolution is as follows (from his memoir of 1880):

Stages of evolution   Representative groups
9. *Eutheria* . . . . *Monodelphia*
                                                          o
8. *Metatheria* . . . . *Marsupialia*
                                                          o
7. *Prototheria* . . . . *Monotremata*
                                                          o
6. *Hypotheria* . . . . *X* . . . . *Sauropsida*   { *Aves*
                                                                                                                         { *Reptilia*
                                                                                                   o
5. *Amphibia* . . . . *Amphibia* . . . . *X*
                                                          o
4. *Herpetichthyes* . . . *Dipnoi* . . . . *X* . . . *Osteichthyes*   { *Ganoidei*
                                                                                                                              { *Teleostei*
                                          o   o

3. *Chondrichthyes* ...*Chimaeroidei* ....*X*.........*X* ....
                        °

                 Selachii.............*X*..........*X* ....
                       °

2. *Myzichthyes*.......*Marsipobranchii*.....*X*.........*X* ....
                       °

1. *Hypichthyes* ....*Pharyngobranchii* ...*X* ....*X* ....

[267, p. 472]

The Evolution of the Vertebrates

In a more general memoir dating from 1876, "On the Evidence as to the Origin of Existing Vertebrate Animals" (235), Huxley explains his reasons for the more sanguine attitude to evolution he had been expressing since the late 1860s. He claims that by 1876 much more evidence for the truth of evolution had accumulated:

Twenty years ago the arguments as to the causes of the phenomena of organic nature, brought forward in support of the then recently advanced views of Mr. Darwin, were largely speculative; all one could hope to show was that no valid objections could be urged against the theory of evolution. But since that time "many have run to and fro and knowledge has been increased"; the question has come out of the region of speculation into that of proof; every day increases our familiarity with the phenomena of life on the globe in antecedent ages, and so gives us the only valid evidence obtainable as to the evolution of living things. [p. 163]

The rest of the memoir concerns the palaeontological evidence for the evolution of the vertebrates, in respect of which Huxley thinks evolution can be considered as a fact (in contrast to his view of the invertebrates, as we shall see shortly). In this memoir much of what was said in works surveyed in this section is summarised. Huxley hints at the evolutionary affinities between fish and amphibians, and remarks that the major difference between the two classes consists of the occurrence of fins and legs respectively, a fact which is related to their different adaptations. However, much more striking than the differences are the resemblances between the two classes, such as the presence of functioning gills early in the life of an amphibian (p. 168).

After the amphibians come the reptiles, which Huxley regards as a higher group than the amphibians. In this memoir an animal is said to be higher than another when the parts of its structure are arranged in a more complex way (p. 170). In this respect, "a reptile is a decidedly higher animal than an amphibian" (p. 172). Moreover, the reptile passes during its embryological development through stages in which it "presents certain amphibian characters, such as the presence of gill-clefts; but these lower stages are passed over; the reptile goes beyond the highest amphibian in its development, and is therefore, in this respect also, to be considered a higher animal" (p. 173).

The last part of the memoir is devoted to the mammals, especially the horse. Following this survey of the vertebrates and their palaeontological history, Huxley concludes that

the accurate information obtained in this department of science has put the *fact* of evolution beyond a doubt; formerly, the great reproach to the theory was, that no support was lent to it by the geological history of living things; now, whatever happens, the fact remains that the hypothesis is founded on the firm basis of palaeontological evidence. [p. 187]

The Invertebrates

After an 1859 memoir entitled "On Some Points in the Anatomy of Nautilus Pompilius" (71), Huxley dealt with invertebrate animals only occasionally. We have seen how confident he became in the application of the concept of evolution to the vertebrates after 1868; so far as the invertebrates are concerned he remained more sceptical. Even in 1868, the year of his "real conversion," he emphasised a sharp line of demarcation between the invertebrates and the vertebrates in a series of lectures delivered to the Royal College of Surgeons. He maintained his old belief in a marked separation of the fundamental types of animal organisation, denying the occurrence of transitional forms between the vertebrates and invertebrates (155, p. 151). But later he began to reconsider his conclusions, and in 1875, during another course of lectures on the invertebrates, he stated:

The Arthropoda, the Mollusca, the Coelenterata, the Protozoa, are such groups, each as distinctly characterised as the Vertebrata, and presenting within itself a multitude of modifications of one fundamental type comparable to those observed in the vertebrate sub-kingdom. But in addition to these, there is a number of smaller and less defined groups which tend to fill up the intervals between the foregoing. The separation of the Invertebrata into sharply characterised assemblages is thus rendered extremely difficult, and the difficulty increases as, with the improvement of our knowledge of morphology, supposed barriers break down, and what were imagined to be distinct groups run into a series, exhibiting different degrees of modification of one and the same fundamental plan. [226, p. 491]

Huxley admits transition within the "great fundamental plan" of the invertebrates, but confirms its separation from the vertebrate plan.

In 1879 Huxley published a monograph entitled *The Crayfish: An Introduction to the Study of Zoology* (257). This is one of Huxley's major contributions to the study of the invertebrates, and shows his tendency to use old concepts for new purposes; in fact, in it he provides an interesting application of the type system to the new questions raised in zoology after the publication of the *Origin of Species.* And he introduces, albeit briefly, the notion of evolution.

The type system was part of Huxley's basic teaching material at this time, as one can see from *A Course of Practical Instruction in Elementary Biology* (360). Its fundamental principle consists of taking exemplars of a few types only, to be studied as illustrations of the animal kingdom. Thus, for example, the analysis of a squid can account for our understanding of the characteristics of molluscs, or at least of the cephalopods. This system is of benefit to the beginner, since it provides a generally clear idea of the structures and affinities of allied forms. The type system became a common working tool in zoological laboratories and, linked with the study of evolutionary systematics, is still valid today. Huxley takes the crayfish here as the reference point for the study of the Crustacea generally.

One should not forget that the study of the Crustacea had provided useful arguments for the theory of evolution, as was shown by Fritz Müller's masterly, although often misguided book, *Für Darwin,* which defended Darwin's views in 1864 by constant reference to the crustaceans (817). Huxley had dealt with the crayfish himself in 1878, a year before the monograph, in a memoir for the Zoological Society entitled "On the Classification and the Distribution of the Crayfishes" (250). As Michael Foster wrote, "He had chosen the crayfish as one of the lessons for the class in general biology . . . and was thus drawn into an interesting study of the crayfishes, by which he was led to a novel and important analysis of the gill plumes as evidence of affinity and separation" (472, vol. 1, p. 429).

In fact, having once discovered and described the "branchial formula" of the common crayfish (*Astacus fluviatilis*), it is possible to compare it to the branchial structures of all other crayfish (250, p. 286). The overall comparison of the branchiae permits the division of crayfish into two families, the Potamobidae and the Parastacidae. Huxley concludes that "the freshwater Crustacea are modifications of a marine prototype, which has more or less completely adapted itself to freshwater conditions" (p. 300). The monograph of 1879 on the same topic is more interesting because it is more complete, and introduces "aetiology" into the study of an invertebrate animal group. In the preface Huxley explains that the major aim of the monograph is to focus upon a single question of zoology and attain from it a clearer and wider view of the more general problems of that science—his approach has clearly not changed greatly from the early days.

I have desired, in fact, to show how the careful study of one of the commonest and most insignificant of animals, leads us, step by step, from every-day knowledge to the widest generalizations and the most difficult problems of zoology; and indeed, of biological science in general. [257, 5th edn., pp. v–vi]

Such a claim justifies the subtitle "an introduction to zoology."

At the beginning of the monograph Huxley remarks that science is nothing more than a sophisticated version of everyday knowledge. Any person of sufficient intelligence can therefore understand its methods and results. The attainment of that goal is one of the main aims of the monograph, and, for that matter, of all Huxley's more "popular" writings on scientific subjects. "Science is simply common sense at its best; that is, rigidly accurate in observation, and merciless to fallacy in logic" (p. 2). The object of science, Huxley argues (p. 3), is simply "the course of nature" as it is (has been, and will be). He is not prepared to accept in a scientific enquiry methods and interpretations borrowed from other disciplines. From a scientific point of view "the phenomena of nature are regarded as one continuous series of causes and effects; and the ultimate object of science is to trace out that series, from the term which is nearest to us, to that which is at the furthest limit accessible to our means of investigation" (ibid.).

After recalling (p. 7) Milne-Edwards's fundamental distinction between the crayfish (*Astacus*) and the lobster (*Homarus*) and explaining the utility of the Latin binominal nomenclature in the manner of Linnaeus (p. 15), Huxley provides a full description of the structure of the object of his enquiry (pp. 18–20). After this prelude, he enters the fundamental discussions of physiology, morphology, distribution, and aetiology, the latter defined as "the crown of biological effort" (p. 47). He now has to decide what order to follow in his description of the crayfish, and chooses a "historical" method. The history of science suggests that the first branch to develop was that of physiology. Men

observed that animals perform various actions; and, when they looked into the disposition and the powers of the parts by which these actions are performed, they found that these parts presented the characters of an apparatus, or piece of mechanism, the action of which could be deduced from the properties and connections of its constituents. [p. 47]

Physiology "consists in the elucidation of complex vital phenomena by deduction from the established truths of Physics and Chemistry, or from the elementary properties of living matter" (p. 48). Huxley regards the body of the crayfish as a sort of "alimentary machine" (p. 67) or better, as a factory fitted out with different pieces of machinery, in which the common processes of chemistry can be detected: "a sort of focus to which certain material particles converge, in which they move for a time, and from which they are afterwards expelled in new combinations" (p. 84).

It is apparent that Huxley holds a strictly mechanist and materialist view of physiology, and, more broadly, of the whole of biological science. It is without doubt one of the most striking features of his outlook that science must be treated in a rigorously mechanist way, evident in his treatment of the problem of the consciousness of "lower" animals. Because it lacks a language, the crayfish is not entitled to have real consciousness, Huxley argues: "No doubt, if the crayfish has any mind at all, his mental operations must more or less resemble those which the human mind performs without giving them a spoken or unspoken verbal embodiment" (p. 88). The discussion about the existence of mind in the crayfish seems to Huxley quite preposterous, since physiology can only tell us of a series of "physical phenomena which intervene between something which happens in the neighbourhood of the animal and that other something which responds to it, as an act of the crayfish" (p. 89). Science deals with the discovery of the order and connection of such physical phenomena. It must consider such physical structures as the nervous system and its interrelations with the environment:

Whatever else it may be, this animal, so far as it is acted upon by bodies around it and reacts to them, is a piece of mechanism, the internal works of which give rise to certain movements when it is affected by particular external conditions; and they do this in virtue of their physical properties and connexions. [p. 90]

Each movement of the body relates to a contraction of the muscles, to which the nervous system is connected. Mechanicism is, in sum, a sufficient means to an understanding of the course of nature, and the study of the crayfish provides the evidence for this claim:

In the crayfish, at any rate, there is not the slightest reason to doubt that every action has its definite physical cause, and that what it does at any moment would be as clearly intelligible, if we only knew all the internal and external conditions of the case, as the striking of a clock is to any one who understands clockwork. [pp. 112–13]

Besides the physiological approach, the crayfish can also be seen from the viewpoint of morphology, the aim of which is to detect the relationships of form between the constituent parts of the animal body (p. 138). Whether the animal is dead or alive does not concern the morphologist. A lengthy section of the monograph concerns the morphology of the crayfish (pp. 141–87); in it Huxley emphasises, for example, that the enucleated cell is to be considered as the morphological unit of both animals and plants (p. 202; see also 151). The importance of the study of the development of the crayfish from the egg is mentioned (p. 205), as well as the fact that the embryological development of the crayfish and the changes which occur in the egg constitute "in the strictest sense of the word, a process of evolution" (p. 221), and the actual development of the crayfish from the gastrula stage is described (p. 222). A further chapter considers comparative morphology. Here, forms allied to the crayfish (e.g., the lobster) are compared with it:

Morphological comparison, fully and thoroughly worked out, furnishes us with means of estimating the position of any one animal in relation to all the rest; while it shews us with what forms that animal is nearly, and with what it is remotely, allied: applied to all animals, it furnishes us with a kind of map, upon which animals are arranged in the order of their respective affinities; or a classification in which they are grouped in that order. [p. 230]

In this passage Huxley once more emphasises the possibility of constructing a classification of animals without reference to evolution. By means of comparative morphology, it is possible to collect various species into larger groupings, termed *genera*. Now, a genus is at least as much an abstraction as a species, Huxley argues (p. 249). In a species we group a set of individuals according to certain common morphological characteristics; likewise, in a genus we group a set of species, following the same morphological criteria. Here Huxley refers once more to the "common plan":

The definition of the genus is simply a statement of the plan of structure which is common to all species included under that genus; just as the definition of the species is a statement of the common plan of structure which runs throughout the individuals which compose the species. [p. 249]

The different crayfish can thus be considered as modifications of a common plan (p. 254), which is to be regarded as a "graphic method of representing the facts which are commonly stated in the form of a definition of the tribe of crayfishes, or *Astacina.*"

Throughout comparative morphology it is possible to establish relations between the crustaceans and the artropods. In both, in fact, the embryo is formed in a very similar manner. In the long run, Huxley thinks it is possible to consider all animals as modifications of the gastrula (p. 285): in some respects, the gastrula has a very similar function to the concept of a "common plan" for all the animals which have so far been mentioned—an interesting case of Haeckelian interpretation of von Baer's embryological views. Moreover, since the gastrula is an aggregate of cells, and plants are also made of cells, one can conclude that "all forms of life are morphologically related to one another" (p. 285). Finally, the truths of morphology and embryology are simple generalisations extracted from our observations of the facts (p. 286). They make plausible the hypothesis that animal and vegetal forms have been evolved from what Huxley calls the common basis of life, the protoplasm (ibid.; see also *151; 610; 693*). But morphology cannot say whether evolution really happened—it can only make it conceivable. "That which is conceivable, however, is by no means necessarily true; and no amount of purely morphological evidence can suffice to prove that the forms of life have come into existence in one way rather than another" (p. 286). That a scientific view must be not only plausible and logical but also empirically testable is the starting point of all Huxley's discussions of the nature of science. As far as the crayfish are concerned, disciplines other than morphology will decide whether there is *evidence* for its evolution.

The last part of the monograph deals with the distribution and aetiology of the crayfish. Distribution is a crucial factor in the understanding of animal evolution. Darwin had understood it perfectly, and Huxley thinks it is a sort of thread which, if properly followed, can connect every variation of the crayfish to the original morphological plan. The modification of the physical conditions in which a species lives favours the development of varieties and races (p. 293); now, once we know that certain forms are allied (as, morphology tells us, the crayfishes are), and we find that in different conditions specific variations are detected, we have evidence that these variations must have evolved from the original forms. Geographical distribution occupies two long chapters in the *Origin of Species* (*656a*, pp. 362–410), the fruit of a not inconsiderable geographical excursion and of a deep knowledge of the relevant literature.

We come then to the "final problem of zoology," on which the study of the crayfish is expected to throw some light. This is "to find out why animals of such structure and active powers, and so localised, exist" (p. 317). Leaving aside the question of abiogenesis (to which Huxley briefly refers in this monograph [p. 318]), since there is a satisfactory article on this topic (*453a*), Huxley claims that, in his time, there were only two possible hypotheses, creation and evolution (*257*, pp. 317–18). It is quite obvious that Huxley cannot accept creation as a scientific hypothesis; evolution is therefore "our only refuge" (p. 319). We must "suppose that the crayfishes have resulted from the modification of some other form of living matter; and this is what, to borrow a useful word from the French language, is known as *transformism*" (p. 318). Evolution is the only conception that can yield a rational understanding of the origin of the crayfish (p. 331), and one for which evidence can be adduced:

I have no doubt that they are derived from ancestors which lived altogether in the sea, as the great majority of the *Mysidae* and many of the prawn do now; and that, of these ancestral crayfishes, there are some which, like *Mysis oculata* or *Penaeus brasiliensis*, readily adapted themselves to fresh water conditions, ascended rivers, and took possession of lakes. These, more or less modified, have given rise to the existing crayfishes, while the primitive stock would seem to have vanished. [p. 331]

Our present knowledge, Huxley argues, does not enable us to draw a precise theory of the aetiology of the crayfish (p. 333).

Although the portion devoted to evolutionary arguments is relatively short, this monograph constitutes Huxley's only attempt in a large-scale work to give an evolutionary account of the invertebrates. He even thought it possible by this stage to draw, perhaps tentatively, a phylogeny of the crustaceans, as this note scribbled for a course of the "Davis Lectures," as far as I know hitherto unpublished, shows:

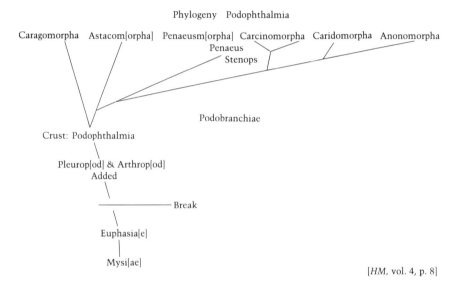

[HM, vol. 4, p. 8]

Figure 13.   Hypothetical Genealogical Scheme of the Podophthalmia.

The distinction between Podophthalmia, whose phylogeny Huxley attempts here, and Edriophthalmia had been made in 1815 by Leach according to the position of the eyes, which are moveable peduncolate in Podophthalmia and sessile in Edriophthalmia (636; see also 762; for the nineteenth century's standard classification of the Crustacea, see 698; also important are 606; 611; and 803, vol. 1, pp. 237–468). There is no possible sequence from the Mysiae to the Euphasiae, and the position of Penaeus is wrong; but I report this phylogeny, which Huxley would certainly have revised had he wished to publish it, not because it touches upon a minor classifactory problem, but because it shows Huxley's increasing confidence in respect of the evolution of the invertebrates.*

* I am grateful to Dr. S. Smith for his help and suggestions regarding this phylogeny.

The Concept of Species

The consideration of Huxley's views of classification has a considerable bearing upon one's understanding of the reasons for his different degrees of confidence in the application of evolutionary arguments to the vertebrates and invertebrates. The first point to be considered is the concept of species.

As E. Mayr (790; 791) and M. T. Ghiselin (699, pp. 78–102) have pointed out, there can be more than one interpretation of "species" even among those who hold evolutionary views. There is the "morphological" concept, the prevailing pre-Darwinian view, in which species are defined in terms of structural resemblances. It is the descriptive concept par excellence. Aristotle, and later Linnaeus, found it the most practical and successful method of grouping organisms. Furthermore, by referring to certain combinations of characters, it is possible to group species into larger categories, and these into yet larger ones, and so on. A taxonomist uses such criteria as colour, structure, and proportion. The morphological classification is typical of the palaeontologist, who has no possible alternative criteria. The follower of the morphological concept of species would define it, Mayr suggests, as "a group of individuals or populations with the same or similar morphological characters" (791, p. 115). Huxley, who worked as a palaeontologist for a large part of his life, favoured the use of the morphological concept.

There is secondly a "biological" concept, which Huxley calls "physiological," in which reproductive isolation and the interbreeding of populations are the major criteria for classification. Thirdly, there is a "genealogical" concept, in which species are grouped according to their "propinquity of descent" (699, p. 82). Huxley used the morphological concept throughout his career and conceived of the biological one—although he never really applied it since he was not truly a physiologist—while his problems started with the genealogical one. He wrote in 1860:

When we call a group of animals, or of plants, a species, we may imply thereby, either that all these animals or plants have some common peculiarity of form and structure; or, we may mean that they possess some common functional character . . . so that we may conveniently speak of . . . two senses, or aspects, of "species"—the one as morphological, the other as physiological. [91, p. 26]

Huxley claims that there is no proof that physiological species are formed by natural selection.

Darwin, on the other hand, emphasises the genealogical concept. He writes in the *Origin of Species*:

Propinquity of descent—the only known cause of the similarity of organic beings,—is the bond, hidden as it is by various degrees of modification, which is partially revealed to us by our classifications. [656a, pp. 413–14]

We use the element of descent in classing the individuals of both sexes and all ages, although having few characters in common, under one species. [p. 433]

Darwin was aware that more evidence than he could provide was necessary to persuade his colleagues to accept the genealogical concept of species, and did not propose any genealogies in the *Origin of Species*. In a slip attached to his copy of the *Vestiges of Creation* of 1848 he noted: "I will not specify any genealogies: much too little known at present" (*Dar. Vestiges; 642c*). Only if we accept this concept of propinquity of descent, Darwin argues, can we build up a "natural system" of classification which is not a mere grouping of forms, but a summary of what has happened during the evolution of those forms (for problems of classification, see also *862*).

For a twentieth-century evolutionist who accepts Darwin's viewpoint, the placing, say, of both man and the apes under the same taxonomic heading means that man and the apes have followed much closer evolutionary paths than, say, man and the dugong or the giraffe. In this way the knowledge of systematics is no longer mere erudition, but a very useful recapitulation of what we know about the evolution of animal and vegetal groups. Thus the unfortunate student of zoology or botany who has to spend a large part of his time learning by heart a long series of names can see why this exercise is not a waste of time, but a way of learning about evolution—he is studying a summary of evolution. The genealogical meaning of species does not preclude the morphological and physiological concepts; rather, it includes them as part of the basis of the taxonomic reconstruction.

As early as 1857 Darwin and Huxley were arguing about genealogical classification, as this letter from Huxley to Darwin indicates:

Cuvier's definition of the object of classification seems to me to embody all that is really wanted in science—it is to throw the facts of structure into the fewest possible *general propostions*. This of course leaves out of view & passes by, all questions of pedigree & possible modifications dealing with existing (?) animals and plants as faits accomplis. If we believe that scientific and logical zoology & botany are not at present possible—for they must be based on sound morphology—a science which has yet to be created out of the old Comparative Anatomy—and the new study of *Development* when the mode of thought and speculations of Oken & Geoffroy S. Hilaire & their servile follower Owen, have been replaced by the principle so long ago inculcated by Caspar Wolff & von Baer & Rathke—& so completely ignored in this country and in France up to the last ten years we shall have in the course of a generation a science of morphology & then a scientific zoology & botany will flow from it as corollaries.

Your pedigree business is a part of Physiology—a most important and valuable part—and in chief a matter of profound interest—but to my mind it has no more to do with pure zoology—than pure pedigree has with the census. [*Dar.* 205.5]

This letter also indicates Huxley's conviction that it is embryology, as recommended by von Baer, which should be the basis for morphology, on which classification should be founded, and that the empirical method of assembling the "facts of structure" into generally summarising propositions is the basis for morphology—Cuvier's method interpreted through von Baer (see chapter 1).

The following is probably Darwin's reply:

I knew, of course, of the Cuverian view of classification; but I think that most naturalists look for something further, and search for "the natural system"—"for the plan on which the Creator has worked," etc. It is this further element which I believe to be simply genealogical. . . . It might be asked why is development so all-potent in classification, as I fully admit it is? I believe it is, because it depends on, and best betrays, genealogical descent. (*662,* vol. 1, p. 284)

Darwin's last point here represents the essence of the "Haeckelian" view that Huxley was later to accept (see chapter 2).

But even in 1864, Huxley was still not convinced that genealogy could be applied to classification. In *The Elements of Comparative History* he wrote:

That classification which I propose to discuss in the present Lectures . . . is meant to subserve the comprehension and recollection of the facts of animal structure; and, as such, it is based upon purely structural considerations, and may be designated a Morphological Classification. I shall have to consider animals, not as physiological apparatuses merely; not as related to other forms of life and to climatal conditions; not as successive tenants of the earth; but as fabrics, each of which is built upon a certain plan. [*117*, p. 2]

It is important to remark that this passage was reprinted in *An Introduction to the Classification of Animals* (*158*) five years later—that is, immediately after one of the most important turning points in his scientific life, the 1868 "conversion." This fact suggests an interesting conclusion: the audience for whom this book was intended was composed of students rather than researchers, and Huxley probably thought it inappropriate to speak to students about something that was not completely established. He expressed this point with great clarity in the *Anatomy of Invertebrated Animals* (*238*) of 1877. It is not advisable to introduce controversial aspects into textbooks:

I have abstained from discussing questions of aetiology, not because I underestimate their importance, or am insensible to the interest of the great problem of Evolution; but because, to my mind, the growing tendency to mix up aetiological speculations with morphological generalisations will, if unchecked, throw biology into confusion.

For the student, that which is essential is a knowledge of the facts of morphology; and he should recollect that generalisations are empty formulas, unless there is something in his personal experience which gives reality and substance to the terms of the propositions in which these generalisations are expressed. [p. iv]

But Huxley did use phylogenies in his work after 1868, as we have seen; and indeed in 1868 wrote a letter to *Ibis* which he must have thought important, since he kept a copy of it in his private papers:

All classification by logical categories, such as that which I have attempted in birds, however, is more or less artificial, and must be regarded as simply a first and most important stage in the progress towards the ultimate goal, which is a *genetic classification*—a classification, that is, which shall express the manner in which living beings have evolved one from the other. [*154; HM* vol. 36, p. 50]

And even in respect of the invertebrates, the problem was not the existence of impediments of principle to an evolutionary survey, but rather that the evidence available was simply insufficient:

The facts of morphology not only present no difficulty in the way of the hypothesis of the evolution of the *Invertebrata* from a common origin, but readily adapt themselves to it. . . .

I will only venture to remark that, in the absence of any adequate palaeontological history of the *Invertebrata*, any attempt to construct their Phylogeny must be mere speculation. [*238*, pp. 686–67]

Interim Conclusions

In these three chapters, after noting how Huxley made his mark as a scientist in the field of invertebrate morphology, we have followed the central thread of his contributions to vertebrate palaeontology, with the further specific aim of elucidating the changes in his attitude to the idea of evolution—from hostility (chapter 1) through apparent inconsistency (chapter 2) to acceptance (chapter 3). Briefly, his original scientific work can be seen primarily as an involvement with and application of two major principles—the Baerian or embryological type concept and the Haeckelian or descent conception of evolution. His more polemical work can be seen primarily as an involvement with and defence of two other major principles—empiricism, and the Darwinian or selective conception of evolution. We have also seen something of his connections with other scientists, especially von Baer, Darwin, Haeckel, and Owen, who are indeed the four principal members of the supporting cast in this drama. By surveying Huxley's positive scientific achievements, and by comparing and distinguishing him from these other characters, we ought therefore to be in a position to offer an assessment of his intellectual temperament and to address the question of the consistency and development of his scientific commitments.

The question of Huxley's consistency may usefully be taken at three principal levels: the level of his method and general approach; the level of theory; and the level of the underlying "philosophical" outlook.

It should already be apparent that Huxley was consistent in method and approach throughout his career. The basis, despite changes of discipline and subject matter over the years, is always the detailed structural examination of specimens, leading to a classification on the basis of the affinities revealed. But this activity, in which the influence of the laboratory is clearly greater than that of the field, was not randomly or rabidly indulged; rather, it was pursued in conjunction with a close reading of relevant literature, and consequently a keen awareness of the interrelationships between particular specimens and theoretical issues of wide import. Let us recall four of Huxley's most important papers, or series of papers—his work on the coelenterates (chapter 1), the ganoids (chapter 2), the dinosaurs (chapters 2 and 3), and the crocodiles (chapter 3). A glance at the discussions of this work will confirm that his favoured approach was to treat a specific taxonomic issue first as a puzzle in itself, then as an illustration, and finally as proof of a basic and general principle.

In respect to the coelenterates he starts with the structural examination of the Medusae, and ends with a new and important criterion (the two membranes) for the grouping of the whole of the coelenterates, leading finally to a reclassification of them as distinct from the Radiata. The full reclassification of the ganoids develops from the problem of the systematic position of *Glyptolemus*. His special interest in the birds and dinosaurs can be traced to the intriguing single example of the so-called *Euskelesaurus*, developing over several papers into a full analysis of the affinities of birds and dinosaurs in general, via the further specific cases of *Archaeopterix* and *Compsognathus*, leading finally to an evolutionary presentation of the data in question. As far as the crocodiles are concerned, an initial involvement with single specimens such as *Stagonolepis* and *Hyperodapedon* leads to a study of the comparative anatomy of crocodiles in general, resulting in their classification into three suborders which can be shown to form a series both morphologically and temporally, and thus to support the claims of evolutionism.

Huxley's familiarity with relevant literature is also clearly visible in these works. A glance at the bibliography will indicate something else of interest about the approaches and rhythms characteristic of Huxley's work: each of these important papers (3; 96; 146; 222) is preceded by two or three years during which less significant memoirs are produced on the same subject and is followed by a similar series of papers fleshing out some of the details of the major publication. (This is also true of *Man's Place in Nature*, as we shall see in the next chapter.) So Huxley's "style" is rather like that of a steady and conscientious professional golfer: he prepares his tee with care, aims true, drives the ball with conviction, and shows a thorough follow-through, with constant off-course reference to the technical manuals.

At the level of scientific theory matters are slightly more complex. We are faced with two periods, broadly speaking, the fifties and sixties being the period of the "type," the seventies and eighties the period of "descent." Now it is clear that each period's dominant principle is applied uniformly in Huxley's scientific research. The work on the coelenterates and the ganoids, for example, is presented in accordance with the theory of the type; the work on the dinosaurs and the crocodiles is presented in accordance with the theory of descent. It is also clear that the conception which provides the element of continuity from one period to the other is for Huxley that of the "embryological archetype," deriving principally from von Baer. The *Descendenz-theorie*, whose basic propositions Huxley came to accept, was in essence the reorganisation of the "embryological archetypes" and their modifications into genealogies rather than abstract correspondences— into "natural" rather than "artificial" patterns: traditionalism with a modern face, so to speak.

But this way of putting it identifies a basic question, not about Huxley's consistency in applying certain theoretical principles, but rather about the internal consistency of those principles themselves. The type, whether considered as an ideal object or as a summary or statement of the average, is an abstraction denoting a stable form and thus a view of nature as organised around static elements. Descent, on the other hand, refers directly to the endless chain of births, reproduction, and deaths, denoting an actual historical process and thus a view of nature as a dynamic continuum. It is not obvious that these conceptions are compatible; certainly it is not clear at this level what picture of nature their combination is supposed to yield. The two conceptions would rather appear to imply choices of picture at a basic level—as we recently saw, for example, concerning the notion of species itself, between the "morphological" and the "genealogical." From the point of view of Huxley's later theoretical commitments, the combination or compromise can itself be seen in two different lights. One blending of the two conceptions would be that there are, at bottom, stable forms, but that movement occurs from time to time from one stable form to another (i.e., moments of process arise in the general stasis; which fits reasonably with Huxley's inclination to emphasise "saltation"). The converse blend would suggest that there is, at bottom, a continuous process of generation and variation within the various animal groupings, but that this process eventually comes to rest in the production of long-lasting forms (i.e., moments of stasis arise in the general process; a view which fits reasonably, for example, with Huxley's emphasis on the continuity of form among the crocodiles). However, the basic point is that Huxley's later theoretical stance represents an uneasy collation of static and dynamic conceptions, rather than a coherent and unified picture.

Another important point arises from this brief discussion. It is possible, as the previous paragraph in fact demonstrates, to state the core of Huxley's later theoretical position without reference to any mechanism(s) by which the phenomena exemplifying "type" and/or "descent" might have been produced. Further, the conceptual ambiguities present in the various possible blendings of the static and dynamic aspects of the theory make it unlikely that a mechanism could be clearly enunciated. Now, we have seen that one of Huxley's principal reasons for welcoming the *Origin of Species* was that Darwin had proposed a mechanism for the transmutation of animal forms; we have also noted how Huxley attacked others for failing to provide a clearly mechanist account of nature. Given therefore that Huxley apparently regarded the identification of a mechanism as an important virtue in a scientific theory, it is odd that the question of the mechanism of descent is nowhere addressed—or even raised—in Huxley's application of the notion. He had doubts about the validity of natural selection, and would not therefore turn to it as an explanatory mechanism; and in any case the focus of research into evolution shifted to groupings above the level of species and into palaeontology, where natural selection was not germane. In spite of, or perhaps even because of, these points, it is strange that Huxley should so readily accept a set of concepts lacking any obvious mechanical interpretation. His post-1868 research principles are not wholly coherent, and are not entirely congruent in any case with his defence of Darwin. In short, despite the clarity and vigour of his polemics on behalf of a mechanical understanding of nature, and the continuity of his research publications, it is not possible to form a picture of what Huxley actually thought nature got up to in the production of the objects he studied.

These comments raise afresh the question of how Huxley came to accept the theory of descent. Chapter 2 answers this question on a biographical and historical level by pointing to the influence of Haeckel and his colleagues; but on a conceptual level the question remains puzzling. However, we should bear in mind what we identified as the element of continuity between Huxley's "early" and "later" theoretical positions: von Baer's view of the type, in which taxonomic decisions were supported, inter alia, by embryological considerations. Huxley's early position, based upon the Baerian conceptions, is thus already one in which the atemporal notion of the type and the historical process of ontogeny are brought into coalition; already, in other words, a blend of "static" and "dynamic" conceptions. Further, the type itself is an abstraction; and it does not of course make sense to ask questions about mechanism(s) in regard to it as such. So the basic conceptual elements of Huxley's later acceptance of the theory of descent are very little different from those of his earlier espousal of the "embryological archetype"—the theory of descent, while clearly a new departure, makes no radical conceptual break with the past. All in all, then, acceptance of the theory of descent was the smallest step in the direction of "evolutionism" that Huxley could have made, given his existing conceptual outlook. The data which previously were to be called evidence for a certain arrangement of the types were now to be called evidence for certain lines of descent; and in the meanwhile the actual business of research could carry on exactly as before—a point in fact prefigured in the demonstration above that Huxley's methodology remained constant throughout his career.

In respect of Huxley's guiding philosophical principles, I have already sufficiently emphasised his commitment to empiricism, especially by reference to his attacks upon theological or metaphysical (Platonic) intrusions into the conduct of science, and his general support for a mechanist and materialist outlook. Furthermore, we have seen this set of preoccupations to be a consistent and recurrent theme in his career: his concern from the outset to detach the concept of the type from its idealist metaphysical associations; his concern to expose poor or insufficient experimentation and observation, which we encountered especially in his confrontations with Owen; his general endorsement of the materialism of Darwin; his instinctive caution about what he saw as rather speculative theorising, which we encounter even in his later period in respect of phylogeny. It was his clear, lifelong view that science should be independent of ethics, politics, metaphysics, and religion, and neutral with respect to any particular positions one might wish to adopt in those areas of endeavour. In chapter 5, we shall witness the intrusion of a degree of inconsistency—by no means peculiar to Huxley—in the application of this conception of the place of science to the particular field of ethnology, where scientific considerations tended to suffer from the impact of broadly "political" considerations.

But *empiricism* is a wide term: for example, chapter 2 also noted that Huxley and Darwin seemed to have divergent opinions in detail upon the requirements of the empirical outlook on the proper conduct of science. Briefly, Huxley demanded "decisive experiment," while Darwin demanded superior explanatory power, as the criterion of the acceptability of a theory. Huxley wanted to see an experimental proof of specific intersterility before raising Darwin's "hypothesis" to the rank of "theory," while Darwin asserted that the theory of natural selection could only sink or swim "according as it groups and explains phenomena."

But let us return to Huxley's espousal of the theory of descent. Here we are dealing in large part with palaeontological data. We can of course observe these data; but clearly we can no longer directly observe the processes of their production, and experimentation is obviously out of the question. The account in terms of "descent," in other words, can only be suggested, not proved; and indeed partly on the basis of an analogical inference from the present, directly observable processes: we observe instances of generation, and the variation of offspring from their parents, and extrapolate that process back into the past, into the production of the fossil record. This argument has the same logical structure, though obviously not the same content, as the analogy between artificial and natural selection which, ironically, partly motivated Huxley's *doubts* about the validity of Darwin's conceptions. Furthermore, given the absence of the possibility of direct observation or experimentation, it is clear that the theory of descent can be persuasive only "according as it groups and explains phenomena"—which, as we have just seen, is not *Huxley's* appreciation of the *Origin of Species*, but the basis of Darwin's *reply* to Huxley's *criticism* of it. In short, it is possible to argue that the logical bases of Huxley's attitude to Darwin on the one hand and to his own research principles on the other were at odds.

Our examination of the consistency of Huxley's work has thus shown a lifelong methodological consistency, a consistent application of the two principles of the type and of the theory of descent, and a consistent commitment in general to empiricism. But at the same time it has proved possible to question the internal consistency of the theoretical and philosophical notions which Huxley deployed, and to question the coherence of aspects of his thought, especially in the later period. The material of these three chapters has shown how Huxley's work falls into distinct periods; but equally it should be clear that the development from one period to another cannot really be seen as an internal development of his own thinking. He does not, in the manner of Darwin, have a complex set of largely novel intuitions which motivate a research programme which in turn moulds the original intuitions into an articulated body of theory. Huxley's phases are marked, rather, by encounters with principles enunciated by others; his development is in that sense external. He reacts rather than initiates, applying the theoretical insights of others to ever wider groups of phenomena.

Huxley's reactions to other colleagues and contemporaries can also give us some insight into his general intellectual temperament. At the beginning of this section I mentioned especially von Baer, Owen, Darwin, and Haeckel, and we are now perhaps in a position, through highlighting some of their traits, to distinguish Huxley's individual temperament.

For example, Haeckel possessed an irritating dogmatism, which Huxley encountered in connection with the notorious *"Bathybius* affair" (see *540; 546*). In 1868 Huxley published "On Some Organisms Living at Great Depths in the North Atlantic Ocean" (*148*). He wrote to Haeckel on 6 October:

> I have as yet received no separate copies of [a] paper (published in the Quarterly Journal of Microscopical Science for this month) which I read before the meeting of the British Association at Norwich.
> It is about a new "Moner" which lives at the bottom of the Atlantic to all appearance, and gives rise to some wonderful calcified bodies.
> I have christened it *Bathybius Haeckelii* and I hope you will not be ashamed of your godchild. I will send you some of the mud itself with the paper. [*571*, p. 18]

Haeckel interpreted the discovery as decisive evidence for his philosophical views, which were entangled with the *Naturphilosophie*, and wrote an enthusiastic reply to Huxley in which he exclaimed "Vivant Monera!" (ibid.). Huxley could well have echoed his cry, since the existence of such beings was good evidence for the view of the descent of all living beings from a common origin. Now, there is nothing more dangerous than a possibly controversial fact which would perfectly fit one's pet theory. Haeckel decided that *Bathybius* was a member of the class Monera. Unfortunately, *Bathybius* was a blunder on Huxley's part, as was shown by the expedition of HMS *Challenger,* whose results were published in 1875; *Bathybius* was simply an organic precipitate (*223; 227*). Huxley was ready to acknowledge his mistake, and even joked about it.

Undoubtedly many facts had suggested the existence of something like *Bathybius;* and had its existence been proved, so much the better for the theory of descent. Nonetheless, Huxley serenely accepted the result of scientific enquiry, whatever its consequence to himself. Haeckel, on the other hand, continued to insist that *Bathybius* was an animal life form, and deplored Huxley's defection (*540*, p. 531). The topic was never again treated in their correspondence, possibly because both feared a personal breach.

Huxley was not prepared to assert his own general view in the face of proven contradictory facts, but the same cannot be said of his German colleague. Huxley's behaviour is a good example of fair play in science; Haeckel's is an excellent specimen of an extremely "aprioristic" attitude. We must conclude that while Huxley and Haeckel agreed on the question of descent, their natures were very different. Huxley objected to the fact that Haeckel was too often carried away by phylogenetic frenzy, and in 1875 he complained that the German thinker tended to mix up "phylogenetic 'Stammbäume' with objective taxonomy" (224, p. 18).

In chapter 1, concerning the *Terebratula*, we noted another episode when Huxley encountered dogmatic obstinacy, that time on the part of Owen. We also saw reason to charge Owen with a distinct lack of integrity; and there was worse to come. From the very beginning Owen had opposed Darwinism, and indeed inspired Wilberforce's attack upon it at the Oxford meeting; but when he felt increasingly overwhelmed by Darwin's friends he claimed that his own views had been of an evolutionary nature even before 1859. MacLeod's argument that Owen realised that Darwin was right and therefore desperately endeavoured somehow to save his prestige is quite convincing (779, p. 278). On this view, Owen became the "archetype" of the enemies of evolution, mainly because of his personal hatred of Huxley and his philosophical dislike of the Darwinian theory (because it was anti-Platonic) (779, p. 264). Owen claimed priority as an evolutionist by drawing attention to his theory of "derivation." He made a complete exposition of this theory in his 1866 paper (843) on the Aye-Aye (*Chyromis madagascariensis*). (It is interesting to note that Owen's grandson did not cite this theory in his rather unreliable *Life of Richard Owen* [846].)

What I have termed the "derivative hypothesis" of organisms, for example, holds that there are comings into being, by aggregation of organic atoms, at all times and in all places, under their simplest unicellular condition; with differences of character as many as are the various circumstances, conditions, and combinations of the causes educing them . . . through forces and conditions acting according to predetermined law. The disposition to vary in form and structure, according to the variation of surrounding conditions, is greatest in these first-formed beings; and from them, or such as them, are and have been derived all other and higher forms of organisms on this planet. And thus it is that we now find energizing in fair proportions every grade of organization from Man to the Monad. Each organism, as such, also propagates its own form for a time under such similitude as to be called its kind. [843, p. 92]

If it is true that Owen's view is in some ways an evolutionary one, it is nonetheless what Mayr would call "Platonic," and as such strongly discordant with Darwin's concept of descent with modifications. Owen had an old-fashioned and traditionally pre-Darwinian view of nature, which was, as M. Rudwick has suggested, that of the old naturalist, such as Buffon and Linnaeus, interested in the "natural history" of natural entities, and in their ordering (875, p. 208).

Yet Owen was shameless enough to claim his priority concerning the natural-selective conception of evolution. In 1866, in reply to a sarcastic criticism of his *Anatomy of Vertebrates* (844) in the *London Review*, Owen wrote:

> If your readers will refer to the IVth volume of *Zool. Trans* "Memoir on Dinornis" (Feb. 1850) [836]—the theory of the extinction and conservation of species.
>
> In that exposition of my theory I speak of those faring better "in the contest which, as a living organism, the individual of each species has to maintain against the surrounding agencies" . . . in the elementary work of 1866, I use the briefer expression "in the battle of life". That is all the difference. [845, p. 516]

One can only conclude from this and the other incidents mentioned that Owen on occasion allowed personal animosity and a concern for his own preeminence to distort his judgment of the facts and his presentation of historical events.

Huxley was less insistent than Haeckel, more honest and level-headed than Owen. On the whole he played fair; and if there were uncertainties surrounding any proposition he endorsed, he would usually say so. We saw that most obviously in connection with his advocacy of Darwin—his caution about natural selection itself, about saltation, and about the concept of species.

The discussion in the opening section of chapter 2 indicated that Darwin's commitment to empirical methods and concepts was one of the reasons for Huxley's endorsement of his general position. Mayr argues that a necessary step towards a new view of organic phenomena was the elimination of Platonism from scientific explanation in refusing to admit the *eidos* as a relevant concept in biology:

> Most of the great philosophies of the 17th, 18th and 19th century were influenced by the idealistic philosophy of Plato, and the school dominated the thinking of the period. . . .
>
> Any attachment to metaphysical idealism, any commitment to an unchanging *eidos*, precludes belief in descent with modifications. The concept of evolution rejects the *eidos*. [792, pp. xix–xx]
>
> Darwin had violated all the rules of the game by placing his argument entirely outside the traditional framework of classical philosophical concepts and terminologies. . . . No other work advertised to the world the emancipation of science from philosophy as blatantly as did Darwin's *Origin*. [pp. xi–xii]

These are what might be called first principles. But beyond that Darwin's notion of natural selection reaches into essentially dynamic processes of the interaction between organisms and their surroundings. His willingness to adapt the concept of species itself to the new design underlines the radical nature of his dissociation from "the traditional framework." For Huxley, on the other hand, who was not a field naturalist, the more static conceptions available from laboratory study remain paramount. It is as if in observing the world, what Huxley saw was the *order* of nature, whereas what Darwin saw was its *process*. The laboratory approach was largely pioneered in Germany in the foundation of the schools of Liebig and Johannes Müller (*612; 638; 794*), and I have stressed Huxley's intellectual involvement in the orientations of his German colleagues. Farber, in discussing the relationships between the "natural history" and laboratory, or "physiological," wings of nineteenth-century biology, reminds us further that the roots of the latter "were not so much in natural history as in medicine and chemistry" (*684*, p. 451). It is thus worth recalling that Huxley's initial training was that of a medical student, and that his participation in the *Rattlesnake* voyage was not officially as a naturalist, but as the ship's medical officer. Something of the discipline of those early studies seems to have remained with him—indeed, one might aphoristically describe his mature attitudes towards both data and theoretical innovation as "cautiously diagnostic." Darwin's concern with the broad picture, the explanatory power of a central idea, to which subvenient notions are brought to conform, shows on the other hand a more creative and insightful disposition.

If Huxley was in some respects less mentally agile and adaptable than Darwin, he proved in the end to be more so than his original mentor, von Baer. It is clear that von Baer's embryological typology is perfectly compatible with Darwin's assumption of divergence from common ancestry when suitably reinterpreted, and indeed furnishes that assumption with evidence. Darwin in fact referred to von Baer's law of development which, to quote E. S. Russell, "states that development is essentially differentiation, and that as a result embryos belonging to the same group resemble one another the more, the less advanced they are in development" (*879*, p. 236; see also *665; 819; 820*). Now Darwin thought that the embryo "is the animal in its less modified state" (*656a*, p. 449), which means that careful examination of the embryo of an existing species can give us useful information about the structure of its ancestors (ibid.). Thus the study of embryology is an abbreviated study of evolution.

Von Baer lived long enough to join in the debates about the *Origin of Species*. In "Über Darwins Lehre" (*597*) of 1876 he expressed his opinion about the connection between his theory and Darwin's; he was conscious of the import of his work for the Darwinian view:

In der That glaube ich für die Begründung derselben einigen Stoff geliefert zu haben, wenn auch die Zeit und Darwin selbst auf das Fundament ein Gebünde aufgeführt haben, dem ich mich fremd fühle. [597, p. 240]

But as he implies here, he was not prepared to accept the doctrine to whose foundation he had contributed, and rejected the *Descendenz-theorie*:

In dem Werke, welches den Titel führt *Entwickelungsgeschichte der Thiere* habe ich allerdings die Umwandlungen der thierischen Organismen in der Ent-wickelung der Individuellen nachgewiesen, allein einer Descendenztheorie, in dem Sinne der Neueren, glaube ich nicht das Wort geredet zu haben. Vielmehr habe ich mich im fünften Scholium des ersten Bandes gegen eine damals herr-schende Ansicht von Transmutation nach ausgesprochen. [597, p. 241; see 819]

When von Baer died an obituary notice appeared in the *Proceedings of the Royal Society* of 1878. The notice is unsigned, but it is not difficult to attribute it to Huxley (255). Referring to von Baer's opposition to Darwinism, the writer noted not only that von Baer's enquiries "mark an epoch" and show that "the embryonic phases of the individuals are tokens of the relations of kind and race" (p. iv), but also that the great embryologist had stopped there, being unable to accept that those types, of which the different living forms are variations, were themselves prod-ucts of evolution (in the post-Darwinian sense of the word). Von Baer opened the way for the "wider doctrine which has swallowed up his own" (p. v).

So von Baer refused the last hurdle, while Huxley, as we saw, man-aged eventually to stay the course. But this is scarcely criticism of von Baer—he was after all in his late sixties when the *Origin of Species* was published, and his crucial and influential insights had been achieved long before.

These comparisons show Huxley as less dogmatic than Haeckel and more straightforward than Owen; less insightful than Darwin but more adaptable than von Baer. A picture emerges of a predominantly open-minded and fair-minded individual—characteristics we shall see con-firmed again in chapters 4 and 5 in connection with Huxley's dispute with Owen about the simian hippocampus minor and his involvement in questions of racial and sexual differences—but one who could not primarily be numbered among the "first" class in Mivart's categorisa-tion of scientists:

Science cannot progress without the action of two distinct classes of thinkers: the first consisting of men of creative genius, who strike out brilliant hypoth-eses, and who may be spoken of as "theorizers" in the good sense of the word; the second of men possessed of the critical faculty, and who test, mould into

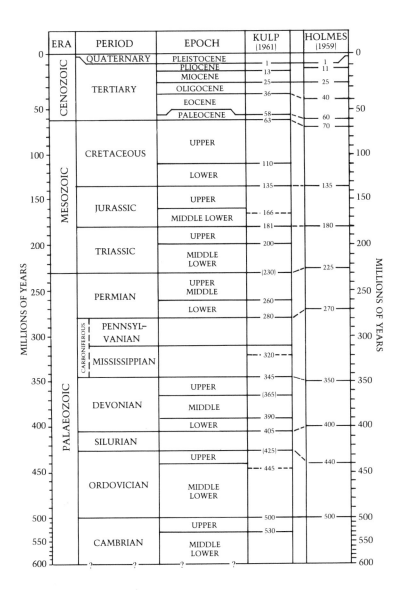

ERA	PERIOD	EPOCH	KULP (1961)	HOLMES (1959)
CENOZOIC	QUATERNARY	PLEISTOCENE	1	1
		PLIOCENE	13	11
		MIOCENE	25	25
	TERTIARY	OLIGOCENE	36	40
		EOCENE	58	60
		PALEOCENE	63	70
MESOZOIC	CRETACEOUS	UPPER	110	100
		LOWER	135	135
	JURASSIC	UPPER	166	
		MIDDLE LOWER	181	180
	TRIASSIC	UPPER	200	
		MIDDLE LOWER	(230)	225
PALAEOZOIC	PERMIAN	UPPER MIDDLE	260	250
		LOWER	280	270
	CARBONIFEROUS PENNSYL-VANIAN			
	MISSISSIPPIAN		320	
	DEVONIAN	UPPER	345	350
		MIDDLE	(365)	
		LOWER	390 405	400
	SILURIAN	UPPER	(425)	440
	ORDOVICIAN	MIDDLE LOWER	445	
	CAMBRIAN	UPPER	500 530	500
		MIDDLE LOWER		

MILLIONS OF YEARS

Figure 14. The time-scales of Kulp (1961) and Holmes (1959). (After Leech et al. 1963, fig. 1, p. 3.)

The scheme is quoted from M. J. Snelling, "A Review of Recent Phanorosoic Time-Scale," in W. B. Harland, A. Gilbert Smith, and B. Wilcock (eds.), *The Phanarosoic Time-Scale* (London, 1964), pp. 29–42, p. 30. [896]

The data come from J. L. Kulp, "Geological Time Scale," *Science* 133 (1961), 1105–14; and A. Holmes, "A Revised Geological Time-Scale," *Trans. Edid. Geol. Soc.* 17 (1959), 183–216.

Fish appeared during the Silurian, amphibians during the Devonian, reptiles during the carboniferous, dinosaurs and mammals during the Triassic, and birds in the Jurassic; while the dinosaurs were extinct, along with the pterosaurs, by the Cretaceous.

shape, perfect or destroy the hypotheses thrown out by the former class. [*807*, p. 48]

Implying that Huxley's proper place is in Mivart's "second" category is not to belittle the quality or importance of his original scientific contribution, merely to acknowledge that his achievements took place in theoretical contexts already mapped by others. Indeed in some cases—perhaps especially in the work on the birds and dinosaurs—his work can be seen as an apotheosis of the theoretical insights of others.

PART TWO
Man

Sagt mir, was bedeutet der Mensch?
Woher ist er kommen? Wo geht er hin?
Wer wohne dort oben auf den goldenen Sternen?
Es murmeln die Wogen ihr ew'ges Gemurmeln,
es wehet der Wind, es fliehn die Wolken,
es blicken die Sternen gleichgültig und kalt,
und ein Narr wartet auf Antwort.

—Heinrich Heine, *Buch der Lieder*

4
The Natural History of Man

What a piece of work is man! how noble in reason! how infinite in faculties! in form and moving, how express and admirable! in action, how like an angel! in apprehension, how like a god! the beauty of the world! the paragon of animals! And yet to me, what is this quintessence of dust?

—W. Shakespeare, *Hamlet*

The Context of *Man's Place in Nature*

The General Context

In *The Death of Adam* (708), Greene reminds us that interest in the question of man's relationship to other living beings was shown by naturalists, philosophers, and learned laymen long before the publication of the *Origin of Species*. The problem of man for natural history concerns three kinds of question. One is the question of classification: the anthropologist is interested in sorting out man's taxonomical position in relation to the other living beings. A second question concerns the antiquity of man. The third is the question of human races: is there one human species, divided into various races, or are races in fact differentiated species (780, pp. 351–52)? These questions exercised many nineteenth-century thinkers. Huxley was to devote a considerable amount of his time to the second question, and, as we shall see in chapter 5, also probed the third.

So far as the first question is concerned, the notion that human structure is essentially similar to that of other animals, especially monkeys and apes, was scarcely a novelty: Aristotle had pointed it out. But the story proper begins with Linnaeus, the inventor of modern systematics, who in the eighteenth century included man in his classification of the animals, and furthermore in the first edition of *Systema Naturae* classed man and the anthropoid apes together as genera belonging to the Anthropomorphae (766). It was beyond Linnaeus to conclude from this that some kind of evolution had taken place. For him, nature was composed of a continuous series of forms, from the lifeless through the simplest living beings to the more complex ones, ending with man and the spiritual world. "Natura non facit saltum" was a favourite aphorism of Linnaeus, Leibnitz, and all those who believed in the continuity of natural forms (and was indeed repeated more than once by Darwin himself [656a, ch. 6]).

Linnaeus would never have conceived that the inclusion of man with the anthropoid apes in the same zoological grouping might suggest that either one had developed from the other or that they both had evolved from some third form. What he meant was merely that the zoologist detects a very close degree of similarity in the structures of those organisms. Linnaeus considered genera to have been created by God in their present form, through distinct acts of creation. For him, genera were "natural" and "fixed," although he was more of a nominalist in respect to other groupings (897, pp. 64–65). Yet his observational rigour and his consequent authority made the idea of man's proximity to the apes scientifically acceptable. Linnaeus's work was, in the long run, more helpful to the establishment of the notion of evolution than that of many thinkers sympathetic to, or instrumental in the exposition of, some kind of evolutionary view. One thinks here of Buffon (936), Chambers (727; 802) and Lamarck (631).

That discussions of the place of man in nature were frequent, and heated, in nineteenth-century England is demonstrated by the William Lawrence affair. In 1819 Lawrence published a series of lectures given at the Royal College of Surgeons in London, including some *Lectures on the Natural History of Man* (761). According to C. Darlington, neither Huxley nor Darwin ever read Lawrence's book, "for neither of them supports or contradicts Lawrence on the theoretical issue he examines" (653, p. 22). Darlington is certainly wrong so far as Darwin is concerned. Darwin's copy of Lawrence's *Lectures* is preserved in the University Library, Cambridge; in 1847 Darwin read the edition dating from 1822, but in his reading list he noted it "poor" (894, p. 399). On the other hand, Lawrence seems to have had very little influence on Huxley (933, p. 350).

Lawrence, who was strongly influenced by Cuvier (905), believed in the dependence of function upon structure, and maintained that the physical, mental, and moral differences which occur in mankind are hereditary. Moreover, he considered man a suitable subject for zoological research and treated him as such in his *Lectures*. He was more concerned with the differences than the resemblances between man and the other animals, and rejected the "scale of beings." He believed in the fixity of species, but recognised the importance of geographical isolation (933, pp. 322–26).

In Huxley's later opinion, Lawrence's book was mild enough: "It was not very long since my kind friend, Sir William Lawrence, one of the ablest men whom I have known, had been well-nigh ostracized for his book "On Man", which now might be read in a Sunday-school without surprising anybody" (*342*, vol. 7, p. vii).

At the time, however, pious, conservative-minded people were alarmed by Lawrence's book, and he was obliged to suppress it lest it ruin his career. Many pirate copies were printed and sold; the *Lectures* were probably more widely read than either the author himself or his adversaries expected. In order to save his career and reputation, Lawrence had to withdraw from such controversial matters; and he went on to devote himself to the more respectable art of surgery. The establishment, once it was no longer threatened by him as a heretic, rewarded him handsomely: Lawrence became president of the Royal College of Surgeons, then sergeant-surgeon to Queen Victoria, and eventually a baronet.

Although he was successful in his career, Lawrence's scientific fate was clearly unfortunate. His book was undoubtedly important, although it should not be overrated, and deserved to make a strong impact on zoology and anthropology. But the intellectual conformism of 1819—forty years before the publication of the *Origin of Species*, which itself encountered heated opposition—afforded him no chance of a fair hearing. There is no doubt that Lawrence's defeat constituted a severe blow to freedom of enquiry. As O. Temkin has shown, such a defeat was engineered by the establishment in the name of patriotism and religion (*905*, p. 114), arguments still used by some of Darwin's opponents when the *Origin of Species* and the *Descent of Man* were published.

When Darwin published the *Origin of Species*, he could see no serious obstacle to the application of his views to man, but he made no statement on this point except the rather cryptic "Light will be thrown on the origin of man and his history" (*656a*, p. 488). It is worth reading the works of Ellegård (*681*) and Irvine (*477*) to appreciate the tremendous impact on the Victorians of Darwinian—or supposedly Darwinian— views of man. For a careful reading of the works of British evolutionists gives the impression that no "Darwinian" was wholeheartedly so. We discover a varied range of opinions among Darwin's friends, very often in disagreement with Darwin himself. Neither Lyell nor Wallace agreed entirely with Darwin's view of human evolution, for example, and Wallace had a long argument with Darwin on sexual selection.

Lyell (*775*), along with the young Lubbock (*770*), addressed himself mainly to questions concerning the antiquity of man. His position on human evolution is well outlined by M. Bartholomew in "Lyell and Evolution: An Account of Lyell's Response to the Prospect of an Evolutionary Ancestry of Man" (604). Bartholomew develops a view expressed by Huxley on Lyell:

I see no reason to doubt that, if Sir Charles could have avoided the inevitable corollary of the pithecoid origin of man—for which, to the end of his life, he entertained a profound antipathy—he would have advocated the efficiency of causes now in operation to bring about the condition of the organic world, as stoutly as he championed that doctrine in reference to inorganic nature. [306, p. 193; 604, p. 261; see also 679, p. 105]

Bartholomew states:

Throughout his life Lyell remained loyal to a set of beliefs about God, nature and man, and . . . these beliefs were integrated into his 'scientific' work, although in the end they were incompatible with the sort of scientific explanation he was advocating. These beliefs slowly became explicit—a few years before his death he made some sad and frank admissions—but they are implicit, though sometimes difficult to establish, in all his early work. [604, p. 269]

Thus, Lyell and Darwin had very different ideas on the relationship between man and the other animals. Lyell wrote:

November 1, 1858. If the geologist dwelling exclusively on one class of facts, which might be paralleled by the existing creation [arrives] at conclusions derogating from the elevated position previously assigned by him to Man, if he blends him inseparably with the inferior animals & considers him as belonging to the earth solely, & as doomed to pass away like them & have no farther any relation to the living world, he may feel dissatisfied with his labours & doubt whether he would not have been happier had he never entered upon them & whether he ought to impart his results to others. [604, p. 293]

Wallace's views on man are also worthy of brief consideration (893). In 1864 he published "The Origin of Human Races and the Antiquity of Man Deduced from the Theory of Natural Selection" (927), in which he propounded the view that no supernatural agency was needed in the explanation of the origin of man. Wallace himself seems to have forgotten this, since in his autobiography he suggests that he had always had this view (930), when in fact he adopted it only later, as M. J. Kottler has shown (751). The main idea expressed in 1864 is that the mind has somehow "shielded" the body of man from the action of natural selection. His views on human evolution, unorthodox from a Darwinian viewpoint, were expressed only later, in 1869, in "Sir C. Lyell and the Geological Climates and the Origin of Species" (928). In his view of man, Wallace now tried to combine value judgments with the tenets of the theory of evolution (893, p. 78). He believed in spiritual purpose behind consciousness, whereas Darwin and Huxley quite obviously did not. Wallace believed that the individuation of purpose in human affairs could be the starting point for the correct attitude both to human evolution and to social views. Under the influence of the philosophical ideas of Herbert Spencer, he believed that evolutionary doctrine and social theory were interdependent (674). Huxley, on the other hand, openly proclaimed the necessity of separating knowledge from value, and therefore of keeping social views apart from discussions of organic evolution (343; 345). Wallace was a convinced spiritualist, whereas Huxley was completely sceptical in this regard (472, vol. 1, pp. 452–55). Of all the evolutionists, Wallace was the one with whom Huxley had the least contact. The two men exchanged little by way of correspondence, and what there is, is of slight interest. Neither Lyell's theological attitude nor Wallace's spiritualism can be found in Huxley's anthropological works. Huxley explained in 1861:

> As the biological sciences have grown in breadth and depth, and as successive generations of naturalists have succeeded in penetrating further and further into the arcana of nature, the questions—in what relation does the thinker and investigator stand to the objects of his enquiries? what is the tie which connects man with other animated and sentient beings?—have more and more forcibly pressed for a reply.
>
> Nor have responses been wanting; but, unfortunately, they have been diametrically opposed to one another. Theologians and moralists, historians and poets, impressed by a sense of the infinite responsibilities of mankind, awed by a just prevision of the great destinies in store for the only earthly being of practically unlimited powers, or touched by the tragic dignity of the ever recurring struggle of human will with circumstance, have always tended to conceive of their kind as something apart, separated by a great and impassable barrier, from the rest of the natural world. On the other hand, the students of natural science, discovering as complete a system of law and order in the microcosm as in the macrocosm, incessantly lighting up new analogies and new identities between life as manifested by man and life in other shapes,—have no less steadily gravitated towards the opposite opinion, and, as knowledge has advanced, have more and more distinctly admitted the closeness of the bond which unites man with his humbler fellows. [99, p. 471]

Huxley, of course, joins hands with the "students of natural science": his main assumption is that man is a suitable subject for a purely zoological study.

Why then did he succeed against the received wisdoms of the "theologians, moralists, historians and poets" where his unfortunate forerunner Lawrence had not? Britain was in Darwin's and Huxley's time more liberal than in 1819, and furthermore Lawrence was probably less resilient than Huxley. Two of Huxley's main qualities were perseverance in attack allied with stubbornness in defence, and what is best expressed by the German word *Schwung* (something like "drive" and "sprint" combined):

When I was a young man, there was just a little—a mere soupçon—in my composition of that tenacity of purpose which has another name; and I felt sure that
all the evil things prophesied would not be so painful to me as the giving up that
which I had resolved to do, upon grounds which I conceived to be right. [342, vol.
7, p. x]

Thus Huxley became popular, while Lawrence was later almost completely forgotten; only recently have scholars begun to consider his
contribution carefully.

We have seen how Darwin's immediate circle came into conflict
with purveyors of received truths, just as Lawrence had; but on the other
side, Darwin's circle also came into conflict with what might be called
"ultra-Darwinians." In Germany there was for example August
Weismann, who belonged to a generation slightly younger than that of
the "historical" evolutionists in Britain, and who, in fact, founded the
school of the "neo-Darwinists." He strenuously denied the notion of
the inheritance of acquired characters, which had been accepted by
Darwin himself. For Weismann, natural selection, and only natural
selection, was the mechanism of evolution. Romanes, who was a "heretic," but an active member of Darwin's group, fought against Weismann's view and advocated—in the name of Darwin—the inheritance
of acquired characters. And in respect to human evolution, Haeckel for
one was wont to push Darwin's positions to radical and misleading
extremes (718).

In short, we see therefore that the general context of thinking upon
the subject of man, even after the publication of the *Origin of Species*,
was rather ragged, especially in respect to human evolution; though the
view of man as a zoological entity related to the apes, deriving principally as we have seen from Linnaeus, was the clear focus of post-
Darwinian approaches to the natural history of man.

Huxley's Specific Motivations

The major problem for anthropology in Darwin's day was therefore not
that of rehearsing the resemblances between man and the apes, but of
drawing useful deductions from those similarities. It is here that the
principal villain of our story reappears. I refer, of course, to Richard
Owen.

Owen denied the existence of the posterior lobe and the hippocampus
minor in the apes. The matter had caused many arguments in the past,
and seemed to have blown over until Owen and Huxley crossed swords
for this, the most spectacular of their duels. Cuvier had claimed the
existence of a hippocampus minor and a posterior lobe in the apes (650),
while Tiedemann had opposed this view (910). Gratiolet and Schröder
van der Kolk (921; 922) had supported Cuvier's opinion. The works of all

these anthropologists were well known to Huxley, who often quoted them in his notes (*HM*, vol. 118, pp. 2–4, 31, 52, 64, 68, 69).

Starting with the alleged absence of the hippocampus minor and the posterior lobe in the apes and their presence in man, Owen put forward a classification in which man and the apes were widely separated: *Homo* was to be considered not as an order but as a subclass of the mammals to be named Archencephala. In a memoir written in 1857 and published in 1858, Owen stated:

In Man the brain presents an ascensive step in development, higher and more strongly marked than that by which the preceding subclass was distinguished from the one below it. Not only the cerebral hemispheres . . . overlap the olfactory lobes and cerebellum, but they extend in advance of the one, and further back than the other. . . . Their posterior development is so marked that anatomists have assigned to that part the character of a third lobe; it is peculiar to the genus *Homo*, and equally peculiar is the 'posterior horn of the lateral ventricle', and the 'hippocampus minor' which characterize the hind lobe of each hemisphere. . . . Peculiar mental powers are associated with this highest form of brain, and their consequences wonderfully illustrate the value of the cerebral character; according to my estimate of which, I am led to regard the genus *Homo*, as not merely a representative of a distinct order, but of a distinct subclass of the Mammalia, for which I propose the name of "Archencephala". [*838*, pp. 19–20]

In a footnote Owen added some dangerous remarks:

Not being able to appreciate or conceive the distinction between the physical phenomenon of a Chimpanzee and of a Boschiman or of an Aztec with arrested brain-growth, as being of a nature so essential as to preclude a comparison between them, or as being other than a difference of degree, I cannot shut my eyes to the significance of that all-pervading similitude of structure—every tooth, every bone, strictly homologous—which makes the determination of the difference between *Homo* and *Pithecus* the anatomist's difficulty. [p. 20n]

Two years later Owen delivered a lecture at Cambridge in which he pointed out that certain characteristics of the human brain cannot be found in the ape (*839*). It was essentially the view expressed in the essay of 1857, but the dangerous words quoted above were wisely omitted.

This was the beginning of the celebrated "hippocampus minor controversy" between Huxley and Owen. Once again Owen denied obvious facts in such a stubborn way as to damage his reputation and give his opponent unexpected advantage.

Huxley received much useful information from colleagues, as the following letter from Allen Thomson dated 24 May 1860 shows; the latter also hints at the inevitable clash with Owen. Thomson explains that the brain of a chimpanzee he had dissected

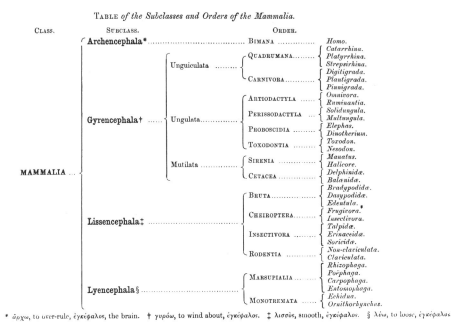

Figure 15.   Owen's classification of the mammalia. [838, p. 37]

was more like the brain of a child than that of an adult, and this corresponds in some degree with more rapid advancement which the chimp makes in its infantile stage. . . . There is a [*sic*] very clearly a posterior lobe separated from the middle one by as deep a groove between the convolutions of the inner side of the hemispheres as in Man, and equally well marked off on the outer side. I should be inclined to say that the posterior lobe is little inferior to that of man, excepting perhaps in vertical depth. The cerebral hemispheres completely covered the cerebellum as seen from above. I took pains to observe this while the brain was still within the cranium, looking down upon it from above at right angles to the longitudinal axis of the cranial cavity and I found the posterior extremity of the cerebral hemispheres projected a little beyond the vertical line passing the back of the cerebellum.

I found an eminence in the floor of the posterior cornu and towards its inner side which I regard as the hippocampus minor and I found it produced in exactly the same manner as in man by the bulging into the ventricle of a portion of the brain by the very deep groove between the convolutions which mark the separation of the posterior and middle lobe.

P. S. Pray don't draw me into any controversy with the great potentate [Owen]. [*HM*, vol. 118, pp. 99–104]

The controversy was pursued by Huxley in his 1861 memoir "On the Zoological Relations of Man with the Lower Animals" (99, p. 471).

There, after quoting Owen's passage on the controversial cerebral structures (p. 476), Huxley launches into the counterattack. He shows that

1. The third lobe is neither peculiar to, nor characteristic of, man, seeing that it exists in all the higher Quadrumana.
2. The posterior cornu of the lateral ventricle is neither peculiar to, nor characteristic of, man, inasmuch as it also exists in the higher Quadrumana.
3. The hippocampus minor is neither peculiar to, nor characteristic of, man, as it has been found in certain of the higher Quadrumana. [Ibid.]

Huxley states, moreover:

Schroeder van der Kolk and Vrolik . . . though they particularly note that "the lateral ventricle is distinguished from that of a man by the very defective proportions of the posterior cornu, wherein only a stripe is visible as an indication of the hippocampus minor", yet the figure 4 in their second Plate shows that this posterior cornu is a perfectly distinct and unmistakable structure, quite as large as it often is in man. It is the more remarkable that Professor Owen should have overlooked the explicit statement and figure of these authors, as it is quite obvious, on comparison of the figures, that his wood-cut of the brain of a Chimpanzee . . . is a reduced copy of the second figure of Messrs. Schroeder van der Kolk and Vrolik's first plate. [p. 482]

But Owen did not change his opinion. On 19 March 1861 he delivered a lecture at the Royal Institution in which he propounded the same views concerning the brain. This lecture was reported in the *Athenaeum* of 23 March:

The osteological distinctions were those which [Owen] had pointed out in detail in his Lecture at the Royal Institution on Friday evening, February 4th, 1859; and which received confirmatory illustrations in the rich series of specimens of skulls and skeletons of both sexes and of different ages of the Gorilla. . . . The advocate for man's origin from a transmuted ape contends that there is a greater difference of structure between the brains of a Gorilla and of a Lemur than between those of a Gorilla and of a Negro. . . . The *hippocampus minor* . . . as developed and extended in the human brain, and as defined in human anatomy, is peculiar to man. . . . There is a gradation of cerebral development from the lowest to the highest vertebrate species; but there are interruptions in this gradation. . . . In the quadrumanous series there is a succession of small steps or improvements of cerebral structures by which the comparative anatomist advances from the brain of the Lemur to that of the Chimpanzee and Gorilla; but the interval of difference between any two steps in this series is truly small indeed, when compared with the vast cerebral expansion and development of new parts, such as posterior lobes overlapping and stretching beyond the cerebellum with their *posterior cornu* and *hippocampi minores* which have no existence in the brains of any lower mammalian animal. [840, pp. 395–96]

The *Athenaeum* showed a diagram which was supposed to reproduce the brain of the gorilla, but was actually incomplete and inaccurate. On 30 March, Huxley sent a letter to the *Athenaeum* pointing out the mistakes and incompleteness of the diagram (*101*). Owen replied in the following issue (6 April), admitting that, with regard to the diagram, "the artist has been less successful in the copy of cerebral diagrams" (*841*). He committed a blunder in claiming that, in order to become acquainted with a correct figure of a simian brain, reference "should be made to the figure of the undissected brain of the Chimpanzee, in my Reade's Lecture "On the Classification etc. of the Mammalia", p. 25, fig. 7, 8vo 1859." Huxley protested, Owen replied, Schröder van der Kolk and Vrolik also complained. But Owen was immovable, although he could produce no evidence to support his arguments.

The controversy ended when W. F. Flower showed that Huxley was right (*687*). Further detail here would reveal no more than what we have already seen; suffice it to say that Owen displayed less than complete integrity over the affair. To label historical figures as saints or sinners is misleading, but Owen's behaviour has little excuse in the eyes of even the most indulgent twentieth-century reader. We have seen in respect to *Terebratula* how inaccurate and arrogant Owen's attitude had been. Arrogance is a moral error, but inaccuracy is a scientific sin, and one of the gravest kind.

The hippocampus minor affair obviously required Huxley to amass relevant material, and drew him into open discussion of the question of man. For it was also in 1861 that Huxley delivered a course on anthropology for working men. These meetings were a great success. He wrote to his wife: "My working-men stick by me wonderfully, the house being fuller than ever last night. By next Friday evening they will all be convinced that they are monkeys" (*472*, vol. 1, p. 205). In 1862 he lectured in Edinburgh on the same subject, the "Relations of Man to the Lower Animals." The audience was said to have been almost as enthusiastic (*430*, p. 65) as the Scottish football fans after a victory over England.

It was at this point that Huxley decided to put together a substantial quantity of the material on man in his possession, a decision which resulted in the book which is undoubtedly his best-known scientific work. *Evidence as to Man's Place in Nature* (*110a*) appeared in 1863. Darwin was one of those who enjoyed it: "I have just finished with very great interest "Man's Place". I never fail to admire the clearness and condensed vigour of your style, as one calls it, but really of your thought" (*662*, vol. 1, p. 237). The book became an international success and was translated into a number of foreign languages, including French, German, Russian, and Italian. Thirty years later in November 1892, Huxley, now an old and revered master, affirmed:

I was looking through *Man's Place in Nature* the other day. I do not think there is a word I need delete, nor anything I need add except in confirmation and extension of the doctrine there laid down. That is great good fortune for a book thirty years old, and one that a very shrewd friend of mine implored me not to publish, as it would certainly ruin all my prospects. I said, like the French fox-hunter in Punch, "I shall try." [472, vol. 2, p. 365]

Certainly the publication of *Man's Place in Nature* might have been dangerous for Huxley's career. He was relatively young, and although his star was rising, his position was less consolidated than that of Owen. Nonetheless, Huxley probably understood from previous clashes that his opponent's throne was tottering, and he judged that the moment had come to deal a possibly decisive blow to the old lion.

The circumstances leading to the production of *Man's Place in Nature* are thus of interest in themselves. We witness simultaneously Huxley's precision of observation and deduction, his willingness to do battle where others held back, his concern for knowledge to reach the widest audience, and his eye for the chance of advancement. In short we see the admixture of scientist, controversialist, educator, and opportunist which ensured his tenacity of purpose and his contemporary reputation and importance.

The Content of *Man's Place in Nature*

Huxley's Existing Material

Huxley had in his possession a series of notes and observations on the primates, and human and simian anatomy. He was attentive to everything published on these subjects and the names and works of Schreber, Rudolf Wagner, Gratiolet, Meckel (e.g., *HM*, vol. 118) are quoted in his private papers, along with Cuvier, Vrolik, Schröder van der Kolk, and G. St. Hilaire. Several notes concern the comparative anatomy of a number of primates, such as *Gorilla* and *Ateles paniscus*; in 1861 Huxley proved that the hippocampus minor can be found in *Ateles*, a low American monkey (100).

Huxley produced a large number of drawings of the brains of various primates, and considered in detail the myology of *Gorilla*, with reference to the muscles of other primates (myology is an important source of evidence in human evolution [see 763]). Simian crania of course occupy an outstanding place in his notes, with numerous comparisons and measurements. He remarks that the gorilla, the chimpanzee, and the gibbon are dolichocephalic (though the gibbon has an inferior cerebral capacity), while the orang is brachycephalic (*HM*, vol. 118, p. 19). As far as dentition is concerned, "*Troglodyta* approaches nearer to man . . . *Gorilla* being more remote, even than *Hylobates*" (*HM*, vol. 118, p. 21). Much space is devoted in these notes to dentition, a crucial point in palaeontological anthropology. Huxley was deeply concerned with the relationships among the primates, hoping to throw light on their classification. For this reason, certain characteristics of dentition and brain structure are pointed out, including a reference to the hippocampus minor: "The brain (of the primates) has a posterior cornu . . . & a . . . fissure (shewn hippocampus minor)" (vol. 119). Other notes concern some readings of Blumenbach and Tyson (vol. 119), the great anthropologists of the eighteenth and seventeenth centuries respectively; a series of measurements comparing the gorilla and chimpanzee to man and woman (vol. 120, pp. 1–2); and the comparison of the pelvis of man and the gorilla (p. 3). All this material, though not properly organised in these notes, was to be of importance in his anthropological work.

In the summer of 1862, having the opportunity to study the skulls of Engis and Neanderthal man, Huxley began to involve himself in the young science of human palaeontology.

Man's Place in Nature falls into three parts, broadly reflecting the foci of this existing material. The first part concerns "The Natural History of the Manlike Apes" (*110a*, pp. 1–56; *110b*, pp. 1–76). Huxley here reports the findings concerning primates and apelike forms known to him. I shall not deal directly with this section of the book. The second part, "On the Relations of Man to the Lower Animals" (*110a*, pp. 57–118; *110b*, pp. 77–156), is the core and raison d'être of the book, and I consider it in some detail. The third part, which investigates the fossil evidence, is examined more briefly.

As the title of the book suggests, Huxley's general purpose was to show the actual position occupied by man in nature, using all the scientific documentation available to him. The best way to achieve this goal, he considered, was to compare man with the anthropoid apes, the animals most resembling man. There was nothing especially novel in this; it is the forcefulness with which he presents his evidence that makes the book striking.

"On the Relations of Man to the Lower Animals"

Darwin commented to Huxley: "I was very much struck with admiration at the opening pages of part II" (*662*, vol. 1, p. 237). What Darwin had appreciated begins:

The question of questions for mankind—the problem which underlies all others, and is more deeply interesting than any other—is the ascertainment of the place which Man occupies in nature and of his relations to the universe of things. Whence our race has come; what are the limits of our power over nature; and of nature's power over us; to what goal we are tending; are the problems which present themselves anew and with undiminished interest to every man born in the world. [*110a*, p. 57; *110b*, pp. 77–78]

These questions are difficult, Huxley argues, and the answers might not be those desired. However, we must accept the results of a candid scientific enquiry even if they diverge from our beliefs, hopes, or expectations. As he wrote in 1874:

I may be permitted to remark that logical consequences are the scarecrows of fools and the beacons of wise men. The only question which any wise and honest man will ask himself, is whether a doctrine is true or false. Consequences will take care of themselves; at most their importance can only justify us in testing with extra care the reasoning process from which they result. [*217*, pp. 244–45]

Man's understanding of his heritage, Huxley believes, and especially of his civilisation, presupposes at least an understanding of his place in nature.

He commences with embryological evidence. Darwin had pointed out more than once that embryology would afford major evidence for his views (*656a*, pp. 439–50), and we know from chapter 1 that Huxley was conversant with that subject chiefly through his sound knowledge of the works of von Baer and the German embryologists:

It is a truth of very wide, if not universal, application, that every living creature commences its existence under a form different from, and simpler than, that which it eventually attains.

The oak is a more complex thing than the little rudimentary plant contained in the acorn; the caterpillar is more complex than the egg; the butterfly than the caterpillar; and each of these beings, in passing from its rudimentary to its perfect condition, runs through a series of changes, the sum of which is called its Development. [*110a*, p. 60; *110b*, pp. 81–82]

The knowledge of embryology is obviously connected with cell theory, and cell theory conduces to the understanding of the stages of life. Both embryology and cell theory, as Huxley had learned from the works of Koelliker, Remak, and von Baer, arrive at the same conclusion: that life can be considered as possessing an inner unity. At the beginning there is no substantial difference between the fertilised eggs of, say, a whale, a toad, and human. Only later, as von Baer had shown so convincingly, does the differentiation of the various species occur.*

---

*In 1853 Huxley wrote a review of cell theory (*23*) the main purpose of which was to emphasise the unity of life. The same year, in fact, Huxley delivered a discourse to the Royal Institution (*20*) in which he supported the view of the identity of structure of plants and animals (the view was not new: it had been propounded by Forbes in 1845 [*688*], and antecedents in the eighteenth century can even be found [*920*]). The same views are expressed by Huxley in "Observations on the Existence of Cellulose in the Tunic of Ascidians," also of 1853 (*21*). In his review of cell theory Huxley does not show himself very sympathetic to Schleiden and Schwann. He refers to an endoplast and a periplast, the former roughly corresponding to the protoplasm. Here Huxley maintains that the most important part of the cell is morphologically and physiologically the periplast (*23*; for cell theory, see *598*; *637*). Huxley was to reverse this view in 1868, in "On the Physical Basis of

Huxley compares the development of dog and chicken embryos. Although there is little superficial likeness between the mature chicken and the dog, their initial cell divisions are quantitatively the same. It is fairly difficult at certain stages to distinguish the chicken embryo from the canine one. The same can be said for all other animals. The casual observer notices the variety of the living world and is unable to account for it. Embryology furnishes a starting point for such an account. *In principio erat ovum*:

The history of the development of any other vertebrate animal, Lizard, Snake, Frog, or Fish, tells the same story. There is always, to begin with, an egg having the same essential structure as that of the Dog:—the yolk of that egg always undergoes division, or '*segmentation*' as it is often called: the ultimate products of that segmentation constitute the building materials for the body of the young animal; and this is built up round a primitive groove, in the floor of which a notochord is developed. Furthermore, there is a period in which the young of all these animals resemble one another, not merely in outward form, but in all essentials of structure, so closely, that the differences between them are inconsiderable, while, in their subsequent course, they diverge more and more widely from one another. And it is a general law, that, the more closely any animals resemble one another in adult structure, the longer and the more intimately their embryos resemble one another; so that for example, the embryos of a Snake and of a Lizard remain like one another longer than do those of a Snake and of a Bird; and the embryo of a Dog and of a Cat remain like one another for a far longer period than do those of a Dog and a Bird; or of a Dog and an Opossum; or even those of a Dog and a Monkey. Thus the study of development affords a clear test of closeness of structural affinity, and one turns with impatience to inquire, what results are yielded by the study of the development of Man. Is he something apart? Does he originate in a totally different way from Dog, Bird, Frog, and Fish, thus justifying those who assert him to have no place in nature and no real affinity with the lower world of animal life? Or does he originate in a similar germ, pass through the same slow and gradually progressive modifications—depend on the same contrivances for protection and nutrition, and finally enter the world by the help of the same mechanisms? [*110a*, pp. 64–65; *110b*, pp. 88–89]

Huxley of course prefers the second alternative: the laws which govern the human species are the same as those which operate in the whole

Life" (*151*). There he claimed that the basic element common to all living things is the protoplasm (see *693*); the reason for this change of mind is not clear. In 1873, Huxley wrote to Michael Foster asking whether he knew of anything on the matter since the publication of W. Kühne's book *Untersuchungen über das Protoplasma und die Contractilität* (*754*) of 1864 (*HP* 4.47). One wonders whether Kühne's book influenced Huxley; but of course this letter provides only a hint, since it was written well after "On the Physical Basis of Life." A more likely influence is Haeckel, since the German thinker, whose views we have already seen to have been important for Huxley, had totally endorsed the protoplasmic theory in *Monographie der Radiolarien* (*715*).

living world. It is worth noting that Huxley's first positive steps into the world of anthropology come from embryology; this is the continuing influence of the German embryologists on his thought. Embryology enables the disinterested naturalist to conclude that, from this viewpoint, man is much closer to the apes than the ape is to the dog. Even in the earliest stages we can observe the difference between the simian and canine embryos, as we cannot in comparing man and ape at corresponding stages. Can we eventually place man and the apes in the same order, or should we consider the latter so distant from the former as to constitute a new order containing man only? Huxley is aware that it is not easy to keep an objective and unbiased mind on such an emotive topic:

Let us imagine ourselves scientific Saturnians, if you will, fairly acquainted with such animals as now inhabit the Earth, and employed in discussing the relations they bear to a new and singular 'erect and featherless biped'. . . . Being happily free from all real, or imaginary, personal interest in the results of the enquiry thus set afoot, we should proceed to weigh the arguments on one side and on the other, with as much judicial calmness as if the question related to a new Opossum. We should endeavour to ascertain, without seeking either to magnify or diminish them, all the characters by which our new Mammal differed from the Apes: and if we found that these were of less structural value, than those which distinguished certain members of the Ape order from others universally admitted to be of the same order, we should undoubtedly place the newly discovered tellurian genus with them. [110a, pp. 69–70; 110b, pp. 95–96]

Two important aspects of Huxley's views can be seen in these passages. The first is that only matters concerning structure, function, and their relationships can be accepted in a zoological enquiry into the position of man; only matters of fact must be considered. Throughout his career Huxley remembered the famous statement Hume makes towards the end of the *Enquiry*:

When we run over libraries, persuaded of these principles, what havoc must we make? If we take in our hand any volume of divinity or school metaphysics, for instance; let us ask: 'Does it contain any abstract reasoning concerning quantity or number? No. Does it contain any experimental reasoning concerning quantity or number? No. Commit it then to the flames: for it contains nothing but sophistry and illusion. [732, sec. 12]

The second aspect, which connects with the first and follows Hume, is Huxley's ideal of neutral, objective science. We must remain detached and unemotional in the face of scientific observations; only thus will we be able to reach genuinely scientific conclusions.

Huxley now entertains a long series of comparisons between the apes and man. His conclusion is that man cannot be classified in a distinct order from that of the apes; confirmation of this comes first from study of the vertebral column and the skull. For any item of the skeleton, for the teeth, for the cranial capacity, the result would be the same: the lower apes differ from the gorilla more than the gorilla differs from man. Moreover, Huxley considers the cranial capacity and the cerebral convolutions of man and the apes, and reaches the same conclusion. As far as the cerebral convolutions are concerned, Lyell had written to Huxley in 1861 to enquire whether stress "had been laid in the greater convolutions of the brain as contrasted with the Apes & has not the European in like manner a more convoluted cerebrum than the Negro? Is there any case where any quadrumanum has a very convolute brain?" (*HP* 6.49–50) Huxley replied by pointing out that not only was the European brain more convolute than the Negro or Hottentot one, but the brains of the orang and the chimpanzee are highly convoluted, though slightly so compared to that of man. He also provided his colleague with cranial measurements which show that the cranial capacity of a Peruvian, at 58 inches, is closer to that of the gorilla, with 34.5, than to that of a European, with 114 (*HP* 30.35). However, the following passage from *Man's Place in Nature* itself does not accord well with his reply to Lyell: "It must not be overlooked, however, that there is a very striking difference in absolute mass and weight between the lowest human brain and that of the highest ape" (*110a*, p. 102; *110b*, p. 140).

Any student of biological science knows that, broadly speaking, any structure detectable in an organism has, or has had, a function; and likewise, any function has a corresponding structure. It is scientifically unimportant whether we consider first the structure and then the function, or vice versa: this mainly depends upon whether we are anatomists or physiologists. Huxley did not of course invent the structure/function relationship; it had even been applied to man as an anatomical and physiological object, although inconsistently. But Huxley's emphasis on the concept was important, as we shall see.

The Christian tradition, both Protestant and Catholic, assumes that man has a "soul," which Christians maintain is neither material nor connected to any material structure. (The principle of psychic dualism is actually much older: C. U. M. Smith has discovered it in Homer [*891*, pp. 24–25].) If this is the case, one must logically conclude that there is a profound difference in kind between man and the animals, which are said to possess no soul. As M. Mandelbaum suggests, it was man's mental characteristics which led pre-Darwinian anthropologists to classify man separately from animals (*780*). There was a remarkable exception in Owen, who sought structural evidence for that separation, but his, as we have seen, was not a very successful attempt.

Dr. W. F. Bynum has shown that the concept of a gap between structure and function is to be found in the works of the great seventeenth-century anthropologist Edward Tyson (*634*). Tyson and his colleagues and successors before Darwin had correctly conceived that the structural differences between the human and simian brains were not enormous. Nonetheless it was apparent that there was a mental difference, and they concluded that it lay in something neither structural nor structurally connected. This difference is the "mind of man," a truly "higher principle." Tyson, according to Bynum, used "an apparent disjunction of the comparative structure/function relationship to erect an absolute barrier between man and brute" (634, p. 463).

The most important antecedent of Huxley's abandonment of this disjunction is the hapless Lawrence. But, as we saw, Lawrence's contribution was largely overlooked, and it is to Huxley and not to Lawrence that modern anthropologists have turned as the first serious example of the application of the structure/function relationship to the case of man in a zoologically rigorous way.

In Huxley's opinion, the mind is a physiological function, whose corresponding structure is the brain. It now becomes necessary to distinguish "mind" and "soul." "Mind" is intended as the faculty of thinking, "soul" as the immortal principle of human nature. Anthropologists before Darwin and Huxley did not respect the difference between the two terms, which in common language are often used synonymously. But given the distinction, there is no problem in admitting that the apes have minds. Huxley is increasingly explicit on this point. In 1878 he was to write:

It is not merely that the observation of the actions of animals almost irresistibly suggests the attribution to them of mental states, such as those which accompany corresponding actions in men. The minute comparison which has been instituted by anatomists and physiologists between the organs which we know to constitute the apparatus of thought in man, and the corresponding organs in brutes, has demonstrated the existence of the closest similarity between the two, not only in structure, as far as the microscope will carry us, but in function, as far as functions are determinable by experiment. There is no question in the mind of any one acquainted with the facts that, so far as observation and experiment can take us, the structure and the functions of the nervous system are fundamentally the same in an ape, or in a dog, and in man. . . .

Structure for structure, down to the minutest microscopical details, the eye, the ear, the olfactory organs, the nerves, the spinal cord, the brain of an ape or of a dog, correspond with the same organs in the human subject. [248, pp. 122–23]

Such thinking enables Huxley to underline his conclusion that man is but one extreme of a long sequence of living beings; and one can only conclude that

in short, it seems hard to assign any good reason for denying to the higher animal any mental state, or process, in which the employment of the vocal and visual symbols of which language is composed is not involved; and comparative psy-

chology confirms the position in relation to the rest of the animal world assigned to man by comparative anatomy. As comparative anatomy is easily able
to show that, physically, man is but the last term of a long series of forms, which
lead, by slow gradations, from the highest mammal to the almost formless speck
of living protoplasm, which lies on the shadowy boundary between animal and
vegetable life; so comparative psychology, though but a young science, and far
short of her elder sister's growth, points to the same conclusion. [p. 125]

"Mind" is therefore a function (or better a family of functions) with
corresponding structure; but this does not imply that "soul" can be seen
as a structureless function. The proper conclusion of the argument, as
Huxley implies, is that "soul" is purely an article of faith, a concept
therefore excluded from the subject matter of science. The gap impeding
the rigorously zoological study of man has been filled.

Huxley was not always consistent in his use of the terms *mind* and
soul. For example, in 1870 he stated: "Modern physiologists . . . adopt
Descartes' principle, and suppose that the soul is lodged in the cortical
part of the brain—at least this is commonly regarded as the seat and
instrument of consciousness" (*184*, pp. 188–89). In an essay of 1874 on
Joseph Priestly, he wrote: "He denied the existence of a soul distinct
from the body" (*219*, p. 22). In both cases, although the term *soul* is used,
Huxley is actually dealing with mind; while in the following extract
from a letter to Kingsley of 22 May 1863, "soul" means "soul" and
reaffirms the proper silence of science in that area: "If you tell me that
an ape differs from a man because the latter has a soul and the ape has
not, I can only say it may be so; but I should uncommonly like to know
either that the ape has not one or that the man has." (*472*, vol. 1, p. 262).

It is worth briefly recalling phrenology at this point (*669; 942*). The
phrenologists also assumed that "the brain is the organ of the mind";
but their manner of specifying the details of the relationship was as
unscientific as the views they intended to oppose. Despite much consequent ridicule, phrenology has a clear place in the history of modern
anthropology and physiological psychology (see *635*, pp. 165–228); it is
perhaps best characterised as an extremely crude forerunner of the materialist conception of mind espoused by Darwin and Huxley. Huxley
does not in fact refer to the phrenologists; it seems unlikely that they
had the kind of influence on Huxley and Darwin that they apparently
had on Wallace (*893*).

It is however possible to trace, or at least suggest, some of the more
direct influences on Huxley. He returned to the question of the mind/
brain relationship in his essay of 1874, "On the Hypothesis That Animals are Automata, and Its History":

Either consciousness is the function of something distinct from the brain,
which we call the soul, and a sensation is the mode in which this soul is affected

by the motion of a part of the brain; or there is no soul, and a sensation is something generated by the mode of motion of a part of the brain. In the former case, the phenomena of the senses are purely spiritual affections; in the latter, they are something manufactured by the mechanism of the body, and as unlike the causes which set the mechanism in motion, as the sound of a repeater is unlike the pushing of the spring which gives rise to it. [217, p. 210]

Huxley's "latter case" here is in close correspondence with the view that "mind" is an "epiphenomenon" of physiological events. Such a view was central in the growing trend towards physiological psychology, one of the foremost representatives of which in Britain was the Scottish researcher Alexander Bain: "There is nothing I wish more than to so unite psychology and physiology that physiologists may be made to appreciate the true ends and drift of their researches into the nervous system, which no one man that I have yet encountered does at the present moment" (quoted from 942, p. 103). The motor theory underlying this trend in psychology was explicitly adopted by Bain from Johannes Müller (see, e.g., 942, p. 116n), with whose work Huxley was also familiar, as we saw in connection with the classification of the ganoids in chapter 2, and who may be taken as the ultimate source from whom the physiological approach to psychology was developed in Britain. Both Bain and Huxley were admirers of the thought of Hume and J. S. Mill, whose thinking on psychological subjects also tended in the direction of the physiological approach.

So embryology, anatomy, and the clarification of the concept of "mind" within the guiding principle of the structure/function relationship can all be seen to point in the same direction: that it is correct to include man in the same class as the apes.

But now a problem presents itself: there is no essential difference of structure, including brain structure, between the apes and man; the difference between the two are of degree rather than kind. Thus, one might expect there to be no real difference of "mind" between man and the apes. But this is not confirmed by any evidence, even of everyday life. After paying tribute to simian intelligence, it is obvious that one can find no Shakespeare, no Galileo, no Mozart among the apes: even Wodehouse's Bertie Wooster, not a particularly bright specimen of our species, would compare favourably to a chimpanzee.

That there are apparent differences of function between man and the apes, Huxley realises; but then it is not true, he claims, that the differences between man and the apes are entirely attributable to the brain. Other major aspects occur:

I by no means believe that it was any original difference of cerebral quality, or quantity, which caused the divergence between the human and the pithecoid stirpes, which has ended in the present enormous gulf between them. It is no doubt perfectly true, in a certain sense, that all difference of function is a result of a difference of structure; or, in other words, of difference in the combination of the primary molecular forces of living substance; and, starting from this undeniable axiom, objectors occasionally, and with much seeming plausibility, argue that the vast intellectual chasm between the Ape and Man implies a corresponding structural chasm in the organs of the intellectual functions; so that, it is said, the non-discovery of such vast differences proves, not that they are absent, but that Science is incompetent to detect them. A very little consideration, however, will, I think, show the fallacy of this reasoning. Its validity hangs on the assumption, that intellectual power depends altogether on the brain—whereas *the brain is only one condition out of many on which intellectual manifestations depend*; the others being, chiefly, the organs of the senses and the motor apparatuses, especially those which are concerned in prehension and the production of articulate speech. . . .

And believing, as I do with Cuvier, that the possession of articulate speech is the grand distinctive character of Man (whether it be absolutely peculiar to him or not), I find it very easy to comprehend, that some equally inconspicuous structural difference may have been the primary cause of the immeasurable and practically infinite divergence of the Human from the Simian Stirps. [*110a*, pp. 102–3n; *110b*, pp. 142–43n; italics added]

It is disappointing that Huxley confined this important issue to a footnote, albeit a long one, and did not delve deeper into this aspect of the problem. Moreover, he refers to the old view of Cuvier that articulate speech is the distinctive character of mankind. However, the point I wish to emphasise arises from the italicised phrase, which implies the view of an organism as an "adaptation of apparatus to function" (*418*, p. 4), that is, that the specificity of a species is to be found in the sum of its differences from its near relatives, the sum of its specific adaptations. It is this deployment of the adaptive interpretation of the structure/function relationship which was later taken as evidence of Huxley's "modernism" in anthropology. To quote Sir Julian Huxley: "Adaptation and function are two aspects of one problem. . . . The problem of adaptation is merely the problem of functional efficiency seen from a slightly different angle" (*742*, p. 417). Adaptation, we now say, is the result of evolution, and every species has its own adaptations; man's are different from those of the apes, or mosquitos, or buttercups. The actual uniqueness of man consists, from a biological point of view, in his adaptations which underlie differences of various sorts. But it can equally be said that apes, mosquitos, and buttercups have their own uniqueness. I therefore disagree with Sir Arthur Keith when he claims that "Huxley and those who followed him forgot that man is a unique animal" (*747*, p. 323); that footnote proves the contrary.

Adaptation is not correlated with one function only. We say that a species is adapted when all functions of the organism are harmoniously balanced and enable it to survive and reproduce itself. Mind can be considered, broadly speaking, as a set of interdependent functions related to the brain. But this set of functions is related to other functions, the result being the adaptation of the organism as a whole. Again with Sir Julian Huxley we say that "adaptation cannot but be universal among organisms, and every organism cannot but be other than a bundle of adaptations, more or less detailed and efficient, coordinated in greater or lesser degree" (742, p. 420).

If we consider the evolution of man in its broadest perspective, we see that, for example, the evolution of the brain alone is not sufficient to explain his present dominance. The evolution of erect posture with the related modification of the bones, and the evolution of the hand are also strictly correlated with the evolution of the brain. All these structures have their functions, which guarantee the adaptation, and therefore the continued existence, of the species. That footnote reminds us that there is no direct cause/effect relationship between the brain alone and the uniqueness of man, and that there is no direct cause/effect relationship of any single structure with respect to widely adaptive functions: relationships of this kind are intrinsically complex. The study of these relationships is indeed the study of the products of evolution, which was what interested Huxley above all. It is a way looking at evolution to whose popularity Huxley contributed, and it is because of this glimpse of future evolutionary views that *Man's Place in Nature* became popular among twentieth-century anthropologists.

The Fossil Remains

In the third part of *Man's Place in Nature* Huxley enquires into the fossil remains known to him. Human palaeontology was taking its first unsteady steps at the time Huxley was dealing with the problems of anthropology, and most of the important discoveries were yet to be made.

In the summer of 1862, Huxley examined the skulls of Engis (discovered in 1837) and Neanderthal man (discovered in 1857). Remains of other human skeletons had also been discovered in a cave at Engihoul, near Engis; but it was the Neanderthal specimen which caused the real sensation. The question it raised was twofold: Was it a human skull? and if so, What place would it occupy in human evolution, accepting the occurrence of evolution in all forms of life?

In order to describe these crania Huxley had to invent new methods of measurement, given his dissatisfaction with existing methods. Thus he made an important contribution to quantitative craniology. The principal method used prior to Huxley's invention was Camper's "Facial angle" technique. But in Huxley's opinion, "No comparison of crania is worth very much that is not founded upon the establishment of a relatively fixed baseline, to which the measurements, in all cases, must be referred" (*110a*, p. 148; *110b*, p. 192). Huxley suggests the use of what he calls the "basicranial axis": "I mean a line drawn through the middle vertical plane of the *basioccipital*, *basisphenoid* and *presphenoid*, from the hinder extremity of the last, at the upper end of the ethmo-presphenoid suture" (*142*, p. 219). As far as Neanderthal man is concerned, Huxley states that

in no sense . . . can the Neanderthal bones be regarded as the remains of a human being intermediate between Men and Apes. At most, they demonstrate

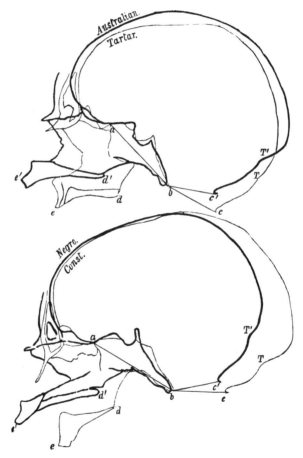

Figure 16. Huxley's basicranial axis. Sections of orthognathous (light contour) and pronathous (dark contour) skulls, *a b*, Basicranial axis; *b c*, *b' c'*, plane of the occipital foramen; *d d'*, hinder end of the palatine bone; *c c'*, front end of the upper jaw; *T T'*, insertion of the tentorium. [*342*, vol. 7, p. 196]

the existence of a Man whose skull may be said to revert somewhat towards the pithecoid type. . . . The Neanderthal cranium . . . forms, in reality, the extreme term of a series leading gradually to the highest and best developed of human crania. [*110a*, p. 157; *110b*, p. 205]

As he had noted in 1862 after measurements made at the College of Surgeons, Huxley considered the Neanderthal skull to be a modification of the lower type of Australian skull (*HP* 30.38). This view of Neanderthal man was mistaken. To quote Sir Arthur Keith:

Huxley regarded this form of humanity as merely an extreme variant of modern man, while, in opposition to him, Prof. King of Galway maintained that the simian characters of the skull were so pronounced that Neanderthal man must be regarded as belonging to a separate and extinct *species* of mankind. Events have proved that King was right. [*485*, p. 722; for King see *750*]

Nowadays it is thought that Neanderthal man was an "unsuccessful" sideline in the evolution of *Homo sapiens*.

Huxley was to maintain the same stance on Neanderthal man in his later scientific memoirs (*118*). However, if we consider the data on which he was working, the fundamental correctness of Huxley's conclusions on the place of man in nature is striking. Furthermore, his basicranial axis is still used by anthropologists for measuring and classifying crania.

The Evaluation of Man's Place in Nature

Huxley's Purposes

Man's Place in Nature is beyond doubt Huxley's best-known scientific work, perhaps the most famous of his writings. It is frequently mentioned, although less frequently quoted, as a contribution of paramount importance not only to modern physical anthropology but also, and especially, to the establishment of a broadly Darwinian attitude towards biological science. Huxley is widely thought of as Darwin's best friend, the man who defeated the church at Oxford, and the author of the first Darwinian book of anthropology. The first point is certainly wrong—Huxley was on good terms with Darwin, who appreciated his work, but no more than that. The second point overstates what really happened at Oxford; historians are now aware that there is no reliable account of the Oxford clash between Huxley and Wilberforce (*411; 543*).

The validity of the third point is also less than clear. The conclusion of Huxley's arguments, as Keith puts it, is that "man, being a member of the animal kingdom, must be classified by the same rules as are applied to animals" (*747*, p. 323). Such a conclusion is perfectly consistent with the evolutionary interpretation of the natural history of man: "There

would be no rational ground for doubting that man might have originated . . . by the gradual modification of a man-like ape; or . . . as a ramifi-
cation of the same primitive stock as those apes" (*110a*, pp. 105–6;
110b, p. 147). Huxley shows that human evolution is possible, even
probable, and points to its products, but he does not explain how it takes
place. He acknowledges that only Darwin's doctrine can solve the problem of man's origin with any degree of rigour:

At the present moment, but one such process of physical causation has any
evidence in its favour; or, in other words, there is but one hypothesis regarding
the origin of species of animals in general which has any specific existence—
that propounded by Mr. Darwin. . . . At the present moment, therefore, the
question of the relation of man to the lower animals resolves itself, in the end,
into the larger question of the tenability or untenability of Mr. Darwin's views.
[*110a*, p. 106; *110b*, pp. 147–48]

Furthermore, the adaptive interpretation of the structure/function relationship is a basic building block of "Darwinism"; and we saw that
Huxley deployed it here, although he relegated it to a footnote.

But in fact when Huxley directly addresses Darwin's view of evolution, his comments are less than extensive, and sound as sceptical as
ever:

But for all this, our acceptance of the Darwinian hypothesis must be provisional
so long as one link in the chain of evidence is wanting: and so long as all the
animals and plants certainly produced by selective breeding from a common
stock are fertile, and their progeny are fertile with one another, that link will be
wanting. For, so long, selective breeding will not be proved to be competent to do
all that is required of it to produce natural species. [*110a*, p. 107; *110b*, p. 149]

This conclusion confirms what we saw in chapter 2, that in 1863 Huxley was not prepared to adopt an actively evolutionary approach to the
questions of natural science.

It follows from this, I believe, that the purpose of advancing the
"Darwinian attitude towards biological science" can only have been
secondary. We must remember the circumstances from which the book
arose. The primary purpose was to pursue the denigration of Owen by
reiterating, and documenting, the correctness of the approach to the
natural history of man deriving essentially from Linnaeus. It was only
much later that the book was hailed as an important forward-looking
treatise. This impression is largely confirmed in reviews from the 1860s
and from the twentieth century.

Man's Place in Nature was reprinted in 1894 as part of Huxley's
Collected Essays (*110b*). Here, however:

The history of the long controversy about the structure of the brain, following
upon the second dissertation, in the original edition . . . is omitted. The verdict

of science has long since been pronounced upon the questions at issue; and no good purpose can be served by preserving the memory of the details of the suit. [*110b*, p. xii]

This amendment was quite misleading: the book was more against Owen than for Darwin. Owen was undoubtedly the most accomplished naturalist in Britain to oppose Darwinism. By showing not only that Owen was wrong, but also that he had to resort to intellectual dishonesty in order to defend his position, Huxley certainly achieved an indirect advancement of Darwinism; but this was not his primary aim.

Contemporary Anticlimax and Generous Hindsight

Let us now assess the reception of *Man's Place in Nature*. The number of contemporary reviews is not very high. Particularly striking is the fact that the fiercest and most influential conservative journal of the time, the *Quarterly Review*, published no review at all, although it did so for the contemporary *Antiquity of Man* by Lyell (775). The *Quarterly* had published (anonymously, as was the custom) Wilberforce's review of the *Origin of Species* (935), which was ferociously critical of Darwin's book, and it was to publish Mivart's negative review of the *Descent of Man* (807). Now, if these anti-Darwinian circles had seen *Man's Place in Nature* as a threat of the same order, one would expect them to have attacked it.

Favourable reviews appeared in the *Natural History Review*, the *Reader*, and the *Westminster Review*; unfavourable reviews in the *Edinburgh Review*, the *Anthropological Review*, the *Medical Times and Gazette*, and the *American Journal of Science and Arts*. One should not forget that Huxley had editorial links with the *Reader* and the *Natural History Review*, and was on very good terms with the progressive *Westminster Review*, for which he had written his piece of 1860 on the *Origin of Species* (91). The review in the *Natural History Review* is not particularly interesting (369). The reviewer quotes passages from the book; he recalls the controversy with Owen and emphasises that Huxley's conclusions regarding the classification of man and the apes corroborate Linnaeus's views. In the *Westminster Review*, W. S. Dallas (730, vol. 3, p. 364) reports on the book in a short section of "Science" (427), and calls it only a "passing note," since the contents of part two, the core of the book, were already known. Dallas, like his colleague of the *Natural History Review*, remarks that the most striking characteristic of the book consists in the fact that it affords evidence supporting the view that man and the apes are zoologically close: "The human species stands in closer zoological relationship to the chimpanzee and the gorilla, than the Anthropoid apes do to the marmozets and lemurs which occupy the lower ranks of the Quadrumana" (427, p. 584).

The most wholeheartedly pro-Huxley review appeared in the *Reader* (*439*), signed F.D.D. (that is Frederic Daniel Dyster [see *HP* 15.125], one of Huxley's best friends). A long passage describes the controversy with Owen on the hippocampus minor, seen from a viewpoint entirely sympathetic to Huxley, and does not refrain from some sarcastic comments about the older man. Of Huxley's book, which he calls "admirable," Dyster emphasises its support of embryology for the conclusion that the difference between man and the apes is one of degree rather than kind. This certainly "will excite much attention, and possibly some controversy," Dyster concludes. But did it really do so? In a letter to Dyster of 12 March 1863, Huxley expressed his surprise at the mild reaction: "I am quite astonished to find how little abuse the book has met" (*HP* 15.125 [126]).

The critical reviews display much more fairness and much less excitement than those of the *Origin of Species* and the later *Descent of Man*. The *Medical Times and Gazette* praises the style of the book, but claims that Huxley's work is scientifically inconclusive, since it fails to demonstrate that the physical natures of man and the apes are the same; it is not possible to argue that man descends from any of the existing apes, while the claim that man derives from some extinct apelike form is mere "speculation," since the evidence available is insufficient (*368a*). A letter sent to the same journal by one "Studens Perplexus," complains that Huxley's long footnote is based on gratuitous assumptions; whoever he is, this "student" realises that the footnote is the most important passage in the book (*368b*).

The *Anthropological Review* criticises Huxley from a "radical" point of view: this is not surprising, since it was the official magazine of the Anthropological Society, led by James Hunt, one of Huxley's fiercest enemies. The reviewer (anonymous, but clearly inspired by Hunt) claims that "Professor Huxley has lost a grand chance of now providing a book which would be for a quarter of a century connected with his name" (*367*, p. 107). He supports Huxley in his controversy with Owen, but complains that Huxley still insists on distinctions between the nature of man and the other animals, and refers to the long footnote as a "refuge for the destitute" (*367*, p. 116). In fact, according to the reviewer, Huxley's "articulate speech" plays the same role as Owen's hippocampus minor. It concludes: "We would advise Professor Huxley not to say anything more about the 'grand distinctive character,' because there is no such thing: no amount of difference in degree ever amounting to the same thing as a difference in kind" (*367*, p. 117). It is clear that the reviewer interpreted Huxley's long footnote as a retrograde step towards the old anthropology rather than as a contribution to the modern one.

The most throughly critical and detailed review of *Man's Place in*

Nature appeared in the *Edinburgh Review,* probably written by C. Carter Blake, a friend of Owen and a foe of Huxley (399). Like all other negative reviews I have considered here, it does not produce the "theological" opposition which Huxley might have expected to meet, but consists mainly of scientific argument. Blake begins by stating where he thinks Huxley stands:

That man should be absolutely identical, both in his physical structure and the psychological results of structural organisation with the beasts of the field— that his direct ancestor should have been like the howling of the Gaboon, and his collateral relation another and more degraded Bornean form—is the great doctrine of which Professor Huxley, in England, is the chief apostle. [p. 546]

Blake relates Huxley's doctrine to Darwin's "theory of development" (p. 547) but he claims that it contains less novelty than one might expect. He refers to the Lamarckian views of Virey, according to which there are gradual shades from the orang to man, and attacks Huxley and Darwin for failing to provide for such a gradation. The reviewer agrees that there are gradual steps in the organisation of the brain from the lower forms to man, but claims that one can support the view expressed by Huxley in the footnote only if one is prepared to admit that language presupposes reason—and that man alone possesses it. He agrees with Owen that the structure of the human hand is very different from that of the gorilla, and sees the controversy on the hippocampus minor from Owen's point of view. The review concludes

that in some Quadrumana (*Gorilla, Mycetes*) the cerebellum is uncovered to a certain proportion of its extent; that in others (*Troglodytes, Pithecus, Macacus, Inuus, Midas*), the cerebral lobes are coextensive with the cerebellum; that in *Cercopithecus, Cynocephalus, Cebus, Chrysothrix* they project slightly beyond it. That in no ape is the portion which projects beyond the cerebellum in any degree equal in bulk or substance to the far larger structure which is termed posterior lobe of man . . .
     That the structure termed hippocampus minor, taking it in the sense in which the term is used by human anatomists, is, strictly speaking, absent in all Quadrumana in none of which is there that characteristic inversion of the grey cortical brain matter, *coincident in its direction with the floor of the posterior cornu,* which forms the hippocampus minor of anthropotomy. [pp. 556–57]

Blake quotes Robert Knox as an authority on this topic for his opposition to the "Darwinite transmutation school" (p. 563); Knox, the author of *The Races of Man* (752) of 1850 had inspired some of James Hunt's opinions as well as Blake's, and was the mentor of a "radical" anthropology which claimed the black races to be the connecting link between man and the apes. This radical school was fighting with the "Darwinian faction" headed by Huxley for control over anthropology, which was by the second half of the nineteenth century one of the major foci of scientific debate in Britain (as we shall see in chapter 5).

In his review in the *Americal Journal of Science and Arts* (*428*), J.D.D. (J. D. Dana) supports Owen's classification of man as distinct from the apes because of his "extreme cephalization"; and refers to his own article "On the Higher Subdivisions in the Classification of Mammals," also published in 1863 (*652*). In man, "the fore-limbs are withdrawn completely from the *locomotive* series, and transferred to the cephalic; and thus, a very large anterior portion of the body is turned over to the service of the head, while the posterior or gastric portion is reduced to a minimum" (*428*, p. 452). Dana agrees with Owen that the cerebrum is wholly beneath the cerebellum, and stresses the want of "missing links" to support the view of a closer relationship between man and the anthropoid apes.

Some interesting conclusions derive from a reading of these reviews. First of all, so far as the supporters of Huxley were concerned, he had made a contribution more to Linnaeus's classification than to Darwinian evolutionary theory and, indeed, most of the book is devoted to that point. Of course, his conclusions were compatible with those required by Darwin's theory, and could therefore equally be used in its support; but this was not the purpose of the book. Its aim was to prove once and for all that Owen was wrong and Linnaeus right. Needless to say, it is a Darwinian viewpoint that man and the apes are closely related, but this is not exclusive to the Darwinian approach to anthropology. It is not necessary to be a follower of Darwin to classify man and the apes in the same order—it is not in fact necessary to be an evolutionist at all. *Man's Place in Nature* is more against Owen than for Darwin; it was Huxley who found support in Darwin's theory in his internecine strife with Owen. As Sir Arthur Keith suggested: "Huxley's guns . . . were infinitely more effective weapons when loaded with Darwin's ammunition than when merely charged with the powder of pure negation" (*485*, p. 270). Thus, by omitting from the 1894 reprint the details of his controversy with Owen, Huxley removed from his book its original raison d'être, and made it appear more Darwinian than it was.

Another notable aspect is that most reviewers, especially those adverse to Huxley, refer to the long footnote as the most important argument in the book. Now, it is apparent that neither friends nor foes refer to that note as Huxley's intention to apply the adaptive interpretation of the structure/function relationship to brain and mind, which I see as the forward-looking element in his treatment of anthropology. I have argued that that is where Huxley's contribution to modern post-Darwinian anthropology can be taken to lie, but apparently his argument was hardly clear or prominent enough to be convincing, and he covered it with a pompous and conventional display of Victorian rhetoric. *Man's Place in Nature* exerted a smaller influence upon contemporary anthropology than we are accustomed to believe; neither Tylor (912) nor Lubbock (772), the pillars of Victorian evolutionary anthropology, quote it in their major works. Even in 1900, Lubbock, by then Lord Avebury, was not especially appreciative of *Man's Place in Nature*. In his survey of Huxley's works (377), he expresses more enthusiasm for his friend's palaeontological results than for his better-known book.

It was well into our century that Huxley's book met with the unconditional appreciation of anthropologists. Perhaps it was Sir Arthur Keith who contributed more than anyone else to the "rehabilitation" of Huxley the anthropologist, and *Man's Place in Nature*, far from the scenario in which it was conceived, became a symbol of the struggle of anthropology to base itself upon Darwinian foundations. Courses of physical anthropology nowadays mention Huxley's book as the beginning of the quest for an evolutionary anthropology. There is a case for such a view—though a weaker one than scientists assume—but paradoxically it is to us a better book than to those who read it over a century ago. This might explain why, when all is said and done, scientists seem to have a higher opinion of Huxley than historians do. Historians find statements like this, written by Keith in 1925, difficult to accept:

In writing "Man's Place in Nature", Huxley laid the basis for a true science of anthropology. By writing that book he rendered a great service to knowledge. . . . Until Huxley appeared as their champion, anthropologists scarcely dared to state the truth as they found it; when he had silenced theological opposition, they were free to apply to the study of man the same methods as they employed in the study of other animals. He paved the way for Darwin's "Descent of Man" which appeared in 1871. [485, p. 722]

Now, the reviews we have seen show that Huxley met not "theological opposition" but scientific criticism from other naturalists. Sir Arthur badly overstates his point—the view of many anthropologists—in claiming that anthropologists before Huxley did not dare tell the truth. Was Blumenbach a liar?

Conclusion

Man's Place in Nature could undoubtedly have been better than in fact it was. Any disappointment felt by the serious reader is due to Huxley's rather cursory treatment of the most important of his arguments. Huxley had always found it difficult to write books, it seems to me; his more congenial style produced what would better be described as articles and lectures. *Man's Place in Nature* is not even a "real" book, not having originally been conceived as such. Writing books requires more patience and reflection than Huxley's commitments allowed.

The second section, which considers the anatomical and embryological evidence for the relationship between man and the anthropoid apes, is by far the most important of the book's three parts. Huxley wants to show that there is a wider gap between the anthropoid apes and the lower pithecoid forms than between man and the anthropoid apes. He succeeds, but surely he ought to have enlarged the part dealing with anatomy and embryology. It must be stated that here the results do not match up to expectations; since he had collected such a vast amount of material, he could have done so easily. Darwin himself had some complaint on this score: "I should have thought you might have enlarged a little on the later embryological changes in man and on his rudimentary structure, tail as compared with tail of higher monkeys, intermaxillary bones, false ribs, and I daresay other points such as muscles of ears, etc., etc." (26 February [?] 1863; *662*, vol. 1, p. 273). In general, therefore, the nineteenth-century reaction was probably a more accurate assessment of the substance of the book than the twentieth-century praise.

The book shows Huxley in mid-career, solidly empiricist and materialist, pursuing the "potentate" Owen, genuflecting before Darwin, glimpsing the future importance of human palaeontology and the concept of adaptation, and providing the "basicranial axis" as a technique of measurement which has withstood the test of time.

But the reading of *Man's Place in Nature* and Huxley's other related works is of interest not only to the scientist and the scholar but to the learned layman as well. It would please the moralist, since it puts the vain human species in its proper place in nature, a species so arrogant as to create a philosophy in its own image, in which any connecting links with supposedly inferior elements were to be discarded as shameful.

Is man therefore no longer the proud centre of the universe, but just a simple molecule which has been lucky in its evolution? This is not Huxley's conclusion, as this passage, couched in a language midway between Victorian rhetoric and a "humanism" that would have appealed to Thomas Mann's Settembrini, shows:

Our reverence for the nobility of manhood will not be lessened by the knowledge that Man is, in substance and structure, one with the brutes; for, he alone possesses the marvellous endowment of intelligible and rational speech, whereby, in the secular period of his existence, he has slowly accumulated and organised the experience which is almost wholly lost with the cessation of every individual life in other mammals; so that now he stands raised upon it as a mountain top, far above the level of his humble fellows, and transfigured from his grosser nature by reflecting, here and there, a ray from the infinite source of truth. [*110a*, p. 112; *110b*, pp. 155–56]

The philosophers before Socrates had stated that the study of the universe should have priority in their interests, and that man should be seen as an element in that universe, and this was also the view of Democritus. But with Socrates, and more especially Plato, the universe was in a very real sense made to centre on man (for a full discussion of such philosophical ideas as the perfectibility of man, see *851*).

Through rigorously scientific enquiry into the facts of organic nature, Huxley and Darwin put things back into the place whence Plato had removed them, and showed empirical reasons for opposing Platonism. It would be foolish for man to forget his ties with the universe; yet it would be wrong to underestimate those aspects which are characteristic of the human species.

If man is an animal, and a strictly zoological enquiry into him is possible and worthwhile from the evolutionary point of view, what is the attitude of the evolutionist to those aspects of human activity which do not seem to be strictly zoological? Once one has accepted biological evolution, how would one answer whether humanism is tenable consistently with "Darwinism"? Thirty years later Huxley was to try to find a solution to that problem consistent with the results of science and the tenets of humanism. The analysis of *Evolution and Ethics* (*343*) is beyond the scope of this study, which is concerned with Huxley's scientific works only. But the reader should bear in mind that Huxley was aware of the importance of the problems which science alone could not solve (see, e.g., *527*).

5
Learned Negroes and Dangerous Myths

A man should, whatever happens, keep to his own caste, race and breed. Let the White go to the White and the Black to the Black.

—R. Kipling, *Plain Tales from the Hills*

Ethnology Versus Philology

Huxley dealt with anthropological questions both in *Man's Place in Nature* and in a series of papers written between 1865 and 1871. In the 1870s he almost completely abandoned the field, returning to it again only in the 1890s. Most of this work concerns what Huxley calls "ethnology"; we today might call it "physical anthropology" with traces of "social anthropology." The principal subject of these papers is the interpretation of the biologically detectable variations of mankind. The main assumption of Huxley's ethnology is that in that discipline one must use the very same criteria as one applies to the study of any living organism; a view consistent with that propounded in *Man's Place in Nature.*

One of Huxley's most interesting works in the field of ethnology is "On the Methods and Results of Ethnology" (*132*) of 1865. This memoir is important primarily because it explains clearly Huxley's conception of the field. It begins with this definition:

Ethnology is the science which determines the distinctive characters of the persistent modifications of mankind; which ascertains the distribution of those modifications in present and past times, and seeks to discover the causes, or conditions of existence, both of the modifications and of their distribution. I say "persistent" modifications because, unless incidentally, ethnology has nothing to do with chance and transitory peculiarities of human structure. And I speak of "persistent modifications" or "stocks" rather than "varieties", or "races", or "species" because each of these last well-known terms implies, on the part of its employer, a preconceived opinion touching one of those problems, the solution of which is the ultimate object of the science; and in regard to which, therefore, ethnologists are especially bound to keep their minds open and their judgment freely balanced. [pp. 209–10]

Thus, for Huxley, (1) ethnology is a branch of physical anthropology, since it describes the variations of human structure treated zoologically; and (2) its aim is to establish scientific divisions between various groups of men, but without presupposition as to the nature of those divisions. But Huxley is aware that there are many other ways of looking at ethnology besides his favoured zoological approach.

One consists of taking language as the major reference point. Thus, if "what is true of speech is true of the speaker—a hypothesis as questionable in science as it is in ordinary life—the ethnologist may apply to mankind themselves the conclusions drawn from a searching analysis of their words and grammatical forms" (pp. 210–11). Another way of looking at ethnology would be to study the conditions of human life (p. 211). Third, one could refer to history, and if that were insufficient, to archaeology and palaeontology. Huxley is sceptical about the real achievements of these methods which, roughly speaking, propound a more "cultural" view of ethnology. So we should not be surprised to find in *Man's Place in Nature* an attitude which a modern social anthropologist would probably say was too loaded with zoological considerations: "Respecting five-sixths of the persistent modifications of mankind, history and archaeology are absolutely silent" (p. 212). So far as the "sociocultural" approach is concerned, Huxley claims, the fact "that two nations use calabashes or shells for drinking-vessels, or that they employ spears, or clubs, or swords and axes of stone and metal as weapons and implements, cannot be regarded as evidence that these two nations had a common origin, or even that intercommunication ever took place between them" (ibid.). Huxley dismisses these approaches in a few pages, with the exception of the philological, or linguistic, view of ethnology, which he takes seriously as a real alternative to his own zoological approach.

It is Huxley's opinion that unity of language does not imply unity of racial stock, and that no necessary anthropological connection between human groups which happen to speak related languages exists (p. 215). He emphasises his criticisms of the philological approach because of its influence in European and British learned circles; he rejects the conclusions of German philologists from Leibnitz onwards, through Humboldt to Schleicher, whose views are quoted by him and were well known in his day. Ernst Haeckel had a high opinion of Schleicher, which was not shared by his English correspondent (572, pp. 10, 21). What Huxley specifically rejects is expressed in the following passage, quoted in Huxley's essay:

If, however, language is the human κατ' ἐξοχήν, the suggestion arises whether it should not form the basis of any scientific systematic arrangement of mankind; whether the foundation of the natural classification of the genus Homo has not been discovered in it.

How little constant are the cranial peculiarities and other so-called race characters! Language, on the other hand, is always a perfectly constant diagnostic. A German may occasionally compete in hair and prognathism with a negro, but a negro language will never be his mother tongue. . . . The externally visible structure of the cerebral and facial skeletons and of the body generally, is less important than that no less material but infinitely more delicate corporeal structure, the function of which is speech. I conceive therefore that the natural classification of languages, is also the classification of mankind. [884, pp. 16–18; quoted from 132, pp. 214–15]

Schleicher was an effective exponent of a trend prominent in German culture which, given the political circumstances of the German-speaking areas of Europe, favoured xenophobia.

For Huxley, the available evidence shows that the philological approach is basically untenable: "There is hardly a country in Europe in which two or more nations speaking widely different languages have not become intermixed; and there is hardly a language of Europe of which we have any right to think that its structure affords a just indication of the amount of that intermixture" (132, p. 216). Moreover, Huxley realises that the philologists' position implies that external conditions affect the physical structures of living beings; in other words, philologists would tend to support Lamarck rather than Darwin. Huxley hints at this implication when he says that, if we accept the philologists' assumptions, we have "to suppose that the different climatal conditions to which these speakers of one tongue have so long been exposed, have caused their physical differences" (p. 217). There is plenty of evidence that the assumptions of the philologists are fallacious; the best is afforded by the Feejans, who are related racially to the Negritoes of New Caledonia and linguistically to the Polynesians (pp. 219–20).

Following the zoological approach, Huxley delineates the major human "persistent modifications": Australians (p. 222); Negritoes* (people from New Caledonia, the New Hebrides, the Louisiade Archipelago, and the extinct Tasmanians [p. 224]); Amphynesians (Polynesians, Micronesians, and Indonesians [p. 226]); Americans (the original ones, naturally [p. 227]); Esquimaux (Arctic America with Greenland [p. 227]); and Mongolians (various people from China to Lapland, without any real continuity [p. 229]). Only the Chinese have attained a high level of civilisation rivalling that of Europe, Huxley remarks (p. 229). Further groupings are the Xanthochroi (basically the population of Northern Europe, the Canary Islands, and the Berber country [p. 230]); Mel-

---

*Defined as "people who have woolly or tufted hair who are not inhabitants of Africa" in "The Negroes," a paper, the proofs of which are still preserved among the Huxley Papers, with Huxley's corrections for the opening pages, but which was never published; the date is probably the early 1860s (HP 33.114 [135]).

anochroi (Mediterranean area [p. 232]); Negroes (from Africa south of the Sahara [p. 233]); Bushmen (South Africa [p. 233]); the "Dravidian populations of the southern Hindustan," who resemble the Australians (p. 233); and the Mincopies of the Andaman Islands, of a type between Negroes and Negritoes (p. 234). Of the Xanthochroi and Melanochroi, Huxley said:

It is needless to remark upon the civilization of these two great stocks. With them has originated everything that is highest in science, in art, in law, in politics, and in mechanical inventions. In their hands, at the present moment, lies the order of the social world, and to them its progress is committed. (p. 232)

In the scale of civilisation, according to Huxley, the bottom step is occupied by the Australians, and—as we have seen and should in any case expect—the top one by Xanthochroi and Melanochroi (ibid.).

It is also possible to divide mankind into two groups according to the shape of the crania: "Brachycephali" (short skulls), in which the transverse diameter of the skull is more than eight-tenths of the longitudinal diameter; and "Dolichocephali" (long skulls), in which the ratio is less than eight-tenths (pp. 235–36n). One could, further, refer to people with fair complexion and fair or red hair (Leucos); those with pale skin but dark hair (Leuchomelanous); those with black hair and yellowish-olive skin (Xanthomelanous), and those with black hair and brown or blackish skin (Melanous) (p. 235). If, finally, we consider the structure of the hair, we can recognise a large group of people with straight or wavy hair (Leiotrichi), and another with woolly, crisp, or tufted hair (Ulotrichi) (pp. 234–35). Thus, on the basis of these data, we obtain the following schema of mankind:

	Leiotrichi		Ulotrichi	
	Dolichocephali	Brachycephali	Dolichocephali	Brachycephali
Leucos				
	. . .Xanthochroi. . .			
Leucomelanous				
	. . .Melanochroi. . .			
Xantomelanous				
	Esquimaux	Mongolians	*Bushmen*	
		Amphinesians		
		Americans		
Melanous				
	Australians		Negroes	*Mincopies* (?)
			Negritoes	

The names of the stocks known only since the fifteenth century are put into italics.   [*132*, p. 235]

According to this scheme, both Huxley and the present writer are Leiotrichi, Leucomelanous, and presumably Dolichocephali (Huxley had dark hair, but it is difficult to determine the conformation of his skull from his photographs): two acceptable specimens of the European middle class.

As I have pointed out more than once, distribution was for Darwin and Huxley an important element in the understanding of zoological problems. Since mankind is here seen by Huxley from a purely zoological point of view, it is a logical consequence that human distribution is relevant to this survey of mankind: the French anthropologist Desmoulins is quoted on this topic (p. 236).

Huxley then addresses the question of whether humanity constitutes a single species, and concludes that there is no satisfactory evidence of intersterility between various races of man (p. 242). One might ask whether crossing, say, a Pygmy and an Eskimo had ever been tried. For if we accept both the physiological definition of species (see chapter 3), and the fact that crossing between every permutation has not occurred, the statement that there is only one species is simply an assumption.

The problem of the unity of mankind arose from the famous controversy on this topic between polygenists and monogenists (634; 708). As Huxley recalls, the monogenists held that mankind originated from one pair (Adam and Eve?), whose progeny spread all over the earth (pp. 242–46); according to the polygenists mankind sprang from more than one stock. We should remember that the majority of British anthropologists and thinkers interested in this topic were monogenists (634, p. x, p. 60); this was mainly because of the influence of James Prichard, a monogenist himself (as were Hunter and Blumenbach), who also believed the philological approach to be important (634, p. 120). It is thought that David Hume was one of the few polygenists in Britain, but his views on this topic are not sufficiently clear for his stance to be determined beyond doubt (644, p. 98).

As far as the monogenists are concerned, one of their propositions is certainly fallacious, Huxley argues: namely, that "the operation of the existing diversities of climate and other conditions upon people . . . is sufficient to account for all the diversities of mankind" (132, p. 244). But Huxley denies the heritability of acquired characters. It is known that

fair Europeans are very readily tanned and embrowned by the sun. Yet I am not aware that there is a particle of proof that the cutaneous change thus affected can become hereditary, any more than that the enlarged livers, which plague our countrymen in India, can be transmitted; while there is very strong evidence to the contrary. [p. 245]

Huxley dismisses the polygenists too, believing that they were unable to provide evidence of the specific diversity of mankind (p. 247).

For Huxley, the solution to the problem of the variation in mankind is provided by Darwin's doctrine. It is "the key to ethnology . . . recon-

ciling and combining all that is good in the Monogenistic and Polygenis-
tic schools" (p. 248). In this essay one finds perhaps the most confident
statement concerning natural selection in all Huxley's writings, 1868
notwithstanding; though we should remember that he is dealing here
with the formation of varieties, not species—he had always accepted the
power of natural selection to produce varieties:

As these rude and primitive families were thrust, in the course of long series of
generations, from land to land, impelled by encroachments of sea or of marsh, or
by severity of summer heat or winter cold, to change their positions, what
opportunities must have been offered for the play of natural selection, in preserving one family variation and destroying another!

Suppose, for example, that some families of a horde which had reached a land
charged with the seeds of yellow fever, varied in the direction of woolliness of
hair and darkness of skin. Then, if it be true that these physical characters are
accompanied by comparative or absolute exemptions from that scourge, the
inevitable tendency would be the preservation and multiplication of the darker
and woollier families, and the elimination of the whiter and smoother haired.
[p. 251]

Superficially it might seem strange that Huxley should be less re-
served about natural selection in the human context—usually the hot-
test potato of all. But the application of the concept in ethnology doubtless flattered the Victorians, since it "explained" how the white races
had become so superior in intelligence and so forth, and "explained" the
irresistible rise of civilisation. More seriously, it is not impossible that
the physiological differences created by natural selection might have
led to the phenomenon of intersterility (p. 252). Huxley speaks only of a
"possibility," since he was aware of the lack of evidence. He might have
wondered what would happen if a Pygmy and an Eskimo were crossed.
However, he did not write to any colonial officer proposing such an
experiment. He had more respect for mankind than many of his contemporaries.

Huxley did show some interest in what we would call "social anthropology." In the archives of Imperial College, London, the proofs of
the lectures on the races of mankind are preserved (ref. B/Huxley/5,
Offprints of papers). These proofs have not been corrected, and as far as I
know were never published. The real scientific value of these five lectures may not be very high, but it is interesting to see how Huxley, a
Victorian gentleman, tried to come to terms with the customs and
habits of cultures as different as those of the Australian Aboriginals and
the Bushmen. Huxley starts with the physical structures of the races he
considers, first of all the Negritoes of Australia (pp. 5ff). But then he goes
on to consider their social context:

No Australian has any house in the proper sense of the word. Very few have fixed
habitations, and many of them are unable to raise more than a mere shed of turf

or fern upon the weather side to protect them from the wind. . . . No Australian has the smallest knowledge of the use of metals. . . . In navigation they have proceeded no further than the manufacture of the roughest kind of canoe. . . . Of clothing, for the purpose of decency, they have always been and are now perfectly innocent. . . . Well now, intellectually speaking, their numerals do not extend beyond four. [pp. 13–14]

Huxley also considers their social condition: "They have no fixed government of any sort, no chiefs, except such as exert some power over them in consequence of strength, or age, or experience, or some accident of that kind" (p. 14). Of course, Huxley must pay lip service to the typical prejudice of Victorian anthropology—a degree of righteous indignation at some of the habits and beliefs distant from European (and especially British) ones:

All, like savage nations in general, are subject to the vilest and basest superstitions; they live in daily and hourly dread of witchcraft and sorcery, and are incapable of believing that any person can die a natural death. Whenever anyone dies, it must be in consequence of witchcraft or sorcery on the part of somebody else; and as it is one of the articles of their code of honour, that all practices of that kind shall be avenged by the death of the sorcerer or some person belonging to his tribe in particular, it follows that every death leads to some kind of murder or violence, and as they are all divided into an immense number of tribes, you may readily imagine what is the kind of social condition and international law that they have amongst them. The men are idle, greedy, selfish, and bloodthirsty and treacherous, as a point of honour. The women are utterly degraded to mere slaves, and not one of them has the remotest scintilla of what chastity means. From their earliest youth they are accustomed to promiscuous intercourse, and if they abstain from it at all during marriage, it is simply because the man who owns them looks upon them as his property. With respect to the mode in which the men treat the women, they regard them as lower than an Englishman would a dog for which he had the smallest care. [pp. 14–15]

The Victorians had reversed Rousseau's myth of the noble savage; the purely natural man is no longer the innocent being who is corrupted by the wickedness of civilisation, it is the lack of civilisation which degrades man. The savage is a brute, and a bloodthirsty one, whose values deserve the civilised man's condemnation. Thus one myth was replaced by another—that of the more humane and human "civilised man."

On Scoundrels Black and White

Needless to say, Huxley was not alone in his interest in anthropology and ethnology. In the first half of the century the views of the influential anthropologist James Prichard had had a strong impact upon British culture (635, pp. 212–14). At the same time, Britain greatly enlarged her empire to include the subcontinent of India under the direct control of the Crown. British anthropologists consequently had both the stimulus and the opportunity for contact with a vast array of different populations. There was no part of the world that a British expedition could not explore, and there was nearly always a naturalist along. Huxley, Darwin, and Hooker were among the most distinguished people who accompanied such expeditions.

New animal and plant species were discovered and described, and human populations like the Fuegians, the Australians, and the doomed Tasmanians were closely studied by scientists, and sometimes even exterminated under the impact of the colonisers. The evident success of the colonisers over the native populations, the dangers of terrible diseases, and the often unpleasant climate must have convinced Europeans of their inborn superiority, thus contributing to the atrophy of any possible sense of guilt over the notorious extermination of the Tasmanians, for example.

In such a situation, learned societies whose aim was the scientific study of human populations met with the approval of both naturalists and interested laymen. In 1844 the Ethnological Society was founded, shortly before the death of its first president, Prichard himself. The phrenologists, attempting to win recognition for their "science," exerted a considerable influence on this society (635, p. 191). The Ethnological Society was an offshoot of the Aborigines Protection Society (901, p. 370); its aims were originally humanitarian. The expanding Europeans, or at least some of them, had realised that other cultures and civilisations were rapidly disappearing under the impact of European civilisation. The actual anthropological interests of the Ethnological Society were thus originally only secondary; but the scope of these increased with the increase of colonial activities and interests, and its leading figure following the death of Prichard was Robert Gordon Latham. In the 1850s anthropological studies developed a racist tone, under the influence of the work of Robert Knox (769, p. 132; see chapter 4); the scope of the interests of the society now also included the origins of the European races. It was then that James Hunt burst onto the scene. Hunt was the major promoter of the dissident Anthropological Society (632), whose central interest was in the distinction between the human races. Hunt, who was deeply influenced by the German and French transcendental biologists (901, pp. 376–78), tended to treat man and all that concerned him purely as a "physical universe." He also objected to Darwin's views and invoked Knox as support in combatting them; he was a polygenist, arguing that modern racial types have been in existence since ancient times, and that races degenerate when they move from their original environment. The polygenist notion of race, which did not die out with Darwin's *Origin of Species*, was a quasi-Platonic one, in which the notion of "racial purity" can be detected, and indeed upheld as the real focus of anthropology (*900*, p. 57). Another influence upon Hunt was Karl Vogt, whose book on man (*915a*) Hunt translated into English (*915b*) one year after it appeared in the original German. Vogt held that the Negro is intermediate between the apes and real man (i.e., the Germanic man: *915b*, pp. 133–71); a conclusion based on the results of his comparison of the skulls and the brains of Negroes and Germans. Since according to his measurements the Negro skulls approached the simian type more closely than did German crania,black races had inferior intellectual capacities—blacks were inferior to whites. Clearly, he used the structure/function relationship in a very naïve way, his starting point being that the cerebrum is the seat of intellectual activity (*915b*, p. 93). In the preface to his translation of Vogt's book, Hunt praised his colleague's conclusions and did not miss his chance to condemn the "wild speculations of Professor Huxley respecting the resemblance of the Neanderthal calvaria to that of the Australian" (*915b*, p. vii). Knox, Hunt and Vogt agreed that ethnology was only a minor branch of anthropology, a view widely held in Victorian Britain, but which they carried to its most radical conclusions. D. A. Lorimer observes that Hunt assumed the same attitude to both "inferior" races and lower social classes (*769*, p. 151).

Not surprisingly, Hunt and Huxley clashed repeatedly. The open war between them ended only with Hunt's untimely death in 1869. In their controversies Huxley expressed the view of the more moderate Ethnological Society, of which he was president from 1869 to 1870.

Huxley explained his view of human races in a series of Hunterian Lectures entitled "Lectures on the Structure and Classification of Mammalia" of 1864. The eighth and ninth lectures address the problem of human races (*124; 125*). Here Huxley emphasises the differences between what were currently called "lower races" and the Europeans, these being, of course, the "higher races." As examples of lower races, he picks Negroes and Fuegians, the latter then quite a fashionable race. In reply to the objection that Huxley was more of a *racist* than a *racial* anthropologist, one should not forget that the idea of the cultural superiority of the European races was commonplace in nineteenth-century Europe, even among the most liberal minds. As W. F. Bynum suggests: "Men in 19th century Britain had a precise and articulate sense of their own superiority over men of other races, and of women and children of their own" (*635*, p. x). Huxley was neither more nor less racist than the average British anthropologist of his day; indeed, his general openmindedness led to his relatively liberal attitude to the question. Perhaps the cardinal sin of Victorian ethnology was the unqualified acceptance of the term *lower* in application to non-European populations.

In the Hunterian Lectures, Huxley deals with the "variations" among mankind. He claims that many such variations can be detected scientifically, and that they are important elements of classification. The structures are always the same, but the dimensions of those structures may vary:

The variation between the proportion of the greatest internal cerebral length to the length of the basicranial axis . . . is also great, the proportion in the higher races of the former to the latter measurement being as 270 to 100, while among the lower races it is as but 230 to 100, indicating a smaller development of the cerebral chamber as compared to the base of the skull and face. [124, p. 344]

To argue that there are dimensional differences among various races does not necessarily imply racism; it is simply a fact, implying no moral judgment. But, undoubtedly, the introduction of such biologically meaningless concepts as "higher" and "lower" leads Huxley to hold a position which is less than scientific, since a value judgment is mistaken for a scientific concept. Huxley's lectures are a good example of the nineteenth-century attitude to race in relatively liberal hands. He reacts calmly to the custom of near nudity among black Africans, and claims that most Negroes are in fact more "decent" than many European ballet dancers (HP 114.148).

His liberal attitude notwithstanding, Huxley was unable to escape entirely the prejudice of his times concerning the "inferiority" of Negroes. In the ninth lecture, he indicates other important structural differences: "On the whole [the cerebral convolutions] are simpler in women than in men, and in the lower races the convolutions have a greater simplicity and symmetry than in the higher" (125, p. 370). This interesting passage also betrays the Victorian conviction that women are basically inferior to men (see 890). Further, Huxley's discussion of race inevitably raises the question of the reliability of the differences he claimed to have observed:

The important question now remains, what is the value of the differences which have been shown to exist in the structure of human beings? This resolves itself into two other questions,—1. Are they sufficient to justify us in supposing them to indicate distinct species of men?—2. Can any of the deviations be considered as transitional towards the lower forms of animals? [124, p. 370]

His answer to both questions is negative: "It is certain that well-defined types occur in different geographical localities; those whose characteristics are most distinct are,—1. European; 2. Mongolian; 3. Negro (or Ethiopian); and 4. Australian" (ibid.). But they are "races", not "species," and "there is at present no evidence of any transitional form or intermediate link between Man and the next succeeding forms in the vertebrate scale" (p. 370).

His views on the black races involved Huxley in a controversy with James Hunt and C. C. Blake. In a pamphlet entitled *On the Negro Place in Nature* (733), James Hunt claimed that the Negro must be classified as a species distinct from the white European.

The general deductions we would desire to make are:—1. That there is a good reason for classifying the Negro as a distinct species from the European, as there is for making the ass a distinct species from the zebra; and if, in classification, we take intelligence into consideration, there is a far greater difference between the Negro and European than between the gorilla and chimpanzee. 2. That the analogies are far more numerous between the Negro and the apes, than between the European and apes. 3. That the Negro is inferior intellectually to the European. 4. That the Negro is more humanised when in his natural subordination to the European than under any other circumstances. 5. That the Negro race can only be humanised and civilised by Europeans. 6. That European civilisation is not suited to the Negro's requirements of character. [pp. 51–52]

One of Hunt's arguments was that "the inferior molars sometimes present in the Negro race five tubercules, and this anomaly is sporadically found in other races. It has been noticed in the Europeans and the Esquimaux, but is affirmed by my friend Mr. Carter Blake to be more frequent in the Negro and Australian than in any other race" (p. 19).

In a letter to the *Reader* of 12 March 1864 (126), Huxley disposes of the claims of Hunt and Blake by emphasising that, since the structure occurs in both white people and black, it is inconclusive evidence for a specific difference between the two races. Huxley's remark convinced neither Hunt nor Blake (615; 734), but pleased one Moses Moore, a "learned negro" who wrote to Huxley to congratulate him (HP 23.3). All this is evidence of Huxley's mild attitude to the question of race, an attitude which was certainly milder than that, for example, of Joseph Hooker, who in a letter refers to the Negro as "a dangerous savage" who must earn his bread by working hard (preferably for whites) (HP 8.318). Hooker wrote to Tyndall in 1867:

My opinion of the character of the Negro is that he is as a rule eminently fickle, impulsive and cruel; not systematically cruel, like the Red Indian, nor a rejoicer in cold-blooded deeds, but one who is easily roused, through fear, superstition or other motive, to the acts of revolting cruelty for his own benefit. Whatever his mental qualities may be in the abstract, as compared with our own races, they desert him altogether in cases of difficulty: at the same time he is capable of an immense amount of passive endurance. Above all he is almost incapable of joint action for a continuous purpose, and in cases of insurrection, meeting or *émeute,* you never know what you are about with him, he has no "guard" and so you can hardly tell when you have him at advantage if you judge him by yourself.

Under discipline or pressure whether artificial, of others, or engendered by the struggle for existence, he will work well and may I doubt not prove a good and useful member of any community, but the circumstances under which his good qualities for self-government have hitherto been called out are so altogether exceptional that I do not think one can judge much from them. [*HP* 8.337]

Clearly, Hooker blames the Negro for not being an English gentleman. The key to understanding Hooker's misconception is the phrase "if you judge him by yourself"—why should he be judged by "yourself" rather than by himself?

The problem concerning the black races was keenly felt in British society at the time, and Huxley's views had their usual strong impact on public opinion. Huxley kept in his papers a pamphlet entitled "Professor Huxley on the Negro Question" of May 1864 (*HM* vol. 16, p. 88), in which Mrs. P. A. Taylor, the authoress, cited Huxley's lectures as an important contribution to the solution of that grave question. The pamphlet also quotes this passage from the *Reader*, which shows how heavily anthropology was enmeshed with politics:

Clearly, therefore, the high scientific authority of Professor Huxley is against the favourite notion of the partisans of slavery that there are signs about the Negro that he has a place of his own in nature inferior to that of the normal man, and against the desired inference that he may fairly have a treatment corresponding to that place, and be excluded from the rights and franchises that are agreed upon amongst men. Professor Huxley might have stopped here—for it was not necessary for him to say, as a man of science, what he might consider these rights and franchises to be. He might have vindicated the title of the Negro physiologically to whatever treatment is proper for human beings as such, and yet he might have believed in the necessity and expediency of slavery within that common society of human beings in which he declined the Negro to be included. But he steps beyond the circle of the physiologist, and speaks strongly and generously his faith as a man. He believes in the doctrine of freedom, or equal personal rights for all men, and he pronounces the system of slavery to be root and branch, an abomination—thus making his physiological definition of the Negro's place among men equivalent to an earnest plea for Negro emancipation. Nay, as will have been noted, he goes farther, and, in virtue of the strength of his feeling with respect to slavery, avows a state of opinion regarding the American War in which many who share his feeling with respect to slavery will refuse to go along with him. [*The Reader* 3 (1864), pp. 287–88]

The American Civil War divided public opinion. Huxley sided with the Union; that passage from the *Reader* refers to the following statement by Huxley:

I am unable to understand how any man of warm heart can fail to sympathize with the indomitable courage, the warlike skill, the self-denying persistence of the Southerner; while I can as little comprehend how any man of clear head can doubt that the South is playing a losing game; and that the North is justified in any expenditure of blood, or of money, which shall eradicate a system hopelessly inconsistent with the moral elevation, the political freedom, or the economical progress of the American people. [125, p. 267]

Huxley's behaviour in the notorious "Jamaica affair" provides further evidence of his relatively liberal mind. In 1804, a Negro revolt took place at Santo Domingo, resulting in the founding of the Negro Republic of Haiti (617; 886; 937). The slave trade ended there in 1808, but was not abolished in the British colonies until 1833; the former slaves were obliged to serve a six-year apprenticeship in the plantations of the West Indies before acquiring complete freedom. In Jamaica the standard of living of the planters gradually declined, and the coup de grâce was administered in 1846 when the protection of the West Indies' sugar trade was ended. In the early sixties, Eyre, a weak and intolerant man, was sent to Kingston as governor. Immediately frictions with the assembly arose, especially with William Gordon, a fierce mulatto. In 1865 disturbances leading to a riot started, and Eyre ordered the hanging of several people, including Gordon. The result of the Gordon riot was that Jamaica became a Crown colony. In Britain, the liberal side of opinion questioned Eyre's behaviour, and J. S. Mill started a campaign for his conviction; a committee including Fawcett and Frederic Harrison was founded for such a purpose. Huxley joined it wholeheartedly. Also Bright, Darwin, Spencer, and Lyell stood with Huxley on Mill's side. The opposing party was represented by Ruskin, Carlyle, Tyndall, Murchison, Tennyson, and Kingsley, who supported Eyre.

Huxley expressed his feelings to Kingsley, whose correspondence he found stimulating (472, vol. 1, pp. 301–04). Justice and the impartial observation of the facts, independent of personal wishes, must direct our judgments and actions. Although a critical reader might argue that Huxley did not always succeed in being fully faithful to these ideals, he tried to fulfil them as far as he was able; the Jamaica affair gave him the chance to express his feelings publicly on the very important issue of the distinction between justice and political opportunity. On 29 October 1866, the *Pall Mall Gazette* remarked:

Sir Charles Lyell and Professor Huxley have given their support to the Jamaica Committee. . . . It would be curious also to know how far Sir Charles Lyell's and Mr. Huxley's peculiar views on the development of species have influenced them in bestowing on the negro that sympathetic recognition which they are willing to extend even to the ape as "a man and brother". [*Pall Mall Gazette* 534 (1866), p. 9]

Huxley replied in the following issue:

Sir—I learn from yesterday evening's *Pall Mall Gazette* that you are curious to know whether certain "peculiar views on the development of species", which

I am said to hold in the excellent company of Sir Charles Lyell, have led me to become a member of the Jamaica Committee.

Permit me without delay to satisfy a curiosity which does me honour. I have been induced to join the committee neither by my "peculiar views on the development of species", nor by any particular love for, or admiration of, the negro—still less by any miserable desire to wreak vengeance for recent error upon a man whose early career I have often admired; but because the course which the committee proposes to take appears to be the only one by which a question of the profoundest practical importance can be answered. That question is, *does the killing of a man in the way Mr. Gordon was killed constitute murder in the eye of the law or does it not?*

You perceive that this question is wholly independent of two others which are persistently confused with it—namely, was Mr. Gordon a Jamaica Hampden, or was he a psalm-singing firebrand? and was Mr. Eyre actuated by the highest and noblest motives, or was he under the influence of panic-stricken rashness or worse impulses?

I do not presume to speak with authority on a legal question; but, unless I am disinformed, *English law does not permit good persons, as such, to strangle bad persons, as such.* . . . The killing of Mr. Gordon can only be defended on the ground that he was a bad and troublesome man; in short, that though he might not be guilty, it served him right.

I entertain so deeply rooted an objection to this method of killing people—the act itself appears to me so frightful a precedent—that I desire to see it stigmatized by the highest authority as a crime. And I have joined the committee which propose to indict Mr. Eyre, in the hope that I may hear a court of justice declare that the only defence which can be set up . . . is no defence, and that the killing of Mr. Gordon was the gravest offence known to the law—murder. [*141*, p. 3]

Eyre was not indicted.

The arguments concerning racial differences had connections not only with the problem of class, but also with the so-called woman question. The passage quoted earlier on cerebral convolutions shows that Huxley believed in one of the most widespread prejudices of his time, the inferiority of women. Nonetheless, his position is reasonably open-minded.

In 1865 Huxley considered the connection between what today we would call "racism" and "sexism," in an essay entitled "Emancipation—Black and White" (*131*). Huxley assumes that "the big chests, the massive brains, the vigorous muscles and stout frames of the best men will carry the day, whenever it is worth their while to contest the prizes of life with the best women" (p. 74). According to Huxley, nature has not made white men, black men, and women equal, but it is the task of society to reduce their inequalities: "The duty of man is to see that not a grain is piled upon that load beyond what nature imposes; that injustice is not added to inequality" (p. 75).

It is interesting to compare Huxley's opinions with those of J. S. Mill, an ardent feminist (800) and the most open-minded of the established figures of his time. In 1850 Mill sent a letter to the editor of the *Fraser's Magazine* in which he expressed his profound dislike of racism (799). Mill, who believed that the woman question and the Negro question were facets of the same problem, pointed out that the paternalistic argument that Negroes are unable to rule themselves is simply an excuse to justify their exploitation for economic reasons; whites rule blacks for their own welfare rather than for the good of the enslaved populations. This conclusion is a corollary of Mill's principle that everybody must be allowed to promote his own good in his own way. Moreover, Mill argues, left to themselves Negroes have proved as industrious and clever as any other group when they have been given the chance. The alleged superiority of the whites is in fact based upon favourable external conditions. Then Mill reaches the core of his argument:

Spontaneous improvement, beyond a very low grade,—improvement by internal development, without aid from other individuals or people—is one of the rarest phenomena in history; and whenever known to have occurred, was the result of an extraordinary combination of advantages; in addition doubtless to many accidents of which all trace is now lost. No argument against the capacity of negroes for improvement could be drawn from their not being one of these rare exceptions. |p. 29|

It seems to me that, between the arguments of Mill and Huxley, there is a difference which, although not at first striking, is of the greatest importance. Both men claim that, even if blacks and women were inferior, this would be no reason for subduing them; but Huxley thinks that they *are* inferior, and that social structure as it is tends to emphasise their inferiority rather than to find appropriate means of attenuating it. On the other hand, Mill holds that there is no doubt that the existing social organisation *makes* people different, and, therefore, we cannot claim the Negro and the woman to be inferior, as we have not removed all the obstacles to full knowledge of human nature. M. Salvadori rightly emphasises that the impact of liberalism was the main factor in the progress of women to emancipation (883), though one should not forget that, from time to time, liberal politicians have opposed women's emancipation on the grounds that they might support conservative tendencies. The difference between Huxley and Mill is the same as that between an open-minded conservative and a true liberal. R. H. Hutton was correct to suggest that Huxley was in fact a "benevolent conservative" (467, p. 106).

Colonial and European Ethnology

Huxley twice tried to amalgamate the Ethnological and Anthropological societies. The endeavour occupied him considerably, as we realise when we see how often it is cited in his correspondence. The amalgamation did not take place until 1871, two years after Hunt's death. Hunt's friends won the fight about the name, since the official name of the new institution became the "Anthropological Institute of Great Britain and Ireland," but the ethnological party won a more substantial prize: John Lubbock, a friend of Huxley's, was elected president (901). Huxley had been very active during the Ethnological Society's last years.

In 1868, Huxley produced "On the Form of the Cranium Among the Patagonians and Fuegians, with Some Remarks upon American Crania in General" (147). Starting from an analysis of the cranial characteristics of the Patagonians and the Fuegians, Huxley tried to establish the geographical distribution of mankind, mainly on the basis of brachycephalism and dolichocephalism (pp. 328–29).

In 1869, Huxley launched what amounted to an ethnological census of the populations of the British possessions:

> The council of the Society over which I have the honour to preside, proposes to direct public attention to the desirableness of subjecting the physical characters, the languages, the civilisation, the religions, in short, the ethnology, of the various people over whom the rule of Britain extends, to systematic investigation.
>
> To this end, we propose to hold a series of meetings in this and succeeding sessions, each of which shall be devoted to the ethnology of one or other of the British possessions. [164, p. 427]

Official requests for information were sent to various parts of the empire. Officials of the Crown responded readily, but some of the natives were less than enthusiastic. Two of the replies from British officials are preserved in Huxley's private papers. In one, from Gibraltar, it is stated that the races there were so mixed that they could be of no ethnological interest (HM vol. 16, p. 85; 29 April 1870). The second, more interesting, letter comes from Australia and complains of the natives' uncooperative behaviour (HM vol. 16, p. 86; 30 March 1870). It seems that the natives did not like to be photographed, especially without clothes. Many Victorians would have found it surprising that the populations under study wore any clothes at all.

As one might expect, the first meeting of the Ethnological Society on colonial ethnology concerned India, the brightest gem in the Crown:

> It seemed fitting that the greatest of the possessions of the Empire should be the first to claim our attention; and, on seeking for that co-operation which was so

essential to the success of our plans among persons familiar with India, we found a store of valuable materials most liberally and kindly thrown open to us. [*164*, p. 427]

In general, the British showed more respect for the Indians than for the Africans (*617*, p. 211), especially for the Brahmins, whose good looks they were ready to praise; and they thought that the Hindu was a "born gentleman."

After the ethnology of India, Huxley's own contribution was "On the ethnology and archaeology of North America" (*165*). He claims that

two widely different forms are distinguishable among the native races of America, namely the Esquimaux, in the extreme north, and the Patagonians, in the heart of South America. The Esquimaux are short of stature, and are extremely dolichocephalic; the Patagonians, on the contrary, are among the tallest of men, and are eminently brachycephalic. [p. 434]

Huxley suggests that a favourable climate must influence the rise of an advanced civilisation—a current positivist opinion.

Whatever may have been the origin of the primitive population of America, the conditions which gave rise to the development of a high state of civilization seem to have been the same in the New World as in the Old. The fertile valley of the Nile and the shores of the Mediterranean determined the locality of the earliest great civilized communities of the Old World. In the Mexican Gulf, sheltered by the great breakwater of the West-India Islands, and artificially warmed by the equatorial current, America has her Mediterranean, and, in the Mississippi, her Nile. [pp. 434–35]

In June 1870, Huxley read to the Ethnological Society a paper entitled "On the Distribution of the Chief Modifications of Mankind" (*180*). In it he singles out four fundamental types of mankind: (1) the Australoid type: medium stature, well-developed torso, slender legs, chocolate-brown skin, raven-black, wavy, rather long hair, dolichocephalic cranium, broad nose, prominent brow ridges, prognathism, large teeth—located in Australia (except Tasmania), and in the area peopled by the ancient Egyptians; (2) the Negroid type: medium stature on average, skin from brown to very dark brown (improperly called black), brown or black eyes, black, short, crisp or woolly hair, dolichocephalic cranium, brow ridges not prominent, forehead somewhat childlike, prognathism, broad, flat nose, coarse, protuberant lips—located principally in South Africa (the Bushmen being a distinct modification of this type); (3) the Xanthochroic type: tall, almost colourless skin, blue or grey eyes, light hair from straw colour to red and chestnut, abundant beard (see Darwin!), cranium from brachycephalic to dolichocephalic extremes—located in northern and central Europe; (4) the Mongoloid type: short, squat features, yellow-brown skin, black, oblique eyes, black, straight,

coarse hair, brachycephalic cranium, flat, small nose—located in Asia
(*180*, pp. 564–68). It is apparent that Huxley omitted from this scheme
what he had called in 1865 the "Melanochroi." He now maintains that
these do not constitute an independent type, but are the result of interbreeding between the Xanthochroi and the Australoids (p. 569). Huxley has a high opinion of this group of people; in some cases they are as
good-looking and intelligent as the Xanthochroi: "A man of this group
may, in point of physical beauty and intellectual energy, be the equal of
the best of the Xanthochroi" (p. 569). The Melanochroi, who include
Irishmen, Welshmen, southern Italians, and Spaniards, have black,
wavy hair, dark eyes, clear, somewhat olive skin, and a shorter stature
than the Xanthochroi (ibid.).

In a paper read on 10 May 1870 entitled "On the Ethnology of Britain"
(*178*), and in "On Some Fixed Points in British Ethnology" the following
year (*185*), Huxley moves on to consider the ethnology of his homeland.
These papers deal with the same problems and reach the same conclusions; the former is simply a report of his speech, the latter he wrote
himself. During the period of the Roman occupation, Huxley maintains, Britain was peopled by two different types: a dark population and
a fair one (*185*, pp. 253–54). Referring to Roman sources (Caesar, Tacitus, and Strabo), it is possible to maintain that the dark variety lived
mainly in the southwest, the fair one elsewhere (pp. 255–56). Huxley's
second important point is that, during subsequent invasions, no new
types were introduced (p. 259). All invasions, in fact, were made by
similar stocks of men, but with a preponderance of the fair type. The
two human types are quite obviously the Xanthochroi and the Melanochroi. According to Huxley, they still occupy roughly the same regions
as in the time of Tacitus (p. 260). These two types also peopled and
continue to people the whole of Europe. Huxley's conclusions are as
follows:

(1) That the Melanochroi and the Xanthochroi are two separate races in the
biological sense of the word race; (2) that they have had the same general distribution as at present from the earliest times of which any record exists on the
continent of Europe; (3) that the population of the British Islands is derived from
them, and from them only. [p. 262]

As to the importance of language to ethnology, Huxley emphasises
once more that community of language implies contact between the
groups concerned but not necessarily a common origin: "Philology has
absolutely nothing to do with ethnology, except so far as it suggests the
existence or the absence of such contact" (pp. 263–64). At the time of
the Roman conquest, only one language was spoken (Celtic), with two
principal dialects, Cymric (in Britain) and Gaelic (in Ireland). Later,
through successive invasions of the British Isles, the Teutonic lan-

guages (Anglo-Saxon) were imported by groups of Xanthochroi. As a result, a basically Teutonic language is now spoken throughout Britain, but this does not mean that the population itself is Teutonic (pp. 265–66).

Similar considerations can be applied to Ireland, where the original ethnological situation was identical to that in Britain. The term *Celt* as a racial label for the Irish does not make any sense; it is in fact a gross error:

> What then, is the value of the ethnological difference between the Englishmen of the western half of England and the Irishmen of the eastern half of Ireland? For what reason does one deserve the name "Celt", and not the other? And further, if we turn to the inhabitants of the western half of Ireland, why should the term "Celts" be applied to them more than to the inhabitants of Cornwall? And if the name is applicable to the one as justly as to the other, why should not intelligence, perseverance, thrift, industry, sobriety, respect for law, be admitted to be Celtic virtues? [p. 268]

Huxley agrees with Robert G. Latham that much Celtic blood flows in English veins; as Latham wrote, and Huxley quoted: "It is certain that the language of England is of Anglo-Saxon origin, and that the remains of the original Keltic are unimportant. It is by no means so certain that the blood of Englishmen is equally Germanic. A vast amount of Kelticism, not found in our tongue, very probably exists in our pedigrees" (pp. 216–17).

These passages hint clearly at the "Irish question," a much debated problem in political, scientific, and learned circles. Huxley realised the political implications of the anthropological discussions concerning the Irish; in a letter to Darwin of 21 January 1870, he spoke of the "political bearing of the Celt question" (*472*, vol. 1, p. 349). Like many of the "progressive" scientists of his time, such as Tyndall, Lubbock, and Stokes, Huxley was a convinced Unionist. He wrote to Donnelly on 15 July 1887: "Much fighting I am likely to do for the Unionist cause or any other! But don't take me for one of the enragés. If anybody will show me a way by which the Irish may attain all they want without playing the devil with us, I am ready to give them their own talking-shop or anything else" (vol. 2, p. 179). These words notwithstanding, Huxley actually opposed any attempt at Irish Home Rule supported by Gladstone, his adversary both in political and theological matters (*294*; *331*; *335*). In this letter of 24 January 1887, John Lubbock, who was politically even more committed than Huxley to the Unionists, asks Huxley for ammunition against the supporters of the Home Rule Bills; the connections between political stand and scientific view is quite clear:

You will no doubt have noticed that the Home Rule Committee continually speak of Scotland & Ireland as separate nationalities, & use them as an argument for the formation of separate Parliaments.

Now you would I fancy agree with me that there is no sufficient scientific basis for such a belief & that in all three countries there is a large admixture of Celtic, Scandinavian & Germanic blood.

No expression of my opinion would be accepted because it would be supposed that I spoke more as a Liberal Unionist than as Ethnologist, but I wish you could give me something which at a fitting opportunity I might quote on your authority.

Would you be disposed to do so? [HP 22.96]

This document belonging to the *Huxley Papers* also concerns the fight against Home Rule, and might be related to Lubbock's letter:

We, the undersigned attentive observers of passing events whose lives are, or have been, devoted to the cultivation of science, and whose tastes, interests, and aims are far removed from the temptations and turmoil of Party Politics, desire, at the present crisis, to record our deliberate conviction that the Irish policy of Mr. Gladstone is fraught, not only with possible danger, but with certain disaster to the British Empire.

Men of science have for centuries, been leaders in the practice and defence of true liberty of thought and speech; but they cannot, without protest, surrender to the modern demagogue, whether English or Irish, the privilege of defining what "true liberty" means.

It is not only Mr. Gladstone's general policy (calamitous as that would be, even if pursued on legitimate lines) that we deprecate. It is his encouragement of the demagogue; his virtual defence of a tyranny which threatens the foundations of civilized society, and which two learned Catholic prelates have recently denounced as operating through terrorism, and culminating in murder; his readiness to compel loyal, trustful subjects of the Queen to bow their necks to the disloyal, from whom they can expect neither clemency nor consideration; it is conduct of this unparalleled character on the part of an ex-Prime Minister that we deplore and condemn.

Persuaded as we are that confusion, and something worse than confusion, must come, if, at the present critical moment, the Executive were to display either pusillanimity or irresolution in the assertion and application of the law, we note with pleasure the signs of inflexible determination, on the part of Her Majesty's Government, to bring law-breakers, without respect of persons, to account. It is thus alone that healthy order can be caused to supplant the amazing disorder which has been permitted to reign so long in Ireland. [HP 8.26; 27 October 1887—the names of the signatories are not given]

To conclude, this is Huxley's general view of the ethnology of Great Britain. Originally western Europe and the British Isles were inhabited by Melanochroi, who spoke dialects allied to the language of the Basques. Then the Xanthochroi spread throughout Europe. Their languages, such as Celtic, belonged to a group different from that spoken by the Melanochroi. The Xanthochroi did not eliminate the Melanochroi, but their language gradually gained the upper hand. Only then did the Roman conquest occur, in any case an event of modest anthropological interest. Here Huxley touches upon the subject of fair haired, tall populations, a subject attracting interest all over Europe through the notion of the "Aryans."

The "Aryan Question"

As Leon Poliakoff has recently shown (858), the "Aryan myth" has complex and distant roots. His rather sarcastic definition of "Aryan" is worth quoting: "On close inspection the true Aryan appeared to be a Westerner of the male sex, belonging to the upper or middle classes, who could be defined equally by reference to coloured men, proletarians or women" (p. 272).

Anthropology flourished all over Europe in the nineteenth century, and many societies were founded to promote it, not only in Britain, as we have seen, but also on the Continent (for example the influential Société d'anthropologie de Paris, founded in 1859 by such eminent scientists as G. St. Hilaire, Armand Quatrefages, and Paul Broca). At the same time philology also became popular; the so-called Aryan question was one of the most conspicuous results of the philological approach to anthropology. Adolf Bastian explained the problem very clearly:

Taking into consideration the fact that civilized peoples are in the course of developing spiritually towards an unquantifiable end, all classifications depending on the corporeal are bound to be sterile and contradictory. Philology, with its auxiliary branches, replaces craniology (applicable to primitive peoples). [858, p. 258]

The philological attitude to anthropology, propounded also by August Schleicher and Theodor Waitz, inevitably introduced a strong measure of value judgment into that field, and was strongly opposed by Rudolf Virchow in Germany and in England by Huxley. Anthropological views became heavily entangled with nationalism, as both France and Germany sought "scientific" support in the internecine rivalry for political hegemony on the continent of Europe.

The real founder of the Aryan myth in its modern guise was F. Schlegel: he stated that the Aryans originated in northern India and then spread westwards. Later this view was abandoned, and the Aryans were thought to have been of Sarmantic origin, as Latham propounded. There was little distinction in German circles between "race" and "language" as concepts. Jacob Grim, the compiler of the famous dictionary, was the most influential supporter of the myth, which was popularised in France by Ernest Renan, and in England by Max Müller. Müller, a German who had settled at Oxford, and was in correspondence with Huxley (*HP* 23.111–22), thought that the English and the Indians were of the same blood, a view which can scarcely have delighted the colonisers of the Indian subcontinent.

The upholders of the Aryan view maintained that the European populations originated from a race of Aryan invaders who spoke Aryan languages from which the present European languages derived. The identity of race and language was their basic proposition. Huxley also contributed to the Aryan debate. He was always attentive to what was happening in European culture, and did not miss the chance to express his view on what he calls the "Aryan question," a myth which was to have the strongest and most unpleasant consequences in our century. Huxley considered the Aryans and their place in Western history in an essay of 1890 entitled "The Aryan Question and Pre-historic Man" (*330*). His opinion in this essay is that there was indeed an Aryan race, but that there is no identity of race with language.

Philology was the starting point of the Aryan question. Philologists, discovering the affinities between the European languages and Sanskrit, claimed that they all descended from a common ancestor (*330*, p. 272). But, Huxley remarks, there is no trace of the original "Aryan" from which all those languages are supposed to have originated. In other words, the Aryan language is merely a hypothetical entity (p. 273). Moreover, it is clear that, if there were in fact a primitive Aryan tongue, there must have been a primitive people who spoke it; and presumably they lived somewhere (pp. 273–74). From the philological point of view, one must conclude that there was an Aryan race, an Aryan language, and an Aryan country (p. 274). The German philologists, whom Huxley disparagingly calls "Uhlans," decided that the Aryans came from the Hindu Kush and Pamir (p. 275). Huxley disagreed with this hypothesis and stood by Latham's Sarmantic hypothesis (p. 303).

Huxley's major argument against the philological approach to the Aryan question is identical to that which we have seen in all his ethnological works: science must develop a purely biological attitude to this problem, and the philologists confuse the concepts of race and language:

Any biologist who studies the history of the Aryan question and, taking the philological facts on trust, regards it exclusively from the point of view of anthropology, will observe that, very early, the purely biological conception of "race" illegitimately mixed itself up with the ideas derived from pure philology. [pp. 277–78]

According to Huxley, the philologists confuse "people" (the set of individuals who speak a language) with "race" (a zoological subdivision of
the species with distinct observable characteristics). The point is, then:
"Community of language is no proof of unity of race, it is not even
presumptive evidence of racial identity" (pp. 279–80). The right attitude to race is ascribed by Huxley to Desmoulins (p. 280n): "the people
who spoke Aryan could have belonged to more than one race" (p. 280).

Huxley endeavours to show that in Europe there is no identity between language and race—he had reached the same conclusion concerning the ethnology of Ireland. But does such a thing as an Aryan race
exist? Huxley is inclined to believe that it does—composed of tall, long-
headed, blond, blue-eyed people; they must have been much older than
the Aryan language: "The blond long-heads . . . must for ages have
been, philologically speaking, non-Aryans, or perhaps one should say
'pre-Aryans'" (pp. 297–98). Huxley concludes that:

There was and is an Aryan race—that is to say, the characteristic modes of
speech, termed Aryan, were developed among the blond long-heads alone however much some of them may have been modified by the importation of non-
Aryan elements. As to the "home" of the Aryan race, it was Europe, and lay
chiefly east of the central highlands and west of the Urals. From this region it
spread west, along the coasts of the North Sea to our islands, where, probably, it
met the brunet long-heads; to France where it found both these and the brunet
short-heads; to Switzerland and South Germany, where it impinged on the
brunet short-heads; to Italy, where brunet short-heads seem to have abounded in
the north and long-heads in the south; and to the Balkan peninsula, about the
earliest inhabitants of which we know nothing. There are two ways to Asia
Minor, the one over the Bosphorous and the other through the Caucasus, and the
Aryans may well have utilized both. Finally, the south-eastern tribes probably
spread themselves gradually over west Turkestan, and, after evolving the primitive Indo-Iranian dialect, eventually colonized Persia and Hindostan, where
their speech developed into its final forms. [p. 305]

According to Huxley, the Aryans were originally Europeans, and, as
he had maintained in 1869, they invaded India from Persia. Thus there
was a historical precedent for the colonisation of India; "Indians" had
never colonised Europe, it had always been the other way round—a
remarkable piece of good fortune for British honour.

Progress and Prejudice

Physical anthropology seems no longer to be at the centre of biological
debate, and ethnology has changed its perspective since the nineteenth
century. Certainly, we find both racism and nationalism in most nineteenth-century anthropology and ethnology. But to maintain that there

are physical differences between human races, once one is capable of proving this claim, is not racist; it *is* racist to claim that those differences make one part of mankind morally superior or inferior to another, or more or less worthy of respect. In other words, it is racist to introduce value judgments into zoological surveys of physical differences detectable in mankind.

In that sense of the word, with the possible exception of J. S. Mill, nearly everyone whose voice was heard on race and nation during the nineteenth century was racist and nationalistic. That was partly because of confusion between the concept of *race* and the highly abstract and scientifically indefinable concept of *nation*. Anthropology and ethnology were constantly entangled with nationalism, exacerbating the degree to which value judgment became part of science. Huxley's attitude is on the whole mild. Everyone is a child of his age, but no one should be its slave. Huxley was certainly a son of his age, and shared with his contemporaries some of the biases of the day; but he was not its slave, and he maintained an attitude to his time that is, in my opinion, critical.

People in the nineteenth century were convinced that the concept of race was basic to the understanding of mankind. For both Robert Knox and Disraeli "race is everything" (858, p. 232). In his historical novels Disraeli attributes all that ever happened in Europe to the Jews: the first Jesuits were Jews, Russian diplomacy was carried on by Jews; Jews held all professorial chairs in German universities, Jews had caused the revolutions of 1848. These commonplace views, which demonstrated to Disraeli's eyes the importance of the role played by his people in European history, were shared by people who were neither Jews themselves nor particularly sympathetic to them: there is the further ghastly example in the twentieth century of Nazism. Marx and Engels were also strongly racist. Marx thought that blacks and the Russians were inferior races because of the influence of the soil. Marx referred such views of his to the influence of Darwin's doctrine, and to the theory of Trémaux. In a letter to Engels he mentions the "sexual swinishness of the savages" (858, p. 246; Marx to Engels, 13 April 1867). The National Front might well be party to such an opinion in our own day. According to Engels, his colleague in the development of "scientific materialism," blacks were congenitally incapable of understanding mathematics (858, p. 244).

Growing nationalist feelings undoubtedly had a strong influence on racial views. France and Germany were not on friendly terms. The French considered themselves the most learned people in Europe and wished to dominate the continent; German philologists devised theories which propounded the superiority of German-speaking people. When the French were humiliated at Sedan in 1870, those philologists must have welcomed such strong evidence of the correctness of their views. Hungarians, Slavs, and Italians rebelled against the short-sighted despotism of Franz Joseph's empire, and laid claim to some mythical national greatness. Throughout the century, many Italians—poets, writers, and politicans such as Gioberti, Mazzini, and Carducci—were convinced of the moral and cultural superiority of their country, referring to a past which was actually remote. Mazzini's claim that each nation was entitled to freedom of expression and expansion was easily turned by unscrupulous politicians into the claim that their nation was so entitled, with the disastrous results known to everybody. Meanwhile in 1868, Wagner's Hans Sachs was exalting "Die heil'ge deutsche Kunst." Certainly there was much conceptual confusion between *nation, race, culture,* and *language.*

The inadequacy of the nineteenth-century approach to science has been pointed out many times. It seems to me that it was not only inadequate but also inconsistent. The scientists claimed that science must be free of value judgments; but they introduced them, copiously, into the fields of anthropology and ethnology, the most controversial subjects of the time. This is what they themselves would call a "cardinal sin." Huxley was perhaps less guilty of this sin than most of his contemporaries. Nevertheless, in his ethnological works his otherwise neutral view of science failed to hold.

Victorian anthropological views indulged freely in moral condemnation, and belittlement, of other people's habits. England was not deeply involved in the great struggle for supremacy in Europe, but she was expanding outside it, and thus came into contact with the habits and customs of people of completely different civilisations. One of the basic tenets of Victorian civilisation was that of "personal responsibility." Nowadays we consider moral censure of people of a different culture not only arrogant, but also scientifically erroneous. The Victorians, however, viewed any alien culture as having a set place in the long scale of progress which culminated in the ultimate culture—their own. They applied abstract judgments according to parameters external to other societies and cultures, and used their own customs and habits as the standard by which to classify others' as right or wrong, good or bad.

The expansion and dominance of Western civilisation in the nineteenth century convinced Victorians that the only type of culture and social tradition worthy of respect and valid as a reference point was their own. Nineteenth-century anthropologists tended to make the truth correspond to their customs and their customs to what they saw as nature. Of course people from other cultures doubtless thought much the same of the Victorians—the view that all "foreigners" can be assumed to be "infidels and curs" cuts both ways.

Conclusion
In Darwin's Shadow

In this book, I have tried to present a survey and discussion of the scientific research of T. H. Huxley. My purpose in doing so has been to show that Huxley was an important scientist independent of the figure of Charles Darwin, even though he is most commonly recalled as Darwin's major exponent; and thus to broaden knowledge of his achievements outside the usual area of emphasis on his role as a public figure. In Part 1 I attempted, in addition, to document his reaction to evolutionism, in order to answer questions about the timing, causes, and nature of his conversion to a broadly evolutionary point of view. Part 2, by contrast, concentrated on his scientific understanding of humanity, demonstrating his difficulty in excluding extrascientific considerations from the analysis of man.

In Part 1, we observed Huxley's passage from the theory of the type to the theory of descent, from the primary influence of von Baer to that of Haeckel, commenting meanwhile on Huxley's cautious endorsement of Darwin's position in the *Origin of Species*. I argued that Huxley's reception of the *Origin of Species* was broadly positive, emphasising its materialist and mechanistic principles and hence its contribution to the understanding of the order of nature and to the emancipation of science from theology and metaphysics. But we also saw that Huxley declined to follow Darwin over saltation, and over the radical revision of the notion of species implied by Darwin's dynamic conceptions. The two men disagreed more fundamentally in their understanding of the logic of scientific explanation, Huxley's criterion of decisive experiment confronting Darwin's criterion of explanatory power. Huxley later accepted the theory of descent, I maintain, because it remained much closer, both in its immediate applicability to palaeontology and in its theoretical basis in the type, to his existing subject matters and conceptual scheme than Darwin's proposals did; and because it shared the same intellectual background of von Baer's embryological typology. In general conclusion, I questioned the internal coherence of Huxley's theoretical and philosophical position, especially in the later period, given the uneasy blending of static and dynamic elements involved in the theory of descent and the impossibility of a decisive experimental proof of the notion of descent itself, while emphasising the consistency of Huxley's application of theoretical principles in each of the stages of his career. I also stressed that Huxley's development could not be regarded as primarily "internal," depending as it did on his reaction to colleagues and contemporaries and his adoption of the theoretical insights of others.

Part 2 concerned *Man's Place in Nature* and Huxley's subsequent work in ethnology. *Man's Place in Nature* should be seen fundamentally as a reiteration of the taxonomic conclusions of Linnaeus, more in order to refute the views of Owen than to support those of Darwin, and therefore the anticlimax which characterised the contemporary reception of Huxley's most famous book was probably more fitting than the generous twentieth-century hindsight, to which it appears as a foundation stone of "modern" anthropology, on the strength of the notion of adaptation implicit in the footnote on which I commented in chapter 4. In chapter 5, Huxley's ethnological works are shown to centre on the establishment of divisions and classifications within mankind. We saw that Huxley rejected the prevailing philological approach, and—in keeping with the main thesis of *Man's Place in Nature*—insisted that physical characteristics were the only proper basis for the classification of mankind. But we also saw the intrusion of biologically irrelevant terms and conceptions into these works, divisions into "higher" and "lower" which were inconsistent with Huxley's championship of the neutrality and independence of science, and which implied that to some extent he shared contemporary prejudices concerning the superiority of males over females, whites over blacks, and Europeans over the "uncivilised" world. On the other hand he demanded that injustice should not be added to these natural "inequalities," and generally opposed the views of overtly racist and/or sexist thinkers.

Chapter 5 also usefully reminds us that Huxley's activities and concerns encompassed extrascientific as well as scientific aspects; the Irish question and the Eyre affair, for example, indicate a direct involvement in some of the political issues of the day, especially later in his life. As the interrelationships between the various elements of Huxley's life and work are crucial to an understanding of his actions, including his "purely" scientific actions, it is important to look briefly at some of these other aspects.

First, let us return, as so often, to the figure of Richard Owen. We have already seen several occasions on which Huxley and Owen came into conflict: the *Terebratula* affair, where Huxley refuted Owen's claim to be able to detect an anus in *Terebratula*; Owen's false claim to part of

Huxley's professorial responsibilities at the Government School of Mines, which sharpened their animosity on a personal level; the dispute concerning the vertebral theory of the skull, which Huxley effectively undermined in his article of 1858 (64); Owen's extraordinary claim of priority in respect to the natural-selective conception of evolution; the hippocampus minor affair, in which Huxley demolished Owen's opinion that the gorilla lacks a hippocampus minor; and so on. These issues provided Huxley with the occasion for overt attacks upon the "potentate"; there were other events in which, inter alia, he pursued a covert attack upon his major adversary. His early work on *Salpa* (7), overtly arguing against Chamisso, was covertly an attack on Owen's notions of parthenogenesis, and was appreciated as such by Allman and Darwin. The famous Oxford meeting was in effect an exchange between Huxley and Owen's proxy. *Man's Place in Nature* must be seen more as a further broadside against Owen than as a positive, forward-looking treatise, despite Huxley's later disavowal. I also wish to emphasise the strategic value Huxley found in supporting Darwin's *Origin of Species*. While it is certainly true, as pointed out in chapter 2, that Huxley praised Darwin's work as a hypothesis of the order of nature, and one which moreover confined itself to materialist and mechanical conceptions, it is also true that Darwin's conceptions, by virtue of that very materialism, were excellent and positive ammunition against Owen's broadly Platonic views of nature. It should also therefore be clear that Owen is a major general target behind Huxley's persistent attacks on Platonism generally, and his support for anti-essentialist, anti-idealist empiricism by contrast, which culminated in the writing of *Hume* (248). Owen's idealist conception of the archetype, for example, was something from which Huxley was always keen to keep his distance.

But we must ask why Huxley was so tenacious in his persistent campaign against Owen. Again, there are clear overt factors. Owen was often wrong on matters of interpretation, and even on matters of observational detail; nor had he refrained from personal injury and sarcasm. But at another level our question requires a different kind of answer. Owen was an established and highly influential figure in British scientific circles: in effect, he was, or at least represented, the scientific establishment. Huxley's rise to success and importance could only be made at the expense of figures such as Owen; and it was fortunate from Huxley's point of view that Owen was such easy prey. Furthermore, his willingness to do battle with established authority brought Huxley increasingly into the limelight, enhancing his prospects of advancement. Huxley duly rose gradually to the presidencies of learned scientific societies—the Geological Society, the Ethnological Society, and eventually the Royal Society itself. Other illustrations of his ambition for success and recognition can be found: his concern to reach a wide audience, and more particularly his concern for the favour of any given audience or readership. He maintained his prominence in the public eye not only by his entry into controversies, both scientific and extrascientific—there were the theological controversies with Gladstone, for example—but also by publishing from time to time in more popular rather than technical journals, and, as we saw in chapter 5, by involvement in political issues. A good illustration of his astuteness in keeping "on the right side" of an audience is provided by an analysis of the fluctuations in his overt endorsement of evolution according to the context in which he was speaking or writing; the following schema gives an indication of this.

Works	Audience expected	Views on evolution
Popular writings and reviews	Learned laymen	Evolution may be true, but since natural selection, its major principle, is not proved, Darwin's hypothesis should be accepted only provisionally
Textbooks	Students of biological science	Phylogeny is interesting, but since we have too little evidence, we should avoid it; morphology suffices
Memoirs for liberal scientific societies	Scientists	Palaeontology affords good evidence for evolution; descent is emphasised; certain genealogical relationships are outlined
Memoirs for the Royal Society [630]	Scientific establishment	Evolution is not mentioned, but evidence is provided for it

The changing viewpoints represented in the right-hand column seem paradoxical until we realise that they serve ambition by presenting their exponent in the most acceptable light possible for each of his different audiences.

So Huxley's underlying desire for success and importance begins to illuminate the reasons behind a range of his activities, both scientific and extrascientific. But we must shift the question again and ask why he wanted to be preeminent, even at the expense of presenting a clear and unambiguous viewpoint. An answer is provided at one level by considering a major aspect of Huxley's extrascientific career—his involvement in the field of education. His textbooks range from general introductory science primers aimed at pre-university students to more specialised works concerning taxonomy, vertebrate anatomy, invertebrate anatomy, physiology, and ecology (see *111, 133, 158, 199, 238, 239, 257, 263, 358, 359, 360*). But far beyond that, he took upon himself a sort of "mission," as he put it, to bring science into the mainstream of education and into the public mind generally. His concern to inform a broader public, to "spread the vogue for science," is indicated in the first place by the publications in the more popular journals, which we have already mentioned, and his *Lectures to Working-men* cited in chapter 4. This concern to spread knowledge, especially scientific knowledge, to those social strata which would not otherwise have been able to obtain it (which was shared by his friend and colleague Tyndall [*HP* 8.55]) can be traced to his time in London prior to the *Rattlesnake* voyage. He had come into contact as a medical student with the miserable conditions of life in the poorest areas of London's East End, which struck his conscience and caused him to abandon his early passion for thinkers like Carlyle (*433*, chap. 1). Later in his career he became increasingly committed to that concern. He wrote articles specifically on the subject of education, especially "A Liberal Education and Where to Find It" (*152*) of 1868, setting out his position on the desirability of a balanced curriculum to include the sciences. He became involved in the parliamentary Select Committee on Scientific Instruction (*157*); in the question of the role of school boards (*186*); and in the National Association for the Promotion of Technical Education (*302*), and rose to the rectorship of Aberdeen University (*218*), a fitting reward for his continuous support and encouragement of the "secular," modern-curriculum universities. His speeches and articles embrace medical, technical, and industrial education, as well as matters affecting schools and universities (e.g., *26, 169, 206, 220, 230, 243, 256, 278, 280, 288, 298, 309*); his involvement was clearly both extensive and intensive, especially from the 1870s onwards. There can be no doubt that Huxley's success in promoting scientific education, through his textbooks, speeches, committee activities, and educational appointments, is one of the lasting monuments of his life; as we have already quoted in the introduction, Irvine said that without Huxley, "science would not have enjoyed such dazzling prestige among politicians and businessmen, nor figured, perhaps, so prominently in the late-nineteenth-century school curriculum" (*477*, p. 118).

It is significant that his absorption in that mission comes in the later period of his career. By the 1870s, because of his personal scientific reputation and his success in undermining the existing scientific establishment, he had risen to the upper echelons of the scientific world. His ability to fulfil his mission is due in no small part to the influence he was consequently capable of wielding as an increasingly dominant and respected authority in scientific matters.

Huxley's educationalist crusade also throws additional light on some of the central features of his scientific behaviour. We have already observed his skill in keeping on the right side of his audience. This desire to maintain respectability is present more generally in the viewpoints he expressed, as well as in his manner of expressing them. We saw in chapter 2 how keen he was to emphasise his reservations about Darwin's hypothesis, to point out from the very beginning the danger that Darwin might have gone too far in dismissing saltation and in presenting his views as the theory of species; Huxley stresses the possibility that Darwin may have been led to overestimate the power of his *"vera causa."* And even in his positive remarks explaining the general welcome he gave to the *Origin of Species,* his underlying attitude is to make clear that, whether true or false, Darwin's publication is to be applauded for its "sobriety and accuracy of thought" (*HP* 30.41). Had Darwin's doctrine been rejected or disproved, Huxley for one could not have been accused of jumping irresponsibly onto the latest bandwagon: he would allow the view a fair trial, and would commend its seriousness, but at the same time keep his escape routes open. The same quality is evident in his later acceptance of the theory of descent: he assures his audience at the outset that there is nothing "wild or illegitimate" about it (*146,* p. 312) and dissociates himself sharply from Haeckel's "phylogenetic frenzy." And we must recall from the early period his constant reminder to his audience that his use of Owen's terminology of the "archetype" did not imply an indulgence in the antiscientific excesses of Platonism.

In other words, even in deploying a theory or concept, he does not *embrace* it; rather, he "lights the blue touch-paper and stands well clear." It is as if he cannot afford his reputation for reliable analytical judgment to be damaged by reversals in the fortunes of theories he has applied or commented upon; and he does not give hostages to fortune in the shape of daring hypotheses or public speculations of his own. He would like to be found supporting the "right" view; but failing that, supporting the "wrong" view at least for the "right" reason, so that his intellect and influence remain respected come what may. Huxley's attachment to "fair play" can also be related to these considerations. Generally speaking, unlike some of his contemporaries, he dealt with issues rather than personalities; and, as we saw in the *Bathybius* affair, was ready to acknowledge his fallibility, to place his trust in evidence rather than intuition. Naturally, these characteristics made it easier for him to establish an influential public persona—after all, in the debates about the educational curriculum, who would be convinced by an advocate of the virtues of a scientific temperament and training who tended to propound or follow "wild" hypotheses, or whose style tended to become acrimonious and dogmatic? So Huxley's educationalism, and the contributory quest for respect and prominence in the scientific and social establishment, exert a considerable influence on his behaviour as a scientist, reaching not only into his public manner but also right into his treatment of theory.

These remarks help us to place into context my comment of chapter 4 that Huxley acted most decisively as a *scientist* when his *extrascientific* concerns were also at issue. *Man's Place in Nature,* for example, was shown to have arisen in a context which activated not only his scientific abilities, but also his concerns for popular education (the *Lectures for Working-men*), public controversy (the clash with Owen over the simian hippocampus minor), and the consequent advancement of his own position. We begin to see how Huxley's scientific commitments, educational interests, and personal career fit together into a broadly coherent enterprise with diverse aspects. These aspects do not appear to cross-fertilise one another at an immediately traceable conceptual level, but rather at the level of underlying strategy and psychological motivation; and it is at this level that the nature of the unity of Huxley's actions is to be sought.

The anxiety attendant upon the pursuit of this life of ever-expanding success is also evident in aspects of Huxley's scientific work. He sustained a punishingly high level of activity over many years, as if addicted to his work. For example, during the period 1860–80, which contains not only the bulk of his important books and memoirs but also the expanding burden of his public offices and commitments, he averaged one publication every six weeks or less throughout that period. In today's vocabulary he would doubtless be branded a "workaholic." A further indication of anxiety can be seen in the episodic, unfinished character of his books, on which I commented in chapter 4. It appears that his state of mind, always looking ahead to the next piece of work, allowed insufficient intellectual repose for the development of "rounded" products of any great length. Most of his publications are of short to medium length and changes of subject matter are frequent and rapid. His scientific work in general, in other words, has an episodic, almost agitated quality; he hops from topic to topic like a cat on a hot tin roof. We should also note the similarly unrounded, eclectic nature of Huxley's actual scientific theory in the period after 1868, as has already been implied in chapter 3; it seems that he also found insufficient intellectual repose to bring the various, partly inconsistent elements, into a more satisfying harmony, and especially to come to terms, in more than the relatively superficial adoption of the notion of descent, with the extent and depth of the conceptual revolution entailed by Darwin's *Origin of Species*. It is of course ultimately a chicken-and-egg problem; whether a high level of activity produces stress or whether, the other way round, constant inner anxiety produces the compulsion to be continuously active. Suffice it to say, in Huxley's case, that he suffered two nervous breakdowns, in 1872 and 1884, the latter of which caused him to resign the presidency of the Royal Society in 1885. He did not however relax much even at that point: the last ten years of his life continued to be highly productive, culminating in the publication in 1893 of *Evolution and Ethics* (343).

But all this still leaves hanging in the air the question where Huxley's formidable drive came from, and how it was sustained. In seeking an answer, let us first note that Huxley's preoccupation with the introduction into the curriculum of scientific subjects, and perhaps more especially with the promotion of industrial and technological education, shows him as an enthusiastic participant in the developing British technocracy—one could indeed describe him as one of its intellectual midwives. His career, from a basically self-taught ship's medical officer to the presidency of the Royal Society, is, further, an example of the ethos which underlay the nineteenth-century extension of the industrial revolution: the Victorian entrepreneurial spirit and the concept of personal and social betterment by individual enterprise.

Notwithstanding the fact that the nineteenth century witnessed a process of liberalisation and secularisation, the place of religion among the foundations of this Victorian ethos should not be underestimated. As Trevelyan wrote in his *English Social History* (910a), "The English of all classes formed in the nineteenth century a strongly Protestant nation; most of them were religious, and most of them (including the Utilitarians and Agnostics) were 'serious' with that strong preoccupation about morality which is the merit and danger of the Puritan character" (p. 506). As G. M. Young explains (940, p. 79), morality and industry were the key virtues of the Victorians; personal success was considered a divine blessing, and competition was an article of faith.

It is therefore worth recalling Huxley's fundamentally Calvinist upbringing; elements of the tenets of Calvinism, and a very great deal of its spirit, are traceable in his later behaviour. Calvinism stresses the independence and responsibility of the individual conscience, minimising the intrusion of an external church authority into the area of practical decision. One's posthumous fate is predetermined. However, Calvinism stresses the importance of moral and worldly effort: one's ability to progress by such personal effort is the earthly or empirical sign that one may posthumously belong to the saved rather than the damned. This treatment of the doctrine of predestination means that Calvinism entails the *essential* insignificance and powerlessness of the individual's life in the divine order, and the *essential* inequality of man, given that the division into the saved and damned, the ultimately superior and inferior, is prearranged; but at the same time the doctrine motivates an escape from earthly insignificance and inequality, through the emphasis on moral and practical effort in this world. Assessing some of Huxley's later attitudes and beliefs against this background from his early, psychologically formative years is interesting. His general insistence in the field of science on the independence of enquiry from theology and metaphysics is clearly congruent with the Calvinist insistence on the independence of decision from central dogma. Calvinist emphasis on the inequality of man recalls the position adopted by Huxley in some of his ethnological works which, as we saw in chapter 5, tend to propose the "natural" superiority of the European, the white, and the male; his belief that social programmes should operate towards the alleviation of inequality echoes the Calvinist belief in the virtue of worldly effort. More generally, Huxley behaves as if he had taken the Calvinist assertion of individual powerlessness and the possible means of earthly escape from that condition psychologically very much to heart: we have noted already his determination to rise to the top through his own efforts, and his punishing work routine. But further, his fervent belief in the necessity of promoting general education has a dual meaning in the light of this Calvinist perspective: his mission represents a personal quest for an earthly salvation from insignificance; and the content of his mission, to bring scientific knowledge and technological skills to the widest possible public, addresses the powerlessness of the mass of individuals through raising the prospect of an increasingly effective domination of the "forces of nature" in the interest of improving the material conditions of life. So the nineteenth-century Calvinist perspective refers us not only to the (in)famous work ethic and the compulsion to succeed but also to the virtuousness of dissatisfaction with existing conditions as an impulse to the making of worldly moral and practical effort.

This last point begins to bring into focus Huxley's quality as a *rebel*. I am struck by how much of his life and work was marked by a rebelliousness which may be described as "adolescent" in nature. By this I do not mean to disparage Huxley—or adolescents. I mean a constant conflict against existing centres of power and influence in order to establish a personal identity, which at the same time feels uneasy or insecure at the vacuum of authority which the conflict itself tends to produce, and which therefore seeks the foundation of its own general "new order." It is therefore an attitude characterised by a preoccupation with demonstrating its individuality and by an ambivalence towards authority and authorities. Its clearest early manifestation in Huxley's thought is his adoption from Goethe of the principle of *thätige Skepsis,* the attitude of dissent from received dogmas which at the same time seeks the foundation of its own truth. Another kind of manifestation can be seen in Huxley's whole preoccupation with nature under the aspect of "order."

Let us look more closely into the "rebellious" aspects of Huxley's career. I have already stressed his insistence on the exclusion of theological considerations from the realm of science; but his rejection of the traditional authority of the church went further than that. He became in fact a committed agnostic, when agnosticism was only newly respectable in public life. James Mill and William Lawrence had been obliged to hide their opinions on this subject, and it was in fact the group led by Huxley, Tyndall, and Morley who contributed to the public recognition of agnosticism as an acceptable alternative to the prevailing religious orthodoxy. We have also already seen more than once Huxley's antagonism to an even more ancient authority, Plato. His agnosticism and anti-Platonism not only define the general context of his scientific opinions, but also underlie a third aspect of his rebellion against received views: his rejection, so far as education is concerned, of the clerical/classical domination of the curriculum in higher education. We have also seen Huxley's persistent undermining of the existing scientific establishment, represented in the figure of Owen, both for reasons of personal advancement and in respect of the rejection of Owen's Platonic views, thus establishing his own distinct identity and pursuing the goal of founding his own "new order." This is also the place to point out that Huxley's favoured methodology, based on laboratory experiment and observation, represents a rejection of the British traditions of natural history, a repudiation of the intellectual environment in which his first steps in the study of animals had been made. But the rebellious attitude can be traced within his scientific work itself at a level of greater detail. One of the features of his style, especially in his earlier periods (see chapters 1, 2, and 4), was to use his data and their theoretical implications to demonstrate that some other, often respected, scientist had "got it wrong." This abrasiveness must have been common knowledge, for in Darwin's papers we find the following:

With respect to Huxley, I was on the point of speaking to Crawfurd and Strelecki (who will be on committee of Athenaeum) when I bethought me of how Owen would look & what he would say. Cannot you fancy him with a red face, dreadful smile & slow & gentle voice, asking "Will Mr Crawfurd tell me what Mr Huxley has done, deserving this honour; I only know that he differs from, & disputes the authority of, Cuvier, Ehrenberg & Agassiz as of no weight at all". [*Dar.* 114.162]

Our present perspective also shows in a fresh light Huxley's behaviour towards his "mentors" at the level of scientific theory. For example, he adopts the views of von Baer—but propounds, rather gratuitously, a greater separation between the types than von Baer's actual work entails (something which in the end actually impeded his recognition of the relationship between the vertebrates and invertebrates). He supports the views of Darwin, but is keen to emphasise his reservations about them; he adopts the views of Haeckel, but dissociates himself from aspects of the "phylogenetic method" (even while effectively using it). Above I alluded to this constant distancing of himself from his theoretical commitments in terms of a cautiousness related to his desire to retain public respectability in the event of a downfall of the theories in question. But our present perspective would rather underline the function that this ambivalence towards his mentors performed of establishing and consolidating Huxley's distinct scientific identity, his claim to individuality. His quest for *public* respect can thus be seen also as a quest for *self*-respect.

The ambivalence we have just touched on in respect to Huxley's relationships with his mentors is also, as we saw at the end of chapter 3, a characteristic of the theoretical and philosophical content of his research principles themselves in the later period. The interim conclusions in chapter 3 draw attention to elements of logical oddness in Huxley's later standpoints; we can now put these matters into a fuller perspective. I noted in particular the uneasy blend of static and dynamic conceptions which the theory of descent appeared to represent: the idea of discrete and stable forms inherent in the notion of the type allied with the idea of a continuous development inherent in the notion of descent. Further, I noted the paradox involved when Huxley's adoption of the theory of descent and his comments about the *Origin of Species* were compared with each other: the support for Darwin on the basis of his having proposed a mechanism for evolution confronting the absence of a ready mechanical interpretation of the theory of descent; and the requirement, in criticism of Darwin, of decisive experimentation confronting the impossibility of such a procedure in respect of the theory of descent. Logically, the combination of these points of view is hard to defend; but our present perspective suggests that what we witness here is Huxley's need for the intellectual security of a regimented framework (the division of nature into "types" and the reliance on the "hard data" provided by experimentation) pushing him into contradiction rather than conceptual revision when the changes of theoretical outlook involved in evolutionism required him to take into consideration the fluid frameworks implied by the dynamics of descent and natural selection, and by the more relativistic scientific criterion of the comparative explanatory power of theories. The view of Huxley as the kind of rebel who at the same time feels uncomfortable in the absence of definitive authority helps to elucidate in some detail the ambivalent conceptions present in his final theoretical position.

This brings me to the last aspect of our present perspective: the quest of the rebel to establish his own system of authority to replace the old order. The shift to the establishment of the new order can be discerned in all aspects of Huxley's career from the late 1860s onwards. He begins to move into positions of power and influence within the scientific world—the presidencies of various societies, and so forth—thus marking the success of the struggle against the old scientific establishment. Like a true campaigner, he maintains his solidarity with his comrades— supporting Hooker's candidacy for the presidency of the Royal Society (*Dar.* 166), securing Lubbock's presidency of the Anthropological In-

stitute (see chapter 5), and so forth. His involvement in the promotion of
the secular, "modernist" educational curriculum becomes an increasingly successful preoccupation—the majority of the publications
and other activities cited in my comments on this topic, above, fall
within the later period of his career. In scientific research itself, there is
something of a significant change in the style of his memoirs: there is a
decreasing emphasis on the polemical aspects, the aspect of the critique
of currently received truths; and an increasing emphasis on the straightforward demonstration that "this is the way in which such-and-such a
corner of the animal kigndom is structured," the aspect of the establishment of the new truths. This change of style is perhaps most clearly
symbolised by Huxley's suppression of the arguments against Owen in
his late reprint of *Man's Place in Nature.*

But what was the "new order"? An aspect is evident in Huxley's
ethnological works. There, as we saw in chapter 5, he devotes most of
his energy to documenting the characteristics of the different races. His
bias—by no means his alone, or in the sense of active political discrimination—towards the white, the European, and the male was also shown.
His picture of humanity, in other words, is one in which each human
grouping has its natural place in the overall pattern. His picture of the
animal world in general is similar: each animal grouping, each type, has
its natural place in the chain of descent. Thus Huxley seeks to vindicate
the use of a definitive framework—this is his final order of nature.

Let us now bring together the various Huxleyan "new truths." We
have the replacement of the old world view of teleology and creationism
with the new world view that every grouping has its place in a natural
order; of the old certainties of the Church with the new certainties of
decisive experiment; of the old metaphysic of idealism with the new
metaphysic of absolute empiricism; of the old authority of "Owenite"
Platonism with the new authority of Huxleyan mechanistic materialism; of the old educational ideology of the clerical and classical disciplines with the new ideology of a popular scientific technocracy. It is
therefore possible at last to discern an inner unity and coherence in
Huxley's life and work; for these elements of the new order—the tough
empirical rationalism, the provision of the order of nature, and the
promotion of a popular technocracy—add up to a fundamental principle: *nature under the control of mind,* conceived both as a world view
and as a programme for action.

In these concluding pages, I have tried to argue that the reasons for
many of the details of Huxley's scientific behaviour have to be sought
outside his science, in the other aspects and projects of his career, and in
his underlying persona. In seeing him as the kind of rebel who seeks to

found his own new order, I have been able to bring the various aspects of his public career—the battle against established authorities, the educationalist mission, the polemical controversies, and the quest for preeminence, as well as his actual scientific thought—ultimately under one principle. First, I related the power struggle against the Owenites to the educationalist crusade in arguing that the quest for preeminence and respect in the scientific world was strongly conducive to the momentum of his campaign for the reform of the curriculum. Then, through the idea that his quest for public respect was also a quest for *self*-respect, I suggested that a mainspring of his formidable drive was a need to establish his own identity and individuality, first in rebelling against existing authorities and later in establishing his own authority in both scientific and extrascientific matters. The question I asked as to why Huxley so desired to rise to the top of the scientific world therefore receives an answer at one level in the campaign for the reform of education, and at a different level in the need to establish his own individuality and his own system of authority. The relationship of these two considerations to the details of Huxley's actual scientific work was also discussed. His apparent failure to embrace fully any of the theoretical principles which he deployed or supported was seen in the first place as cautiousness aimed at retaining public respect and in the second place as part of a more general ambivalence towards mentors and authorities; the latter aspect, of the search for a combination of security and individuality, being reflected further in the logically curious combination of "old" and "new" elements present in his later theoretical position. Subsidiary considerations in elucidating qualities of Huxley's scientific work were the aspect of anxiety and the probable influence of his Calvinist upbringing. Finally it was possible to propose as the essence of Huxley's new order the aphorism: nature under the control of mind.

What were Huxley's lasting achievements and relevance? His contribution to the modernisation of the educational curriculum has already been stressed. His contribution to the analysis of the coelenterates; his views on saltation as an anticipation of mutationist theory (and, of the recent notion of "punctuated equilibrium"); and his view on the evolution of the birds as the forerunner of a still-unfinished controversy all are of the first importance. And we have also seen how twentieth-century writers, whether fully justified or not, hail Huxley as one of the founding fathers of modern anthropology. But scientifically speaking, his strongest influence was on the reception of evolutionism. For it would appear that Huxley's static interpretation of evolution, with its emphasis on the laboratory, was at first more influential than Darwin's dynamic one—the "naturalist's interpretation." To quote Sir Gavin de Beer:

But no sooner was [Darwin's] great work in the hands of biologists than they rushed indoors, into their laboratories, and for fifty years they devoted their energies and thoughts to research in comparative anatomy and embryology, and neglected the study of variation, selection, and adaptation in natural populations of animals and plants. The reason for this paradoxical situation was that the dominant influences in teaching were those of Huxley and Haeckel. The classic researches of the former inspired students with interest in what could be learnt from the structure and functions of the organs of a type, while the latter kindled enthusiasm in the search for ancestral types to place on the appropriate levels of ancestral trees. [668, p. 196]

As Geison has shown (694), Michael Foster, who was deeply influenced by Huxley, became the father figure of the great physiologists who sprang from the Cambridge School. At the same time, E. R. Lankester emphasised the role of microscopy for the study of evolution. Another of Huxley's protégés, H. N. Martin, emigrated to Johns Hopkins University in Baltimore, where H. T. Morgan was to start his scientific career. With his studies on the genetics of *Drosophila*, Morgan made a contribution of paramount importance to the modern regeneration of Darwinism; for it was not until the 1930s and 1940s, with the "Synthetic theory" of evolution propounded by Fisher (686), Haldane (720), J. Huxley (742), and others, that steps were taken to return to the Darwinian origins of the theory of evolution—a more field-oriented, dynamic conception.

In the introduction I quoted Irvine, who asked, in effect, What would Darwin have been without Huxley? My final question returns the compliment: What would Huxley have been without Darwin? I think it is possible to say, in the manner of Irvine, that although the details of his career would obviously have been different, his reputation "would have been nearly as great." After all, his star was rising, both scientifically and extrascientifically, by the time the *Origin of Species* appeared. His scientific methodology and theoretical perspectives were already well ingrained; his motivation to succeed was already powerful. The theory of descent itself might even have seen the light of day independently of the publication of the *Origin of Species*. Although I suggest in chapter 2 that Darwin was important to the proponents of other evolutionary conceptions in having been the first to rehabilitate the notion of evolution in any form at all in the eyes of science, it is clear that the central principle of the theory of descent in Haeckel's formulation, the principle that "phylogeny recapitulates ontogeny," might have arisen in any case directly from the marriage of von Baer's attention to embryology and the increasing quantity of palaeontological data. Be that as it may, it is possible to argue that, despite the strategic value to Huxley of the *Origin of Species*, its comprehensively dynamic doctrines threatened his increasingly successful theoretical perspectives with confusion, and that the time and energy he spent in the defence of Darwin's publication constituted a distraction from his already well-developed studies and pursuits. What is certain is that he never fully came to terms either with Darwin's "dynamic" attitude to nature or his "pragmatic" conceptions of the logic of science. Huxley's temperament and underlying motivation led him to the rationalism of the stable order of nature and its human exploitation through science and technology. On the other hand, Darwin—the radical, by contrast with Huxley the rebel—reached through to the elementalism of a great, restless drama.

ABBREVIATIONS

Aberdeen Univ. Rev.	Review of the University of Aberdeen
Abh. bayer. Akad. Wiss.	Abhandlungen der bayerischen Akademie der Wissenschaft
Abh. K. Akad. Wiss. Berlin	Abhandlungen der Kaiserliche Akademie der Wissenchaft Berlin
Adult Ed.	Adult Education
Am. J. Sci.	American Journal of Science
Am. J. Sci. Arts	American Journal of Science and Arts
Am. Nat.	American Naturalist
Ann. Ist. Fil. Univ. Fir.	Annali dell'istituto di filosofia dell'Università di Firenze
Ann. Mag. Nat. Hist.	Annals and Magazine of Natural History
Ann. Rep. Smithsonian Inst.	Annals and Reports of the Smithsonian Institute
Ann. Rev. Earth Plan. Sci.	Annals and Review of Earth and Planetary Science
Ann. Sci.	Annals of Science
Ann. Sci. Nat.	Annales de science naturelle
Anthr. Rev.	Anthropological Review
Brit. Ass. Rep.	Reports of the British Association
Brit. For. Med.-Chir. Rev.	British and Foreign Medico-Chirurgical Review
Brit. J. Ed. Stud.	British Journal of Educational Studies
Brit. J. Hist. Sci.	British Journal of the History of Science
Brit. J. Phil. Sci.	British Journal of the Philosophy of Science
Bull. Brit. Mus. (Nat. Hist.) Hist. Ser.	Bulletin of the British Museum (Natural History), Historical Series
Bull. Med. Hist.	Bulletin of the History of Medicine
Cont. Rev.	Contemporary Review

Ed. Rev.	Educational Review
Edin. New Phil. J.	Edinburgh New Philosophical Journal
Fort. Rev.	Fortnightly Review
Geol. Mag.	Geological Magazine
Hist. Sci.	History of Science
Int. Rev.	International Review
J. Aesth. Art Crit.	Journal of Aesthetics and Art Criticism
J. Anat. Physiol.	Journal of Anatomy and Physiology
J. Brit. Stud.	Journal of British Studies
J. Geol. Soc.	Journal of the Geological Society
J. Hist. Beh. Sci.	Journal of the History of Behavioural Sciences
J. Hist. Biol.	Journal of the History of Biology
J. Hist. Ideas	Journal of the History of Ideas
J. Hist. Med.	Journal of the History of Medicine
J. Linn. Soc. (Bot./Biol./Zool.)	Journal of the Linnean Society of London (Botanical, Biological, Zoological)
J. Physiol.	Journal of Physiology
J. Royal Inst. Chem.	Journal of the Royal Institute of Chemistry
J. Hist. Phil. Life Sci.	Journal of the History and Philosophy of the Life Sciences
J. Proc. Linn. Soc.	Journal of the Proceedings of the Linnean Society of London
J. Queckett Micro. Club	Journal of the Queckett Microscopical Club
J. Soc. Bibliphy Nat. Hist.	Journal of the Society of the Bibliography of Natural History
Jewish Soc. Stud.	Jewish Social Studies
Lit. Gaz.	Literary Gazette
Lond. Med. Gaz.	London Medical Gazette
Macmillan's Mag.	Macmillan's Magazine
McClure's Mag.	McClure's Magazine
Med. Times Gaz.	Medical Times and Gazette
Mem. Geol. Surv. India	Memoirs of the Geological Survey of India
Mem. Geol. Surv. U.K.	Memoirs of the Geological Survey of the United Kingdom
Nat. Hist. Rev.	Review of Natural History
Nat. Sci.	Natural Science
National Rev.	National Review
Nin. Cent.	Nineteenth Century
North Am. Rev.	North American Review
Notes Rec. Royal Soc.	Notes and Records of the Royal Society of London

Perspect. Biol. Med.	Perspectives in Biology and Medicine
Phil. Mag.	Philosophical Magazine
Phil. Trans. Royal Soc.	Philosophical Transactions of the Royal Society of London
Proc. Am. Ass. Adv. Sci.	Proceedings of the American Association for the Advancement of Science
Proc. Aus. Phil. Soc.	Proceedings of the Australian Philosophical Society
Proc. Camb. Phil. Soc.	Proceedings of the Philosophical Society of Cambridge
Proc. Linn. Soc.	Proceedings of the Linnean Society of London
Proc. Philad. Acad. Nat. Sci.	Proceedings of the Philadelphia Academy of Natural Science
Proc. Royal Inst.	Proceedings of the Royal Institution of London
Proc. Royal Soc.	Proceedings of the Royal Society of London
Proc. Royal Soc. Edin.	Proceedings of the Royal Society of Edinburgh
Proc. Zool. Soc.	Proceedings of the Zoological Society of London
Quart. J. Micro. Soc.	Quarterly Journal of the Microscopical Society of London
Quart. Rev.	Quarterly Review
Rev. Engl. Stud.	Review of English Studies
Rev. Quest. Sci.	Revue de questions scientifiques
Royal Coll. Sci. Mag.	Magazine of the Royal College of Science
Sat. Rev.	Saturday Review
Sci. Am.	Scientific American
Scrib. Mag.	Scribner's Magazine
Smithsonian Rep.	Smithsonian Reports
Southern Quart.	Southern Quarterly
Stud. Hist. Biol.	Studies in the History of Biology
Stud. Hist. Phil. Sci.	Studies in the History and Philosophy of Science
Trans. Am. Phil. Soc.	Transactions of the American Philosophical Society
Trans. Edin. Geol. Soc.	Transactions of the Edinburgh Geological Society
Trans. Ethnol. Soc.	Transactions of the Ethnological Society
Trans. Geol. Soc.	Transactions of the Geological Society
Trans. Inst. Brit. Geog.	Transactions of the Institute of British Geographers

Trans. Linn. Soc.	Transactions of the Linnean Society
Trans. Micro. Soc.	Transactions of the Microscopical Society
Trans. Royal Irish Acad.	Transactions of the Royal Irish Academy
Trans. S. Afr. Phil. Soc.	Transactions of the South African Philosophical Society
Trans. Zool. Soc.	Transactions of the Zoological Society
Univ. Edin. J.	Journal of Edinburgh University
Univ. Toronto Quart.	University of Toronto Quarterly
Vict. Stud.	Victorian Studies
West Rev.	Westminster Review
Wiss. Zeitschr. der Friedrich-Schiller Uni. Jena	Wissenschaftliche Zeitschriften der Friedrich-Schiller Universität Jena
Zeitsch.	(Tiedemann's) Zeitschrift für Physiologie
Zool. Res.	Zoological Researches

BIBLIOGRAPHY

This bibliography is divided into four sections.

Section A contains unpublished material from archives.

Section B is a list of Huxley's works. This does not claim to be complete but contains everything I was able to find. Little is likely to be missing. Items published anonymously are indicated by (A). The works are listed chronologically, and within each year as follows:
1. books and pamphlets;
2. articles reprinted in *The Scientific Memoirs of Thomas Henry Huxley*;
3. articles reprinted in *Collected Essays*;
4. works not reprinted in either of these;
5. works written in collaboration with others.

Section C contains works on Huxley, alphabetically arranged; some of these are taken from Mrs. Pingree's files.

Section D contains an alphabetical list of other works of relevance.

Section A

The Huxley Papers (*HP*) and the Huxley Manuscripts (*HM*), Imperial College of Science and Technology, London.

The Darwin Papers (*Dar.*), Manuscripts Room, University Library, Cambridge.

The Owen Papers (*OP*), British Museum (Natural History), London.

Section B

1. "On a Hitherto Undescribed Structure in the Human Hair Sheath," *London Med. Gaz.* 1 (1845): 1340; *The Scientific Memoirs of Thomas Henry Huxley* (hereafter *Scientific Memoirs*), vol. 1, pp. 1–3.
2. "Examination of the Corpuscles of the Blood of Amphioxus lanceolatus" (1847), *Brit. Ass. Rep.*, part ii, p. 95; *Scientific Memoirs*, vol. 1, pp. 4–5.
3. "On the Anatomy and the Affinities of the Medusae," *Phil. Trans. Royal Soc.* (1849), part ii, p. 413; *Scientific Memoirs*, vol. 1, pp. 9–32.
4. "Description of the Animal of Trigonia, from Actual Dissection," *Proc. Zool. Soc.* 17 (1849): 30–32; *Ann. Mag. Nat. Hist.* 5 (1850): 141–43; *Scientific Memoirs*, vol. 1, pp. 6–8.

5. "Notes on Medusae and Polypes," *Ann. Mag. Nat. Hist.* 6 (1850): 66–67; *Scientific Memoirs*, vol. 1, pp. 33–35.

6. "Observations sur la circulation chez les mollusques des genres Firole et Atlante" (extraites d'une lettre addressée à M. Milne-Edwards), *Ann. Sci. Nat.* 14 (1850): 193–95; *Scientific Memoirs*, vol. 1, pp. 36–37.

7. "Observations upon the Anatomy and Physiology of Salpa and Pyrosoma," *Phil. Trans. Royal Soc.* (1851), part ii, pp. 567–94; *Ann. Mag. Nat. Hist.* 9 (1852): 242–44; *Scientific Memoirs*, vol. 1, pp. 38–68.

8. "Remarks upon Appendicularia and Doliolum, Two Genera of the Tunicata," *Phil. Trans. Royal Soc.* (1851), part ii, pp. 595–606; *Scientific Memoirs*, vol. 1, pp. 69–79.

9. "Zoological Notes and Observations Made on Board H.M.S. 'Rattlesnake' During the Years 1846–50," *Ann. Mag. Nat. Hist.* 7 (ser. 2) (1851): 304–06, 370–74; 8:433–42; *Scientific Memoirs*, vol. 1, pp. 80–95.

10. "Observations on the Genus Sagitta," *Brit. Ass. Rep.* (1852), part ii, pp. 77–78; *Scientific Memoirs*, vol. 1, pp. 96–97.

11. "An Account of Researches into the Anatomy of the Hydrostatic Acalephae," *Brit. Ass. Rep.* (1852), part ii, pp. 78–80; *Scientific Memoirs*, vol. 1, pp. 98–101.

12. "Description of a New Structure of Sponge-like Animal," *Brit. Ass. Rep.* (1852), part ii, p. 80; *Scientific Memoirs*, vol. 1, p. 102.

13. "Report upon the Researches of Prof. Müller into the Anatomy and Development of the Echinoderms," *Ann. Mag. Nat. Hist.* 8 (ser. 2) (1851): 1–19; *Scientific Memoirs*, vol. 1, pp. 103–21.

14. "Über die Sexualorgane der Diphydae und Physophoridae" (1851), *Müllers Archiv für Anatomie, Physiologie und Wissenschaftliche Medicin*, pp. 380–84; *Scientific Memoirs*, vol. 1, pp. 122–25.

15. "Lacinularia socialis: A Contribution to the Anatomy and Physiology of the Rotifera," *Trans. Micro. Soc.* (n.s.) 1 (1853): 1–19 (read 31 Dec. 1851); *Scientific Memoirs*, vol. 1, pp. 126–45.

16. "Upon Animal Individuality," *Proc. Royal Inst.* 1 (1851–54): 184–89 (abstract of discourse delivered on 30 April 1852); *Scientific Memoirs*, vol. 1, pp. 146–51.

17. "On the Morphology of the Cephalous Mollusca, as illustrated by the Anatomy of Certain Heteropoda and Pteropoda Collected During the Voyage of H.M.S. 'Rattlesnake' in 1846–50," *Phil. Trans. Royal Soc.* 143 (1853), part i, pp. 29–66; *Scientific Memoirs*, vol. 1, pp. 152–93.

18. "Researches into the Structure of the Ascidians," *Brit. Ass. Rep.* (1852), part ii, pp. 76–77; *Scientific Memoirs*, vol. 1, pp. 194–96.

19. "On the Anatomy and Development of Echinococcus veterinorum," *Proc. Zool. Soc.* 20 (1852): 110–26; *Scientific Memoirs*, vol. 1, pp. 197–215.

20. "On the Identity and Structure of Plants and Animals," *Proc. Royal Inst.* 1 (1851–54): 298–302 (delivered 1853); *Edin. New Phil. J.* 53 (1853): 172–77; *Scientific Memoirs*, vol. 1, pp. 216–20.

21. "Observations on the Existence of Cellulose in the Tunic of Ascidians," *Quart. J. Micro. Sci.* 1 (1853): 22–24; *Scientific Memoirs*, vol. 1, pp. 221–23.

22. "On the Development of the Teeth, and on the Nature and Import of Nasmyth's 'Persistent Capsule'," *Quart. J. Micro. Sci.* 1 (1853): 149–64; *Scientific Memoirs*, vol. 1, pp. 224–41.

23. "The Cell-Theory" (review), *Brit. For. Med.-Chir. Rev.* 12 (1853): 285–314; *Scientific Memoirs*, vol. 1, pp. 242–78.

24. *(Taylor's) Scientific Memoirs*, "Natural History," ed. A. Henfrey and T. H. Huxley (1853).

25. "Fragments Relating to Philosophical Zoology, Selected from the Works of K. E. von Baer," *(Taylor's) Scientific Memoirs*, "Natural History" 3 (1853): 176–238.

26. *On the Educational Value of the Natural History Sciences* (London, 1854: originally an address delivered at St. Martin's Hall and printed as a pamphlet); *Collected Essays*, vol. 3, *Science and Education*, pp. 38–65; *Lay Sermons, Addresses and Reviews* (1870).

27. "Vestiges of the Natural History of Creation, Tenth Edition" (review), *Brit. For. Med.-Chir. Rev.* 13 (1854): 425–39; *Scientific Memoirs*, suppl., pp. 1–19.

28. "On the Vascular System of the Lower Annulosa," *Brit. Ass. Rep.* (1855), part ii, p. 109; *Scientific Memoirs*, vol. 1, pp. 279–80.

29. "On the Common Plan of Animal Forms" (delivered 12 May 1854), *Proc. Royal Inst.* 1 (1851–54): 444–46; *Scientific Memoirs*, vol. 1, pp. 281–83.

30. "On the Structure and Relation of the Corpuscula Tactus (Tactile Corpuscles or Axile Corpuscles) and the Pacinian Bodies," *Quart. J. Micro. Sci.* 2 (1854): 1–7; *Scientific Memoirs*, vol. 1, pp. 284–90.

31. "On the Ultimate Structure and Relations of the Malpighian Bodies of the Spleen and of the Tonsillar Follicles," *Quart. J. Micro. Sci.* (1854): 74–82; *Scientific Memoirs*, vol. 1, pp. 291–99.

32. "Contributions to the Anatomy of the Brachiopoda," *Proc. Royal Soc.* 7 (1854–55): 106–17, 241–42; *Scientific Memoirs*, vol. 1, pp. 325–36.

33. "Professor Edward Forbes, F. R. S." (obituary), *Lit. Gaz.* (1854): 1016–18 (A).

34. "Science at Sea," *West. Rev.* 5 (n.s.) (1854): 98–119 (A).

35. "Schamyl, the Prophet-Warrior of the Caucasus," *West. Rev.* 5 (n.s.) (1854): 480–519 (A).

36. "Science" (notices), *West Rev.* 5 (n.s.) (1854): 254–70, 580–95; 6 (1854): 42–56, 572–80; 7 (1855): 239–53, 558–63; 8 (1855): 240–55, 5–74; 9 (1856): 261–71 (A) (? vols. 8 and 9).

37. "On Certain Zoological Arguments Erroneously Adduced in Favour of the Hypothesis of the Progressive Development of Animal Life in Time," *Proc. Royal Inst.* 2 (1854–58): 82–85 (delivered 1855); *Scientific Memoirs*, vol. 1, pp. 300–04.

38. "On Hermaphrodite and Fissiparous Species of Tubicolar Annelidae," *Edin. New Phil. J.* 1 (1855): 113–29; *Scientific Memoirs*, vol. 1, pp. 337–50.

39. "On the Structure of Noctiluca miliaris," *Quart. J. Micro. Sci.* 3 (1855): 49–54; *Scientific Memoirs*, vol. 1, pp. 351–56.

40. "On the Enamel and Dentine of the Teeth," *Quart. J. Micro. Sci.* 3 (1855): 127–30; *Scientific Memoirs*, vol. 1, pp. 357–60.

41. "Memoir on Physalia," *Proc. Linn. Soc.* 2 (1855): 3–5; *Scientific Memoirs*, vol. 1, pp. 361–62.

42. "On the Anatomy of Diphyes, and on the Unity of Composition of the Diphidae and Physophoridae, etc.," *Proc. Linn. Soc.* 2 (1855): 67–69; *Scientific Memoirs*, vol. 1, pp. 363–64.

43. "Principles of (General and) Comparative Physiology," by W. B. Carpenter, M. D., F. R. S., 4th edn. London: "Churchill, 1854" (review), *West. Rev.* 7 (n.s.) (1855): 239–53, 241–47 (A).

44. "Mollusca," in C. Knight, ed., *English Cyclopedia, Natural History*, vol. 3 (1855), pp. 855–74 (A).

45. "Tegumentary Organs" (1855–56), in R. B. Todd, ed., *The Cyclopedia of Anatomy and Physiology; Scientific Memoirs*, vol. 1, pp. 365–431.

46. "On Natural History as Knowledge, Discipline, and Power," *Proc. Royal Inst.* 2 (1854–58): 187–95 (delivered 15 Feb. 1856); *Scientific Memoirs*, vol. 1, pp. 305–14.

47. "Lectures on General Natural History," *Med. Times Gaz.* 12 (1856): 429–32, 481–84, 507–11, 563–67, 618–28; 13 (1856): 27–30, 131–34, 157–60, 278–81, 383–86, 462–63, 537–38, 586–88, 635–38; 14 (1857): 133–35, 181–83, 255–57, 353–55, 505–08, 638–40; 15 (1857): 159–62, 186–89, 238–41, 467–71.

48. "On the Method of Palaeontology," *Ann. Mag. Nat. Hist.* 18 (1856): 43–54; *Scientific Memoirs*, vol. 1, pp. 432–44.

49. "Observations on the Structure and Affinities of Himantopterus," *Quart. J. Geol. Soc.* 12 (1856): 34–37; *Scientific Memoirs*, vol. 1, pp. 445–48.

50. "Further Observations on the Structure of Appendicularia Flabellum (Chamisso)," *Quart. J. Geol. Sci.* 4 (1856): 181–91; *Scientific Memoirs*, vol. 1, pp. 449–60.

51. "Note on the Reproductive Organs of the Cheilostome Polyzoa," *Quart. J. Micro. Sci.* 4 (1856): 191–92; *Scientific Memoirs*, vol. 1, pp. 461–62.

52. "On the Present State of Knowledge as to the Structure and Function of Nerve," *Proc. Royal Inst.* 2 (1854–58): 432–37 (delivered 15 May 1857); *Med. Times Gaz.* 15 (1857): 1–2; *Scientific Memoirs*, vol. 1, pp. 315–20.

53. "Description of a New Crustacean (Pygocephalus Cooperi, Huxley) from the Coal-Measures," *Quart. J. Geol. Soc.* 12 (1857): 363–69; *Scientific Memoirs*, vol. 1, pp. 463–70.

54. "On Dysteria, a New Genus of Infusoria," *Quart. J. Micro. Sci.* 5 (1857): 78–82; *Scientific Memoirs*, vol. 1, pp. 471–75.

55. "Dr. Hannover's Memoir 'Über die Entwickelung und den Bau des Säugethierzahns' " (review), *Quart. J. Micro. Sci.* 5 (1857): 166–71; *Scientific Memoirs*, vol. 1, pp. 476–81.

56. "Letter to Mr. Tyndall on the Structure of Glacier Ice," *Phil. Mag.* 14 (1857): 241–60: *Scientific Memoirs*, vol. 1, pp. 482–501.

57. "Glaciers and Glacier Theories," *West. Rev.* 11 (n.s.) (1857): 418–44 (A).

58. *On Tape and Cystic Worms*, by C. Th. E. von Siebold (translated from German for the Sydenham Society) (London, 1857).

59. Contribution to *Icones Zootomicae*, by J. V. Carus (Leipzig, 1857).

60. "On Cephalaspis and Pteraspis," *Quart. J. Geol. Soc.* 14 (1858): 267–80; *Scientific Memoirs*, vol. 1, pp. 502–16.

61. "On the Phenomenon of Gemmation," *Proc. Royal Inst.* 2 (1854–58): 534–38 (delivered 21 May 1858); *Am. J. Sci. Arts* 38 (1859): 206–09; *Scientific Memoirs*, vol. 1, pp. 321–24.

62. "Observations on the Genus Pteraspis," *Brit. Ass. Rep.* (1858), part ii, pp. 82–83; *Scientific Memoirs*, vol. 1, pp. 517–21.

63. "On a New Species of Pleiosaurus (*P. Etheridgii*) from Street, near Glastonbury; with Remarks on the Structure of the Atlas and Axis Vertebrae and of the Cranium in that Genus," *Quart. J. Geol. Soc.* 14 (1858): 281–94; *Scientific Memoirs*, vol. 1, pp. 522–37.

64. "On the Theory of the Vertebrate Skull," *Proc. Royal Soc.* 9 (1857–59): 381–457; abridged in *Ann. Mag. Nat. Hist.* 3 (1859): 414–39; *Scientific Memoirs*, vol. 1, pp. 538–606.

65. "On the Structure and Motion of Glaciers," *Phil. Trans. Royal Soc.* 147 (1857): 327–46; *Scientific Memoirs*, vol. 2, pp. 1–25.

66. "On the Agamic Reproduction and Morphology of Aphis," *Trans. Linn. Soc.* 22 (1858): 193–220, 221–36; *Scientific Memoirs*, vol. 2, pp. 26–80.

67. "Glaciers and Glacier Theories," *Sat. Rev.* 6 (1858): 58–59 (A).

68. "The Clouds," *Sat. Rev.* 6 (1858): 207–08 (A).

69. "Chalk, Ancient and Modern," *Sat. Rev.* 6 (1858): 500–02 (A).

70. *The Oceanic Hydrozoa* (London, 1859); a short abstract with review appears in *Nat. Hist. Rev.* 7 (1860): 1–11.

71. "On Some Points in the Anatomy of Nautilus pompilius," *J. Linn. Soc. (Zool.)* (1859): 36–44; *Scientific Memoirs*, vol. 2, pp. 81–89.

72. "On the Persistent Types of Animal Life" (June 1859), *Proc. Royal Inst.* 3 (1858–62): 151–53; *Scientific Memoirs*, vol. 2, pp. 90–93.

73. "On the Stagonolepis Robertsoni (Agassiz) of the Elgin Sandstone; and on the Recently Discovered Footmarks in the Sandstones of Cummingstone," *Quart. J. Geol. Soc.* 15 (1859): 440–60; *Scientific Memoirs*, vol. 2, pp. 94–119.

74. "On Some Amphibian and Reptilian Remains from South Africa and Australia," *Quart. J. Geol. Soc.* 15 (1859): 642–49; *Scientific Memoirs*, vol. 2, pp. 120–29.

75. "On a New Species of Dicynodon (D. Murrayi) from near Colesberg, South Africa; and on the Structure of the Skull in Dicynodonts," *Quart. J. Geol. Soc.* 15 (1859): 649–58; *Scientific Memoirs*, vol. 2, pp. 130–40.

76. "On Rhamphorhynchus Bucklandi, A Pterosaurian from the Stonesfield Slate," *Quart. J. Geol. Soc.* 15 (1859): 658–70; *Scientific Memoirs*, vol. 2, pp. 141–56.

77. "On a Fossil Bird and a Fossil Cetacean from New Zealand," *Quart. J. Geol. Soc.* 15 (1859): 670–77; *Scientific Memoirs*, vol. 2, pp. 157–65.

78. "On the Dermal Armour of Crocodilus Hastingsiae," *Quart. J. Geol. Soc.* 15 (1859): 678–80; *Scientific Memoirs*, vol. 2, pp. 166–69.

79. "British Fossils. Part 1—On the Anatomy and Affinities of the Genus Pterogotus," *Mem. Geol. Surv. U.K.*, mon. 1 (1859): 1–36; *Scientific Memoirs*, vol. 2, pp. 170–202.

80. "On Daryceps Bucklandi (Labyrinthodon Bucklandi, Lloyd)," *Mem. Geol. Surv. U.K.* (1859): 52–56; *Scientific Memoirs*, vol. 2, pp. 263–68.

81. "On a Fragment of a Lower Jaw of a Large Labyrinthodont from Cubbington," *Mem. Geol. Surv. U.K.* (1859): 56–57; *Scientific Memoirs*, vol. 2, pp. 269–70.

82. "Observations on the Development of Some Parts of the Skeleton of Fishes," *Quart. J. Micro. Sci.* 7 (1859): 33–46; *Scientific Memoirs*, vol. 2, pp. 271–85.

83. "The Darwinian Hypothesis," *The Times*, 26 Dec. 1859; *Collected Essays*, vol. 2, pp. 1–21 (A).

84. "Time and Life: Mr. Darwin's *Origin of Species*," *Macmillan's Mag.* 1 (1859): 142–48.

85. "Structure of Glaciers," *Sat. Rev.* 7 (1859): 333–35 (A).

86. "The Theory of Glaciers," *Sat. Rev.* 8 (1859): 80–81 (A).

87. "On the Dermal Armour of Jacare and Caiman, with Notes on the Specific and Generic Characters of Recent Crocodilia," *J. Linn. Soc. (Zool.)* 4 (1860): 1–28: *Scientific Memoirs*, vol. 2, pp. 286–312.

88. "On Species and Races and Their Origin," *Ann. Mag. Nat. Hist.* 5 (1860): 344–46; *Proc. Royal Inst.* 3 (1858–62): 195–200; *Scientific Memoirs*, vol. 2, pp. 388–94.

89. "On the Structure of the Mouth and Pharynx of the Scorpion," *Quart. J. Micro. Sci.* 8 (1860): 250–54; *Scientific Memoirs*, vol. 2, pp. 395–99.

90. "On the Nature of the Earliest Stages of the Development of Animals," *Proc. Royal Inst.* 3 (1858–62): 315–17; *Scientific Memoirs*, vol. 2, pp. 400–02.

91. "The Origin of Species," *West. Rev.* 17 (n.s.) (1860): 541–70; *Collected Essays*, vol. 2, pp. 22–79 (A).

92. "On the Study of Zoology" (1860), *Lectures Addressed to Teachers*; reprinted as "A Lobster, or the Study of Zoology" in *Collected Essays*, vol. 8, pp. 196–228 (erroneously dated 1861).

93. "The Glaciers of the Alps," *Sat. Rev.* 10 (1860): 81–83 (A).

94. "On a New Species of Macrauchenia (M. boliviensis)," *Quart. J. Geol. Soc.* 26 (1861): 73–84; *Scientific Memoirs*, vol. 2, pp. 403–16.

95. "On Pteraspis dunensis (Archaeoteuthis dunensis, Roemer)," *Quart. J. Geol. Soc.* 26 (1861): 163–65; *Scientific Memoirs*, vol. 2, pp. 417–20.

96. "Preliminary Essay upon the Systematic Arrangement of the Fishes of the Devonian Epoch" (1861), *Mem. Geol. Surv. U.K.: Figures and Descriptions Illustrative of British Organic Remains*; *Scientific Memoirs*, vol. 2, pp. 421–60.

97. "Glyptolaemus Kinnairdi," *Mem. Geol. Surv. U.K.* (1861): 41–46; *Scientific Memoirs*, vol. 2, pp. 461–66.

98. "Phaneropleuron Andersoni," *Mem. Geol. Surv. U.K.* (1861): 47–49; *Scientific Memoirs*, vol. 2, pp. 467–71.

99. "On the Zoological Relations of Man with the Lower Animals," *Nat. Hist. Rev.* 1 (n.s.) (1861): 67–84; *Scientific Memoirs*, vol. 2, pp. 471–92.

100. "On the Brain of Ateles paniscus," *Proc. Royal Soc.* (1861): 247–60; *Scientific Memoirs*, vol. 2, pp. 493–508.

101. "Letter to the *Athenaeum* on the Brain . . ." (30 March 1861), *Athenaeum* (1861): 433.

102. "On the Anatomy and Development of Pyrosoma," *Trans. Linn. Soc.* 23 (1862): 193–250; *Scientific Memoirs*, vol. 2, pp. 313–87.
103. "On Fossil Remains of Man" (1862), *Proc. Royal Inst.* 3 (1858–62): 420–22; *Scientific Memoirs*, vol. 2, pp. 509–11; *Med. Times Gaz.* 24 (1862): 159–61.
104. "Geological Contemporaneity and Persistent Types of Life" (anniversary address to the Geological Society), *Quart. J. Geol. Soc.* 18 (1862): xl–liv; *Scientific Memoirs*, vol. 2, pp. 512–29; *Collected Essays*, vol. 3, pp. 272–304; *Lay Sermons, Addresses and Reviews* (London, 1870).
105. "On New Labyrinthodonts from the Edinburgh Coal-Field," *Quart. J. Geol. Soc.* 18 (1862): 29–96; *Scientific Memoirs*, vol. 2, pp. 530–35.
106. "On a Stalk-Eyed Crustacean from the Carboniferous Strata near Paisley," *Quart. J. Geol. Soc.* 18 (1862): 420–22; *Scientific Memoirs*, vol. 2, pp. 536–38.
107. "On the Premolar Teeth of Diprotodon, and on a New Species of That Genus," *Quart. J. Geol. Soc.* 18 (1862): 422–27; *Scientific Memoirs*, vol. 2, pp. 539–45.
108. "On the Methods and Results of Palaeontology" (report), *Med. Times Gaz.* 24 (1862): 36.
109. "The Brain of Man and Apes" (letter, 25 Oct. 1862), *Med. Times Gaz.* 25 (1862): 449.
110a. *Evidence as to Man's Place in Nature* (London, 1863); reprinted [110b] in *Collected Essays*, vol. 7, pp. 1–208.
111. *On Our Knowledge of the Causes of the Phenomena of Organic Nature* (London, 1863); reprinted in *Collected Essays*, vol. 2, pp. 303–475.
112. "Description of a New Species of Glyptodon Recently Acquired by the Royal College of Surgeons of England" (1863), *Proc. Royal Soc.* 12 (1862–63): 316–26; *Scientific Memoirs*, vol. 2, pp. 546–55; *Med. Times Gaz.* 26 (1863): 705–07, 233–34.
113. "Letter on the Human Remains Found in the Skull-Mounds," *Trans. Ethnol. Soc.* 2 (1863): 265–66; *Scientific Memoirs*, vol. 2, pp. 556–57.
114. "Description of Anthracosaurus Russelli, a New Labyrinthodont from the Lanarkshire Coal-Field," *Quart. J. Geol. Soc.* (1863); 56–68; *Scientific Memoirs*, vol. 2, pp. 558–72.
115. "Six Lectures on Classification at the Royal College of Surgeons," *Med. Times Gaz.* 26 (1863): 259–62, 285–86, 311–14, 337–39, 363–65, 391–93, 417–19, 443–46, 471–72, 499–500, 527–30, 553–56, 607–10, 633–35.
116. "Lectures on the Vertebrate Skull," *Med. Times Gaz.* 26 (1863): 607–10, 633–35; 27 (1863): 1–6, 57–58, 107–10, 189–92, 371–74, 425–29, 475–78, 529–31, 579–80, 607–09, 633–36, 663–68.
117. *Lectures on the Elements of Comparative Anatomy* (London, 1864).
118. "Further Remarks upon the Human Remains from the Neanderthal," *Nat. Hist. Rev.* 4 (n.s.) (1864): 429–46; *Scientific Memoirs*, vol. 2, pp. 573–90.
119. "On the Angwántibo (Arctocebus calabarensis, Gray) of Old Calabar," *Proc. Zool. Soc.* (1864): 314–45; *Scientific Memoirs*, vol. 2, pp. 591–612.

120. "On the Cetacean Fossil termed 'Ziphius' by Cuvier, with a Notice of a New Species (Bolemnoziphius compressus) from the Red Crag," *Quart. J. Geol. Soc.* 20 (1864): 388–96; *Scientific Memoirs*, vol. 3, pp. 1–10.

121. "On the Structure of the Belemnitidae; with a Description of a More Complete Specimen of 'Belemnites' Than Any Hitherto Known, and an Account of a New Genus of Belemnitidae 'Xiphoteuthis'," *Mem. Geol. Surv. U.K.: Figures and Descriptions Illustrative of British Organic Remains* 2 (1864); *Scientific Memoirs*, vol. 3, pp. 11–36.

122. "On the Osteology of the Genus Glyptodon," *Phil. Trans. Royal Soc.* 155 (1865): 31–70 (written in Dec. 1863, read Jan. 1864); *Scientific Memoirs*, vol. 3, pp. 37–84.

123. "Criticisms of 'The Origin of Species'," *Nat. Hist. Rev.* 4 (n.s.) (1864): 566–80 (published anonymously); *Collected Essays*, vol. 2, pp. 80–106; also in *Lay Sermons, Addresses and Reviews* (London, 1870).

124. "Hunterian Lectures on the Structure and Classification of Mammalia" (abstracts), *Med. Times Gaz.* 28 (1864), 153–54, 177–78, 203–04, 229–30, 256–57, 284–85, 312–13, 343–44, 369–70, 398–99, 428–29, 456–57, 486–87, 509–10, 537–38, 564–65, 595–96, 617–18, 647–48, 671–72.

125. "Hunterian Lectures on the Structure and Classification of the Mammalia" (report), *The Reader* 3 (1864): 205–06, 239–40, 266–68, 300–01, 330–31, 364–65, 493–94, 525–26.

126. "The Negro's Place in Nature," letter to *The Reader* 3 (12 March 1864): 334–35.

127. "On the Structure of the Stomach in Desmodus rufus," *Proc. Zool. Soc.* (1865): 386–90; *Scientific Memoirs*, vol. 3, pp. 85–89.

128. "On a Collection of Vertebrate Fossils from the Panchet Rocks, Ranigunj, Bengal" (1865), *Mem. Geol. Surv. India: Palaeontologia Indica, ser. 4: Indian Protertiary Vertebrata*, vol. 1, pp. 3–24; *Scientific Memoirs*, vol. 3, pp. 90–120.

129. "On the Methods and Results of Ethnology" (1865), *Proc. Royal Inst.* 4 (1862–66): 461–63 (abstract and report); *Scientific Memoirs*, vol. 3, pp. 121–24.

130. "Explanatory Preface to the Catalogue of the Palaeontological Collection in the Museum of Practical Geology" (1865) (originally the preface to the catalogue compiled by Etheridge), *Scientific Memoirs*, vol. 3, pp. 125–79; reprinted as "Principles and Methods of Palaeontology," *Smithsonian Rep.* (1869): 363–88; written in 1859.

131. "Emancipation—Black and White," *The Reader* 5 (20 May 1865): 561–62; *Collected Essays*, vol. 3, pp. 66–75; also in *Lay Sermons, Addresses and Reviews* (London, 1870).

132. "On the Methods and Results of Ethnology" *Fort. Rev.* 1 (1865): 257–77; *Collected Essays*, vol. 7, pp. 209–52.

133. *Lessons in Elementary Physiology* (London, 1866); enlarged by J. Bancroft in 1915.

134. "British Fossils. Illustrations on the Structure of the Crossopterygian Ganoids" (1866), *Mem. Geol. Surv. U.K., Decade xii; Scientific Memoirs*, supplement, pp. 20–68.

135. "Notes on the Human Remains," in S. Laing, *Prehistoric Remains of Caithness* (London, 1866).
136. "On a Collection of Fossil Vertebrates, from the Jarrow Colliery, County of Kilkenny, Ireland," *Trans. Royal Irish Acad.* 24 (1871): 351–69 (read 1866); *Scientific Memoirs*, vol. 3, pp. 180–97.
137. "On Some Remains of Large Dinosaurian Reptiles from the Stormberg Mountains, South Africa," *Quart. J. Geol. Soc.* 23 (1867): 1–6 (read 1866); *Scientific Memoirs*, vol. 3, pp. 198–204.
138. "On a New Specimen of Telerpeton Elginense," *Quart. J. Geol. Soc.* 23 (1867): 77–84 (read 1966); *Scientific Memoirs*, vol. 3, pp. 205–13.
139. "On the Advisableness of Improving Natural Knowledge," *Fort. Rev.* 3 (1866): 626–37; *Collected Essays*, vol. 1, pp. 18–41.
140. "Address to St. Mary's Hospital," *Med. Times Gaz.* 32 (1866): 534–37.
141. "Letter to the *Pall Mall Gazette* on the Jamaica Committee," *Pall Mall Gazette* 4 (31 Oct. 1866): 3.
142. "On Two Widely Contrasted Forms of the Human Cranium," *J. Anat. Physiol.* 1 (1867): 60–77; *Scientific Memoirs*, vol. 3, pp. 214–30.
143. "On Acanthopholis horridus, a New Reptile from the Chalk-Marl," *Geol. Mag.* 4 (1867): 65–67; *Scientific Memoirs*, vol. 3, pp. 231–34.
144. "On the Classification of Birds; and on the Taxonomic Value of the Modifications of Certain of the Cranial Bones Observable in That Class," *Proc. Zool. Soc.* (1867): 415–72; *Scientific Memoirs*, vol. 3, pp. 239–97.
145. "On 'Saurosternon Bainii' and 'Pristerodon McKayi,' Two New Fossil Lacertilian Reptiles from South Africa," *Geol. Mag.* 5 (1868): 201–05; *Scientific Memoirs*, vol. 3, pp. 298–302.
146. "On the Animals Which Are Most Nearly Intermediate Between Birds and Reptiles," *Geol. Mag.* 5 (1868): 357–65; *Scientific Memoirs*, vol. 3, pp. 303–13; *Ann. Mag. Nat. Hist.* 2 (1868): 66–75; a short report also in *Med. Times Gaz.* 36 (1868): 184–85.
147. "On the Form of the Cranium Among the Patagonians and Fuegians, with Some Remarks upon American Crania in General," *J. Anat. Physiol.* 2 (1868): 253–71; *Scientific Memoirs*, vol. 3, pp. 314–29.
148. "On Some Organisms Living at Great Depths in the North Atlantic Ocean," *Quart. J. Micro. Sci.* 8 (n.s.) (1868): 203–12; *Scientific Memoirs*, vol. 3, pp. 330–39.
149. "Remarks upon Archaeopterix lithographica," *Proc. Royal Soc.* 16 (1868): 243–48; *Scientific Memoirs*, vol. 3, pp. 340–45.
150. "On the Classification and Distribution of the Alectoromorphae and Heteromorphae," *Proc. Zool. Soc.* (1868): 294–319; *Scientific Memoirs*, vol. 3, pp. 346–73.
151. "On the Physical Basis of Life," *Fort. Rev.* 5 (n.s.) (1868): 129–45; *Collected Essays*, vol. 1, pp. 130–65; also in *Lay Sermons, Addresses and Reviews* (London, 1870); a report also appeared in *Med. Times Gaz.* 38 (1869): 248–49.
152. "A Liberal Education and Where to Find It," *Macmillan's Mag.* 17 (1868): 367–78; *Collected Essays*, vol. 3, pp. 76–110; also in *Lay Sermons, Addresses and Reviews* (London, 1870).

153. "On a Piece of Chalk," *Macmillan's Mag.* 18 (1868): 396–408; *Collected Essays*, vol. 8, pp. 1–36; also in *Lay Sermons, Addresses and Reviews* (London, 1870).

154. "Reply to Objections on My Classification of Birds," *Ibis* 4 (1868): 357–62.

155. "Lectures on the Invertebrates at the Royal College of Surgeons," *Med. Times Gaz.* 36 (1868): 151, 208, 235–36, 265–67, 292–93, 320–21, 344–45, 398–99, 450–51, 504–06, 583–85.

156. "Speech at the Prehistoric Congress at Norwich," *Med. Times Gaz.* 37 (1868): 271 (very short report).

157. "Questions 7954–8032 of *Select Committee on Scientific Instruction, Report to Be Printed*" (London, 1868).

158. *An Introduction to the Classification of Animals* (London, 1869).

159. *The Views of Hume, Kant, and Whately upon the Logical Basis of the Doctrine of the Immortality of the Soul* (17 Nov. 1869, printed for the Metaphysical Society).

160. "On Hyperodapedon," *Quart. J. Geol. Soc.* 25 (1869): 138–52; *Scientific Memoirs*, vol. 3, pp. 374–90.

161. "On a New Labyrinthodont from Bradford," *Quart. J. Geol. Soc.* 25 (1869): 309–11; *Scientific Memoirs*, vol. 3, pp. 391–93.

162. "On the Upper Jaw of Megalosaurus," *Quart. J. Geol. Soc.* 25 (1869): 311–14; *Scientific Memoirs*, vol. 3, pp. 394–96.

163. "Geological Reform" (anniversary address of the president to the Geological Society of London), *Quart. J. Geol. Soc.* 25 (1869): xxviii–liii; *Scientific Memoirs*, vol. 3, pp. 397–426; *Collected Essays*, vol. 8, pp. 305–39; also in *Lay Sermons, Addresses and Reviews* (London, 1870).

164. "On the Ethnology and Archaeology of India" (opening address of the president of the Ethnological Society of London), *J. Ethnol. Soc.* 1 (n.s.) (1869): 89–93; *Scientific Memoirs*, vol. 3, pp. 427–31.

165. "On the Ethnology and Archaeology of North America" (address of the president to the Ethnological Society of London), *J. Ethnol. Soc.* 1 (n.s.) (1869): 218–21; *Scientific Memoirs*, vol. 3, pp. 432–35.

166. "On the Representatives of the Malleus and the Incus of the 'Mammalia' in the Other 'Vertebrata'," *Proc. Zool. Soc.* (1869): 391–407; *Scientific Memoirs*, vol. 3, pp. 436–53.

167. "On the Classification of the Dinosauria, with Observations on the Dinosauria of the Trias," *Quart. J. Geol. Soc.* 26 (1870): 32–50; *Scientific Memoirs*, vol. 3, pp. 487–509.

168. "The Natural History of Creation—by Dr. Ernst Haeckel (*Natürliche Schöpfungsgeschichte* von Dr. Ernst Haeckel, Professor an der Universität Jena, Berlin, 1868)," *The Academy* 1 (1869): 12–14, 40–43; *Collected Essays*, vol. 2, pp. 107–19 (abridged under the title "The Genealogy of Animals"); also in *Lay Sermons, Addresses and Reviews* (London, 1870).

169. "Scientific Education: Notes of an After-Dinner Speech," *Macmillan's Mag.* 20 (1869): 177–84; *Collected Essays*, vol. 3, pp. 111–33.

170. "The Scientific Aspects of Positivism," *Fort. Rev.* 5 (n.s.) (1869): 653–70;

also in *Lay Sermons, Addresses and Reviews* (London, 1870; new edn., London, 1880), pp. 147–73.

171. "Nature: Aphorisms by Goethe" (1869), *Nature* 1 (1869–70): 9–11.

172. "Triassic Dinosauria" (1869), *Nature* 1 (1869–70): 23–24; *Scientific Memoirs*, vol. 3, pp. 599–600.

173. *Lay Sermons, Addresses and Reviews* (London, 1870).

174. *Has a Frog a Soul, and of What Nature Is That Soul, Supposing It to Exist?* (1870, printed for the Metaphysical Society).

175. "On Hypsilophodon Foxii, a New Dinosaurian Form from the Wealden of the Isle of Wight," *Quart. J. Geol. Soc.* 26 (1870): 3–12; *Scientific Memoirs*, vol. 3, pp. 454–64.

176. "Further Evidence of the Affinity Between the Dinosaurian Reptiles and Birds," *Quart. J. Geol. Soc.* 26 (1870): 12–31; *Scientific Memoirs*, vol. 3, pp. 465–86.

177. "Anniversary Address of the President to the Geological Society of London," *Quart. J. Geol. Soc.* 26 (1870): xxix–lxiv; *Scientific Memoirs*, vol. 3, pp. 510–50; partly reprinted in *Nature* 1 (1869–70): 437–43 (abridged).

178. "On the Ethnology of Britain," *J. Ethnol. Soc.* 2 (n.s.) (1870): 382–84; *Scientific Memoirs*, vol. 3, pp. 551–53.

179. "Anniversary Address of the President to the Ethnological Society of London," *J. Ethnol. Soc.* 2 (n.s.) (1870): xvi–xxiv; *Scientific Memoirs*, vol. 3, pp. 554–63.

180. "On the Geographical Distribution of the Chief Modifications of Mankind," *J. Ethnol. Soc.* 2 (n.s.) (1870): 404–12; *Scientific Memoirs*, vol. 3, pp. 564–71.

181. "Address to the British Association at Liverpool" (1870), *Brit. Ass. Rep.* (1871): lxxiii–lxxxix; *Scientific Memoirs*, vol. 3, pp. 572–94; *Collected Essays*, vol. 8, pp. 229–70; a report also in *Med. Times Gaz.* 41 (1870): 344–47.

182. "On the Milk Dentition of Palaeothesium magnum," *Geol. Mag.* 7 (1870): 153–55; *Scientific Memoirs*, vol. 3, pp. 595–98.

183. "On the Relations of Penicillium, Torula and Bacterium," *Quart. J. Micro. Sci.* 10 (n.s.) (1870): 355–62; *Scientific Memoirs*, vol. 3, pp. 601–07.

184. "On Descartes's 'Discourse Touching the Method of Using One's Reason Rightly, and of Seeking Scientific Truth'," *Macmillan's Mag.* 22 (1870): 69–80; *Collected Essays*, vol. 1, pp. 166–98; also in *Lay Sermons, Addresses and Reviews* (London, 1870).

185. "On Some Fixed Points in British Ethnology," *Cont. Rev.* 14 (1870): 511–20; *Collected Essays*, vol. 7, pp. 253–70; also in *Critiques and Addresses* (London, 1873).

186. "The School Boards: What They Can Do and What They May Do," *Cont. Rev.* 16 (1870): 1–15; *Collected Essays*, vol. 3, pp. 374–403; also in *Critiques and Addresses* (London, 1873).

187. "On Medical Education" (1870, address at University College, London), *Collected Essays*, vol. 3, pp. 294–302; also in *Critiques and Addresses* (London, 1873).

188. "On Tobacco Smoking," *Med. Times Gaz.* 41 (1870): 377 (report of Huxley's intervention at the meeting of the British Association at Liverpool, September 1870, in the discussion after R. Wilkinson's *Statistics on Tobacco, Brit. Ass. Rep.* [1870], pp. 206–07).

189. "Kant's View of Space" (1870), *Nature* 1 (1869–70): 314 (letter to the editor).

190. "The Forefathers of the English People" (1870), *Nature* 1 (1869–70): 514–15.

191. "The Deep-Sea Soundings and Geology" (1870), *Nature* 1 (1869–70): 657–58.

192. "Life in the Deep Sea," *Nature* 2 (1870): 187 (letter to the editor).

193. "Remarks on Mr. Gladstone," *Nature* 2 (1870): 414–15.

194. "Speech on Vivisection," *Nature* 2 (1870): 466 (report).

195. "Dr. Bastian and Spontaneous Generation," *Nature* 2 (1870): 473 (letter to the editor).

196. "On the Maxilla of Megalosaurus," *Phil. Mag.* 34 (1870): 385–86.

197. "On the Pedigree of the Horse," *Proc. Royal Inst.* 6 (1870): 129 (report).

198. *Essays Selected from Lay Sermons, Addresses and Reviews* (London, 1871).

199. *Manual of the Anatomy of Vertebrated Animals* (London, 1871).

200. "On Coral and Coral Reefs," *Good Words* 12 (1871): 104–12; also in *Critiques and Addresses* (London, 1873); and *Science Lectures for the People* (2nd ser.), pp. 3–17, with variations.

201. "Mr. Darwin's Critics," *Cont. Rev.* 18 (1871): 443–76; *Collected Essays*, vol. 2, pp. 120–86; also in *Critiques and Addresses* (London, 1873).

202. "Yeast," *Cont. Rev.* 19 (1871): 23–36; *Scientific Memoirs*, vol. 3, pp. 608–22; also in *Science Lectures for the People* (3rd ser.), pp. 3–16, as "On Yeast," with variations.

203. "Administrative Nihilism," *Fort. Rev.* 10 (n.s.) (1871): 525–43; *Collected Essays*, vol. 1, pp. 251–89.

204. "Bishop Berkeley on the Metaphysics of Sensation," *Macmillan's Mag.* 24 (1871): 147–60; *Collected Essays*, vol. 6, pp. 243–87.

205. "After Dinner Speech at the Royal Academy," *Med. Times Gaz.* 42 (1871): 517 (report).

206. "Prof. Huxley on Medical Education" (distributing prizes at the Charing Cross Medical Hospital), *Med. Times Gaz.* 42 (1871): 692–93 (report).

207. "Lectures on the Elementary Physiology of Motion, Consciousness and the Senses," *Med. Times Gaz.* 43 (1871): 563, 593–94, 650–51, 714–15, 743–45, 802–03 (report).

208. "The Duties of the State" (report of a speech delivered at Birmingham on 4 October 1871 as president of the Birmingham and Midland Institute), *Nature* 4 (1871): 462, 495–96.

208a. "British Fossils, Decade XIII, Plate X," *Mem. Geol. Soc. U.K.* (1872); *Scientific Memoirs*, suppl., p. 68.

209. *Critiques and Addresses* (London, 1873).

210. "The Problems of the Deep Sea" (1873), *Collected Essays*, vol. 8, pp. 37–68; *Cont. Rev.* 21 (1873): 825–41.

211. "Forbes and Tyndall," *Nature* 8 (1873): 64 (letter to the editor).
212. "On the Structure of the Skull and of the Heart of Menobranchus lateralis," *Proc. Zool. Soc.* (1874): 186–204; *Scientific Memoirs,* vol. 4, pp. 1–22.
213. "Note on the Development of the Columella Auris in the Amphibia," *Nature* 11 (1874–75): 68–69; *Brit. Ass. Rep.* (1874), part ii, pp. 141–42; *Scientific Memoirs,* vol. 4, pp. 23–25.
214. "Preliminary Note upon the Brain and Skull of Amphioxus lanceolatus," *Proc. Royal Soc.* 23 (1875): 127–32 (written 1874); *Scientific Memoirs,* vol. 4, pp. 26–31.
215. "On the Bearing of the Distribution of the Portio Dura upon the Morphology of the Skull," *Proc. Camb. Phil. Soc.* 2 (1876): 348–51 (read 1874); *Scientific Memoirs,* vol. 4, pp. 32–34.
216. "On the Classification of the Animal Kingdom," *J. Linn. Soc. (Zool.)* 12 (1876): 199–226 (read 1874); *Nature* 11 (1874–75): 101–02; *Scientific Memoirs,* vol. 4, pp. 35–60.
217. "On the Hypothesis That Animals Are Automata, and Its History" (address at Belfast, 1874), *Nature* 10 (1874): 362–66; *Collected Essays,* vol. 1, pp. 199–250; *Science and Culture, and Other Essays* (London, 1881).
218. "Universities, Actual and Ideal" (address at Aberdeen as rector of that university, 1874), *Nature* 9 (1873–74): 337–39; *Cont. Rev.* 23 (1874): 657–79; *Collected Essays,* vol. 3, pp. 189–234; also in *Science and Culture, and Other Essays* (London, 1881).
219. "Joseph Priestly," *Macmillan's Mag.* 30 (1874): 473–85; *Collected Essays,* vol. 3, pp. 1–37; also in *Science and Culture, and Other Essays* (London, 1881).
220. "Speech at Manchester" (opening of the Medical School at Owen College, 1874, report), *Nature* 10 (1874): 455–57.
221. "On the Recent Work of the 'Challenger' Expedition, and Its Bearing on Geological Problems," *Proc. Royal Inst.* 7 (1874): 354–57; *Scientific Memoirs,* vol. 4, pp. 61–65.
222. "On Stagonolepis Robertsoni, and on the Evolution of the Crocodilia," *Quart. J. Geol. Soc.* 31 (1875): 423–38; *Scientific Memoirs,* vol. 4, pp. 66–83.
223. "On Some of the Results of the Expedition of H.M.S. Challenger, " *Cont. Rev.* 25 (1875): 639–60; *Collected Essays,* vol. 8, pp. 69–109.
224. *"Antropogenie: Entwickelungsgeschichte des Menschen* von Ernst Haeckel. Zweite Auflage (Leipzig: Engelmann, 1874)," *The Academy* 139 (review) (1875): 16–18.
225. "Birds" (1875), *Encyclopaedia Britannica,* 9th ed., vol. 3, pp. 726–27 (abstract of a paper on "Respiratory and vocal organs"); see also *Nature* 13 (1875–76): 247.
226. "Notes on the Invertebrata" (lectures delivered at Edinburgh), *Med. Times Gaz.* 50 (1875): 491–96, 517–19, 545–47, 571–73, 599–601, 627–29, 655–57, 695–97.
227. "Notes from the Challenger, " *Nature* 12 (1875): 315–16.

228. *The Evidence of the Miracle of the Resurrection* (1876), printed for the Metaphysical Society.
229. "Three Lectures on Evolution" (1876), *Collected Essays,* vol. 4, pp. 46–138; also in *American Addresses* (London, 1877).
230. "Address on University Education" (delivered at Johns Hopkins University, Baltimore), *Nature* 14 (1876): 546–50; *Collected Essays,* vol. 3, pp. 235–61; also in *American Addresses* (London, 1877).
231. "Contribution to Morphology. Ichthyopsida No. 1. On Ceratodus Fosteri; with Observations on the Classification on Fishes," *Proc. Zool. Soc.* (1876): 24–59; *Scientific Memoirs,* vol. 4, pp. 84–124.
232. "On the Position of the Anterior Nasal Apertures in Lepidosiren," *Proc. Zool. Soc.* (1876): 180–81; *Scientific Memoirs,* vol. 4, pp. 125–27.
233. "On the Nature of the Craniofacial Apparatus of Petromyzon," *J. Anat. Physiol.* 10 (1876): 412–29; *Scientific Memoirs,* vol. 4, pp. 128–44.
234. "On the Border Territory Between the Animal and the Vegetable Kingdoms," *Macmillan's Mag.* 33 (1876): 373–84; *Collected Essays,* vol. 8, pp. 162–95; also in *Science and Culture, and Other Essays* (London, 1881): *Scientific Memoirs,* vol. 4, pp. 145–62.
235. "On the Evidence as to the Origin of Existing Vertebrate Animals," *Nature* 13 (1876): 388–89, 410–12, 429–30, 467–69, 514–16; 14 (1876): 33–34; *Scientific Memoirs,* vol. 4, pp. 163–87.
236. "Dinner to the 'Challenger' Staff" (report of a speech by Huxley, followed by C. Wyville Thomson's reply), *Nature* 14 (1876): 238–41.
237. *American Addresses* (London, 1877).
238. *Anatomy of Invertebrated Animals* (London, 1877).
239. *Physiography* (London, 1877).
240. "The Crocodilian Remains Found in the Elgin Sandstones, with Remarks on the Ichnites of Cummingstone" (1877), *Mem. Geol. Surv. U.K.,* mon. 3; *Scientific Memoirs,* vol. 4, pp. 188–241.
241. "On the Study of Biology," *Nature* 15 (1877): 219–24; *Amer. Nat.* 11 (1877): 210–21; *Scientific Memoirs,* vol. 4, pp. 248–64.
242. "Elementary Instruction in Physiology," *Nature* 16 (1877): 233–34; *Collected Essays,* vol. 3, pp. 294–303; also in *Science and Culture, and Other Essays* (London, 1881).
243. "Technical Education," *Fort. Rev.* 23 (n.s.) (1877): 48–58; *Collected Essays,* vol. 3, pp. 404–26.
244. "A Note on the Number of Species of Insects" (1877), *Nature* 15 (1876–77): 275.
245. "A Modern Symposium: Influence upon Morality of a Decline in Religious Belief," *Nin. Cent.* 1 (1877): 536–39.
246. "A Modern Symposium: The Soul and Future Life," *Nin. Cent.* 2 (1877): 334–41.
247. "On the Geological History of Birds," *Proc. Royal Inst.* 8 (1877): 347–48.
248. *Hume* (London, 1878); reprinted in *Collected Essays,* vol. 6, pp. 3–240.
249. "Address to the Anthropological Department of the British Association, Dublin, 1878. Informal Remarks on the Conclusions of Anthropology," *Nature* 18 (1878): 445–48; *Scientific Memoirs,* vol. 4, pp. 265–74.

250. "On the Classification and the Distribution of the Crayfishes," *Proc. Zool. Soc.* (1878): 752–88; *Scientific Memoirs*, vol. 4, pp. 275–315.
251. "On a New Arrangement for Dissecting Microscopes" (president's address, 1878), *J. Quekett Micro. Club* 5 (1878–79): 144–45; *Scientific Memoirs*, vol. 4, pp. 316–18.
252. "William Harvey," *Fort. Rev.* 23 (n.s.) (1878): 169–90; also in *Scientific Memoirs*, vol. 4, pp. 319–44; also in *Science Lectures for the People*, as "The Circulation of the Blood," pp. 5–24 (with variations); also a report in *Med. Times Gaz.* 56 (1878): 625–26.
253. "Evolution in Biology" (1878), *Encyclopaedia Britannica*, 9th edn., vol. 8: 744–51; *Collected Essays*, vol. 2, pp. 187–226; also in *Science and Culture, and Other Essays* (London, 1881).
254. "On the Use of Historical National Names and Scientific Terms," *Nature* 18 (1878): 479–80 (report of Huxley's intervention after A. C. Lewes read his paper "On the Evils Arising from the Use of Historical National Names and Scientific Terms").
255. "Obituary Notices of Fellows Deceased; Karl Ernst von Baer," *Proc. Royal Soc.* 27 (1878): i–v (A).
256. "Report on the Promotion of Technical Education," in *Livery Companies Committee: Report on Technical Education* (London, 1878).
257. *The Crayfish: An Introduction to the Study of Zoology* (London, 1879).
258. "On the Characters of the Pelvis in the Mammalia, and the Conclusions Respecting the Origin of Mammals Which May Be Based on Them," *Proc. Royal Soc.* 28 (1879): 395–405; *Scientific Memoirs*, vol. 4; pp. 345–56.
259. "On Sensation and the Unity of Structure of Sensiferous Organs," *Nin. Cent.* 5 (1879): 597–611; *Scientific Memoirs*, vol. 4, pp. 357–73; *Collected Essays*, vol. 6, pp. 288–319.
260. "The President's Address" (1879), *J. Quekett Micro. Club* 5 (1878–79): 250–55; *Scientific Memoirs*, vol. 4, pp. 374–79.
261. "On Certain Errors Respecting the Structure of the Heart Attributed to Aristotle," *Nature* 21 (1879): 1–5; *Scientific Memoirs*, vol. 4, pp. 380–92; also in *Science and Culture, and Other Essays* (London, 1881).
262. "Prefatory Note to E. Haeckel, *Freedom in Science and Teaching* (English translation)" (London, 1879).
263. *Introductory Science Primer* (London, 1880); see 359.
264. "On the Epipubis in the Dog and Fox" (1880), *Proc. Royal Soc.* 30 (1879–80): 162–63; *Scientific Memoirs*, vol. 4, pp. 393–94; a report in *Nature* 21 (1880): 362.
265. "The Coming of Age of the Origin of Species," *Nature* 22 (1880): 1–4; *Scientific Memoirs*, vol. 4, pp. 395–403; *Collected Essays*, vol. 2, pp. 227–43; also in *Science and Culture, and Other Essays* (London, 1881).
266. "On the Cranial and Dental Characters of the Canidae," *Proc. Zool. Soc.* (1880): 238–88; *Scientific Memoirs*, vol. 4, pp. 404–56.
267. "On the Application of the Laws of Evolution to the Arrangement of the Vertebrata and More Particularly of the Mammalia," *Proc. Zool. Soc.* (1880): 649–61; *Scientific Memoirs*, vol. 4, pp. 457–72; report in *Nature* 23 (1880–81): 227–31.

268. "Science and Culture" (1880), *Collected Essays*, vol. 3, pp. 134–59; also in *Science and Culture, and Other Essays* (London, 1881).

269. "On the Method of Zadig," *Nin. Cent.* 7 (1880): 929–40; *Collected Essays*, vol. 4, pp. 1–23.

270. "The First Volume of the Publications of the 'Challenger'" (1880), *Nature* 23 (1880–81): 1–3 (correction of a misprint, ibid., p. 33).

271. *Science and Culture, and Other Essays* (London, 1881).

271a. "The Herring" (1881), *Nature* 23 (1880–81): 607–13; *Scientific Memoirs*, vol. 4, pp. 473–92.

272. "The Connection of the Biological Sciences with Medicine," *Nature* 24 (1881): 342–46; *Scientific Memoirs*, vol. 4, pp. 493–507.

273. "The Rise and Progress of Palaeontology," *Nature* 24 (1881): 452–55; *Scientific Memoirs*, vol. 4, pp. 508–19; *Collected Essays*, vol. 4, pp. 24–45; also in *Essays on Some Controverted Questions* (London, 1892).

274. "A Contribution to the Pathology of the Epidemic known as the 'Salmon Disease'," *Proc. Royal Soc.* 33 (1882): 381–89; *Scientific Memoirs*, vol. 4, pp. 520–28.

275. "On the Respiratory Organs of Apteryx," *Proc. Zool. Soc.* (1882): 560–69; *Scientific Memoirs*, vol. 4, pp. 529–39.

276. "On Saprolegnia in Relation to the Salmon Disease," *Quart. J. Micro. Sci.* 22 (n.s.) (1882): 311–33; *Scientific Memoirs*, vol. 4, pp. 540–62.

277. "Charles Darwin" (1882, obituary), *Nature* 25 (1881–82): 597; *Collected Essays*, vol. 2, pp. 244–47.

278. "On Science and Art in Relation to Education" (1882), *Nature* 27 (1883): 396–98; *Collected Essays*, vol. 3, pp. 160–88.

279. "A Glimpse Through the Corridors of Time," *Nature* 25 (1881–82): 241 (letter to the editor).

280. "On Education" (1882, report of a speech at Liverpool Institute), *Nature* 27 (1882–83): 187–89.

281. "Contribution to Morphology. Ichthyopsida—No. 2. On the Oviducts of Osmerus; with Remarks on the Relations of the Teleostean with the Ganoid Fishes," *Proc. Zool. Soc.* (1883): 132–39; *Scientific Memoirs*, vol. 4, pp. 563–71.

282. "Oysters and the Oyster Question" (1883), *Proc. Royal Soc.* 10 (1884): 336–58; *Engl. Ill. Mag.* (1883–84): 47–55, 112–21; *Scientific Memoirs*, vol. 4, pp. 572–609.

283. "Evolution, as Illustrated by the Pearly Nautilus" (the Rede Lecture), *Nature* 28 (1883): 187–89; *Scientific Memoirs*, supplement, pp. 69–79.

284. "Presidential Address to the Royal Society" (1883), *Proc. Royal Soc.* 36 (1883–84): 60–73; *Nature* 29 (1883–84): 136–40.

285. "Inaugural Address: Fisheries Exhibition, London, 1883," *The Fisheries Exhibition Literature* 4 (1885): 3–22.

286. "Unwritten History (of Egypt)," *Macmillan's Mag.* 48 (1883): 26–41.

287. "State Intervention in Medical Affairs" (report), *Med. Times Gaz.* 67 (1883): 428–29, 436–37 (delivered at the London Hospital).

288. "Address at Finsbury Technical College" (1883), *Nature* 29 (1883–84): 158 (report).

289. "The State and the Medical Profession" (revised version of speech at the London Hospital, 1883), *Nin. Cent.* 15 (1884): 228–38; *Collected Essays,* vol. 3, pp. 323–46.

290. "On Parasites in Mackerel," *Nature* 30 (1884): 199 (letter to J. L. Sayer).

291. "The Darwin Memorial" (1885), *Collected Essays,* vol. 2, pp. 248–52.

292. "The Interpreters of Genesis and the Interpreters of Nature," *Nin. Cent.* 18 (1885): 849–60; *Collected Essays,* vol. 4, pp. 139–63; also in *Essays on Some Controverted Questions* (London, 1892).

293. "Presidential Address to the Royal Society," *Proc. Royal Soc.* 39 (1885): 278–99; *Nature* 33 (1885–86): 112–19.

294. "Mr. Gladstone and Genesis," *Nin. Cent.* 19 (1886): 191–205; *Collected Essays,* vol. 4, pp. 164–200; also in *Essays on Some Controverted Questions* (London, 1892).

295. "The Evolution of Theology: An Anthropological Study," *Nin. Cent.* 19 (1886): 346–65, 485–506; *Collected Essays,* vol. 4, pp. 287–372.

296. "Science and Morals," *Fort. Rev.* 40 (1886): 788–802; *Collected Essays,* vol. 9, pp. 117–46; also in *Essays on Some Controverted Questions* (London, 1892).

297. "From the Hut to the Pantheon," *The Youth's Companion* (1886).

298. *Memorandum of Proceedings at a Drawing-Room Meeting for the Promotion of Technical Education Held at the House of E. C. Robins on the Evening of the 5th March 1887, Under the Presidency of Professor Huxley* (London, privately printed, 1887), pp. 39–40.

299. "Preliminary Note on the Fossil Remains of a Chelonian Reptile, Ceratochelys Sthenurus, from Lord Howe's Island, Australia," *Proc. Royal Inst.* 42 (1887): 232–38; *Nature* 35 (1886–87): 615–17; *Scientific Memoirs,* vol. 4, pp. 606–11.

300. "Further Observations upon Hyperodapedon Gordoni," *Quart. J. Geol. Soc.* 43 (1887): 675–94; *Scientific Memoirs,* vol. 4, pp. 636–57.

301. "The Progress of Science," in T. H. Ward, *The Reign of Queen Victoria* (London, 1887), vol. 2, pp. 322–87; *Collected Essays,* vol. 1, pp. 42–129.

302. "Address on Behalf of the National Association for the Promotion of Technical Education" (1887), *Collected Essays,* vol. 3, pp. 427–51.

303. "Scientific and Pseudo-scientific Realism," *Nin. Cent.* 21 (1887): 191–205; *Collected Essays,* vol. 5, pp. 59–89; also in *Essays on Some Controverted Questions* (London, 1892).

304. "Science and Pseudo-science," *Nin. Cent.* 21 (1887): 481–98; *Collected Essays,* vol. 5, pp. 90–125; also in *Essays on Some Controverted Questions* (London, 1892).

305. "An Episcopal Trilogy," *Nin. Cent.* 22 (1887): 625–40; *Collected Essays,* vol. 5, pp. 126–59; also in *Essays on Some Controverted Questions* (London, 1892).

306. "On the Reception of the Origin of Species," in F. Darwin, *The Life and Letters of Charles Darwin* (London, 1887), vol. 2, pp. 179–204.

307. "The Imperial Institute" (1887), *Nature* 35 (1886–87): 265–66.

308. "On the True Functions of the Imperial Institute" (letter to *The Times,* January 1887), *Nature* 35 (1886–87): 304–05.

309. "The Organisation of Industrial Education" (letter, 1887), *Nature* 35 (1886–87): 493.
310. "The Connection Between Science and Art and Literature," *Nature* 36 (1887): 14 (report of a speech at the Royal Academy, 5 May 1887).
311. "The British Race-Types of Today" (letter to *The Times*, October 1887), *Nature* 36 (1887): 563 (report and abstract).
312. "Politics and the Presidency of the Royal Society," *Nature* 37 (1887): 49–51 (A).
313. "An Olive-Branch from America," *Nin. Cent.* 22 (1887): 620–24.
314. Passage on W. B. Carpenter's *Principles of . . . Physiology*, in Carpenter, *Nature and Man: Essays Scientific and Philosophical* (London, 1887), pp. 66–67.
315. "The Struggle for Existence in Human Society," *Nin. Cent.* 23 (1888): 161–80; *Collected Essays*, vol. 9, pp. 195–236.
316. "The Value of Witness to the Miraculous," *Nin. Cent.* 24 (1889): 438–53; *Collected Essays*, vol. 5, pp. 160–91; also in *Essays on Some Controverted Questions* (London, 1892).
317. "Obituary Notices of Fellows Deceased; Charles Robert Darwin," *Proc. Royal Soc.* 44 (1888): i–xxiv; *Collected Essays*, vol. 2, pp. 253–302.
318. "The Gentians: Notes and Queries," *J. Linn. Soc. (Bot.)* 24 (1888): 101–24; *Scientific Memoirs*, vol. 4, pp. 612–35.
319. "The Duke of Argyll's Charges Against Men of Science" (9 February 1888), *Nature* 37 (1887–88): 342 (letter to the editor).
320. "Agnosticism," *Nin. Cent.* 25 (1889): 169–94; *Collected Essays*, vol. 5, pp. 209–62; also in *Essays on Some Controverted Questions* (London, 1892).
321. "Agnosticism: A Rejoinder," *Nin. Cent.* 25 (1889): 481–504; *Collected Essays*, vol. 5, pp. 263–308; also in *Essays on Some Controverted Questions* (London, 1892).
322. "Agnosticism and Christianity," *Nin. Cent.* 25 (1889): 937–64; *Collected Essays*, vol. 5, pp. 309–65; also in *Essays on Some Controverted Questions* (London, 1892).
323. "Prof. Huxley and M. Pasteur on Hydrophobia" (letter of 25 June 1889, reported 4 July 1889), *Nature* 40 (1889): 224–25.
324. "Autobiography," in L. Engel, ed., *From Handel to Hallé: Biographical Sketches with Autobiographies of Professor Huxley and Professor Herkomer* (London, 1890); *Royal Coll. Sci. Mag.* 3 (1890): 33–40; 7 (1894): 65–72; *Hosp. Gaz.* (23 May 1891): 7–11; *Collected Essays*, vol. 1, pp. 1–17; *see also* De Beer, Gavin (*q.v. infra*, no. 432, 1974).
325. "The Natural Inequality of Men," *Nin. Cent.* 27 (1890): 1–23; *Collected Essays*, vol. 1, pp. 290–335.
326. "Natural Rights and Political Rights," *Nin. Cent.* 27 (1890): 173–95; *Collected Essays*, vol. 1, pp. 336–82.
327. "Capital the Mother of Labour," *Nin. Cent.* 27 (1890): 513–32; *Collected Essays*, vol. 9, pp. 147–87.
328. "Government: Anarchy or Regimentation," *Nin. Cent.* 27 (1890): 843–66; *Collected Essays*, vol. 1, pp. 383–430.

329. "The Lights of the Church and the Light of Science," *Nin. Cent.* 28 (1890): 5–22; *Collected Essays*, vol. 4, pp. 201–38; also in *Essays on Some Controverted Questions* (London, 1892).

330. "The Aryan Question and Pre-Historic Man," *Nin. Cent.* 28 (1890): 750–77; *Collected Essays*, vol. 7, pp. 271–328.

331. "The Keepers of the Herd of Swine," *Nin. Cent.* 28 (1890): 967–79; *Collected Essays*, vol. 5, pp. 366–92; also in *Essays on Some Controverted Questions* (London, 1892).

332. "On Medical Education" (letter to *The Times*, 4 August 1890), *Nature* 42 (1890): 353 (report).

333. *Social Diseases and Worse Remedies* (London, 1891) (originally letters to *The Times*, Dec. 1890–Jan. 1891); *Collected Essays*, vol. 9, pp. 237–334.

334. "Possibilities and Impossibilities" (1891), *Agnostic Annual* (1892); *Collected Essays*, vol. 5, pp. 192–208.

335. "Illustrations of Mr. Gladstone's Controversial Methods," *Nin. Cent.* 29 (1891): 455–67; *Collected Essays*, vol. 5, pp. 393–419; also in *Essays on Some Controverted Questions* (London, 1892).

336. "Hasisadra's Adventure," *Nin. Cent.* 29 (1891): 904–24; *Collected Essays*, vol. 4, pp. 239–86; also in *Essays on Some Controverted Questions* (London, 1892).

337. *Essays on Some Controverted Questions* (London, 1892); "Prologue" reprinted in *Collected Essays*, vol. 5, pp. 1–58.

338. "An Apologetic Irenicon," *Fort. Rev.* 52 (n.s.) (1892): 557–71.

339. "Science and the State," *Nature* 46 (1892): 416 (letter to the editor, 1 Sept.).

340. "Gib diesen Todten mir heraus" (memorial verses to Tennyson), *Nin. Cent.* 32 (1892): 831–32.

341. "Introductory Letter" to T. J. Parker, *William Kitchen Parker: a Biographical Sketch* (London, 1893): pp. xi–xv.

342. *Collected Essays* (London, 1893–94): vol. 1, *Method and Results*; vol. 2, *Darwiniana*; vol. 3, *Science and Education*; vol. 4, *Science and Hebrew Tradition*; vol. 5, *Science and Christian Tradition*; vol. 6, *Hume, with Helps to the Study of Berkeley*; vol. 7, *Man's Place in Nature*; vol. 8, *Discourses, Biological and Geological*; vol. 9, *Evolution and Ethics, and Other Essays*.

343. *Evolution and Ethics* (London, 1893); *Collected Essays*, vol. 9, pp. 46–116.

344. "Two Statements" (2 Feb. 1893), *Nature* 47 (1892–93): 316 (letter to the editor).

345. "Prolegomena to Evolution and Ethics" (1894); *Collected Essays*, vol. 9, pp. 1–45.

346. "Owen's Position in the History of Anatomical Science" (1894), in Rev. Richard Owen, *The Life of Richard Owen* (London, 1894), vol. 2, pp. 273–332; *Scientific Memoirs*, vol. 4, pp. 658–89.

347. "Professor Tyndall" (obituary), *Cont. Rev.* 35 (1894): 1–11.

348. "Past and Present" (1894), *Nature* 51 (1894–95): 1–3.

349. "Report of a Speech," *The Times* (9 Aug. 1894).

350. "Report of a Speech," *The Times* (1 Dec. 1894).
351. "Palaeontology and the Royal School of Mines" (3 Jan. 1895), *Nature* 51 (1894–95): 223 (letter to the editor).
352. "Mr. Balfour's Attack on Agnosticism," *Nin. Cent.* 37 (1895): 527–40.
353. Preface to first edn. of G. B. Howes, *Atlas of Elementary Zootomy* (London, 1902).
354. *T. H. Huxley's Diary of H.M.S. Rattlesnake* (ed. J. S. Huxley, London, 1935).
355. *The Scientific Memoirs of Thomas Henry Huxley* (ed. M. Foster and E. R. Lankester, London, 1898–1903).
356. *Kölliker's Manual of Human Histology* (tr. and ed. T. H. Huxley and G. Busk, London, 1853).
357. *An Elementary Atlas of Comparative Anatomy, in Twelve Plates* (with B. W. Hawkins, London, 1864).
358. *The Elements of Physiology and Hygiene: (a Textbook for Educational Institutions)* (with W. J. Youmans, New York, 1868).
359. *Science Primers* (with H. E. Roscoe and S. Balfour, eds., London, 1874).
360. *A Course of Practical Instruction in Elementary Biology* (with H. N. Martin, London, 1875; later edn. 1877; rev. by G. B. Howes and D. H. Scott, 1888).
361. *Report on the Specimen of the Genus Spirula Collected by H.M.S. Challenger* (with P. Pelseneer, London, 1895) (report of scientific results of the voyage of H.M.S. *Challenger*, appendix [Zoology part 83]).
362. *Evolution and Ethics, 1893–1943* (with J. S. Huxley, London, 1947).
363. *Poems. See* Huxley, Henrietta Anna, 738 (1913).
364. "Recent Science," *Nin. Cent.* 1 (1877): 156–76; 2 (1877): 309–28, 884–98; 3 (1878): 548–66, 1133–53; 4 (1878): 149–67, 765–84; 5 (1879): 890–907; 6 (1879): 728–45; 7 (1880): 521–37; 8 (1880): 844–60: articles by J. Knowles, aided and revised by T. H. Huxley.

Section C

365. Anonymous, *Report of a Sad Case Recently Tried Before the Lord Mayor, Owen versus Huxley* . . . (London, 1863).
366. Anonymous, *Protoplasm, Powheads, Porwiggles and the Evolution of the Horse from the Rhinoceros, Illustrating Professor Huxley's Scientific Mode of Setting Up the Creation and Upsetting Moses* (London, 1875).
367. Anonymous, "On the Relations of Man to the Inferior Animals," *Anthro. Rev.* 1 (1863): 107–17.
368. Anonymous, (a) "Evidence as to Man's Place in Nature," *Med. Times Gaz.* 26 (1863): 218–19; (b) Letter of "Studens Perplexus," ibid. 308–09.
369. Anonymous, "Man's Place in Nature," *Nat. Hist. Rev.* 3 (1863): 381–84.
370. Adam, I., "A Huxley Echo in 'Middlemarch'," *Notes and Queries* 209 (1964): 227.
371. Adams, R. M., "T. H. Huxley and His Clan," *Sci. Am.* 219 (1968): 135–39.
372. Armstrong, A., "Samuel Wilberforce v. T. H. Huxley: A Retrospect," *Quart. Rev.* 296 (1958): 426–37.

373. Armstrong, H. E., "Huxley's Message in Education," in "The Centenary of Huxley," *Nature* 115 (1925): 697–752, 743–47.

374. _____, *Our Need to Honour Huxley's Will* (London, 1933).

375. Armytage, W., "Matthew Arnold and T. H. Huxley: Some New Letters, 1870–1880," *Rev. Engl. Stud.* 4(n.s.) (1953): 346–53.

376. Ashforth, A. A., *Thomas Henry Huxley* (New York, 1969).

377. Avebury, John Lubbock, Lord, "Huxley's Life and Work," *Nature* 63 (1900): 92–96, 116–19.

378. Ayres, G., *Huxley* (New York, 1932).

379. Balfour, J. H., "Proposed Alterations in the Medical Curriculum," *Nature* 9 (1873): 121–22 (about Huxley's proposals while rector at Aberdeen).

380. Bartholomew, M., "Huxley's Defence of Darwin," *Ann. Sci.* 32 (1975): 525–35.

381. Barrett, M., *H.M.S. Rattlesnake's Australia–New Guinea Cruise, 1846 to 1850* (Melbourne, 1966).

382. Bastian, H. C., "Reply to Professor Huxley's Inaugural Address at Liverpool on the Question of the Origin of Life," *Nature* 2 (1870): 410–13, 431–34.

383. _____, *The Modes of Origin of Lowest Organisms; Including a Discussion of the Experiments of M. Pasteur, and a Reply to Some Statements by Professors Huxley and Tyndall* (London and New York, 1871).

384. Bateson, W., "Huxley and Evolution," in "The Centenary of Huxley," *Nature* 115 (1925): 697–752, 715–17.

385. Beale, E., *Kennedy of Cape York* (Adelaide, 1970) (Huxley took part in the beginning of Kennedy's ill-fated expedition).

386. Beckett, E., *A Review of Hume and Huxley on Miracles* (London, 1883).

387. Bibby, C., "The Huxley-Wilberforce Debate: A Postscript," *Nature* 176 (1955): 363.

388. _____, "The South London Working Man's College: A Forgotten Venture," *Adult Ed.* 28 (1955): 211–21.

389. _____, "T. H. Huxley and the Training of Teachers," *Ed. Rev.* 8 (1956): 137–45.

390. _____, "A Victorian Experiment in International Education," *Brit. J. Ed. Stud.* 5 (1956): 25–36.

391. _____, "T. H. Huxley and the Universities of Scotland," *Aberdeen Univ. Rev.* 37 (1957): 134–49.

392. _____, "Science as an Instrument of Culture: An Examination of the Views of T. H. Huxley," *Researches and Studies* 15 (1957).

393. _____, "Thomas Henry Huxley and University Development," *Vict. Stud.* 2 (1958): 97–116.

394. _____, *T. H. Huxley, Scientist, Humanist and Educator* (London, 1959).

395. _____, *Scientist Extraordinary: The Life and Scientific Work of Thomas Henry Huxley, 1825–95* (London, 1972).

396. _____, "T. H. Huxley and Medical Education," *Charing Cross Hosp. Gaz.* 54 (1956): 191–95.

397a. _____, ed., *The Essence of T. H. Huxley* (London, 1967).

397b. _____, ed., *T. H. Huxley on Education: A Selection from His Writings* (London, 1971).

398. Birmingham, University of, *Huxley Memorial Lectures, 1914* (contributions by O. Lodge, M. Foster, E. B. Poulton, P. Gardner, H. Bergson, J. Joly).
399. Blake, C. C., "Evidence as to Man's Place in Nature," *Edin. Rev.* 117 (1863): 541–69 (A).
400. Blinderman, C. S., "Thomas Henry Huxley," *Sci. Mon.* 84 (1957): 171–82.
401. _____, "The Oxford Debate and After," *Notes and Queries* 202 (1957): 126–28.
402. _____, "T. H. Huxley's Theory of Aesthetics: Unity in Diversity," *J. Aesth. Art. Crit.* 21 (1962): 49–55.
403. _____, "Semantic Aspects of T. H. Huxley's Literary Style," *J. Comm.* 12 (1962): 171–78.
404. _____, "T. H. Huxley: A Revaluation of His Philosophy," *Rationalist Annual* (1966): 50–62.
405. _____, "Thomas Henry Huxley and the Jews," *Jewish Soc. Stud.* 25 (1969): 57–61.
406. _____, "The Great Bone Case," *Perspect. Biol. Med.* 14 (1971): 370–93.
406a. _____, "Huxley, Pater and Protoplasm," *J. Hist. Ideas* 43 (1982): 477–86.
407. Boys, C. V., "Personal Impressions," in "The Centenary of Huxley," *Nature* 115 (1925): 697–752, 751.
408. Bower, F. O., "Teaching of Biological Science," in "The Centenary of Huxley," *Nature* 115 (1925): 697–752, 712–14.
409. Brodrick, G. C., "Professor Huxley: Personal Reminiscences," *Fort. Rev.* 58 (n.s.) (1895): 308–12.
410. Brooks, W. K., "The Lesson of the Life of Huxley," *Ann. Rep. Smithsonian Inst.* (1901): 701–11.
411. Browne, E. J., "The Charles Darwin-Joseph Hooker Correspondence: An Analysis of Manuscript Resources and Their Use in Biography," *J. Soc. Bibliography Nat. Hist.* 8 (1978): 351–66 (part deals with the Oxford meeting).
412. Cadman, S., *Charles Darwin and Other English Thinkers* (London, 1911): 45–87 (Huxley).
413. Cambridge, University of, *Speeches Delivered by the Public Orator in the Senate House of Cambridge* (10 June 1879): 5–6 (citation of Huxley for Hon. LL.D.).
414. Carpenter, W. B., Bishop of Ripon, "The Bishop of Ripon on Huxley and Science," *Nature* 54 (1896): 31–32.
415. Clark, R. W., *The Huxleys* (London, 1968).
416. Clarke, W., *Huxley and Phillips Brooks* (London, n.d.).
417. Clodd, E., *Pioneers of Evolution, from Thales to Huxley* (London, 1897; rev. edn. 1907).
418. _____, *Thomas Henry Huxley* (London, 1902).
419. _____, *Memories* (London, 1916).
420. _____, "Evolution and Man," in "The Centenary of Huxley," *Nature* 115 (1925): 697–752, 724–26.
421. *See* 432a (1858).
422. Cockerell, T. D. A., "Huxley's Message to the Modern World," in "The Centenary of Huxley," *Nature* 115 (1925): 697–752, 750.

423. Cockshut, A., *The Unbelievers: English Agnostic Thought, 1840–1890* (London, 1964), pp. 86–98 (Huxley).

424. Cohen, C., *God and the Universe: Eddington, Jeans, Huxley and Einstein, with a Reply by A. S. Eddington* (London, no date).

425. Courtney, J. E., *Freethinkers of the Nineteenth Century* (London, 1920), pp. 138–70 (Huxley).

426. Courtney, W. L., "Professor Huxley as a Philosopher," *Fort Rev.* 58 (n.s.) (1895): 317–22.

427. Dallas, W. S., "Science," *West. Rev.* 23 (1863): 580–90 (review of *Evidence as to Man's Place in Nature*: 584–85 [A]).

428. Dana, J. D., "Evidence as to Man's Place in Nature," *Am. J. Sci. Arts* 35 (n.s.) (1863): 451–54 (signed J.D.D.).

429. Davitashvili, L. Sh., "V. O. Kowalewsky and T. H. Huxley as Naturalist-Evolutionists" (in Russian), *Tr. Inst. Ist. Est.* 3 (1949): 351–67.

430. Davis, J. R. A., *Thomas H. Huxley* (London, 1907).

431. Dawson, W. R., ed., *The Huxley Papers* (catalogue) (London 1946).

432. De Beer, G., ed., *Charles Darwin and Thomas Henry Huxley: Autobiographies* (Oxford, 1974).

432a. Dewey, J., "Evolution and Ethics," *The Monist* 8 (1858): 321–44.

433. Di Gregorio, M. A., "On the Side of the Apes: T. H. Huxley and the Method and Results of Science" (unpublished Ph.D. thesis, London University, 1979).

434. _____, "The Dinosaur Connection: A Reinterpretation of T. H. Huxley's Evolutionary View," *J. Hist. Biol.* 15 (1982): 397–418.

435. _____, "Order or Process of Nature: Huxley's and Darwin's Different Approaches to Natural Sciences," *J. Hist. Phil. Life Sci.* 2 (1981): 217–41.

436. Dockrill, D. W., "The Origin and Development of Nineteenth-Century English Agnosticism," *Hist. J.* (Univ. of Newcastle, New South Wales) (1971): 3–31.

437. _____, "T. H. Huxley and the Meaning of Agnosticism," *Theology* 74 (1971): 461–77.

438. Drachman, J. M., *Studies in the Literature of Natural Science* (New York, 1936) (Huxley, pp. 294–385).
Dundreary, Lord. *See* 487.

439. Dyster, F. D., "Evidence as to Man's Place in Nature," *The Reader* 1 (1863): 234–35 (signed F.D.D.).

440. Eisen, S., "Huxley and the Positivists," *Vict. Stud.* 7 (1964): 337–58.

441. Ellegård, A., "Public Opinion and the Press: Reactions to Darwinism," *J. Hist. Ideas* 19 (1958): 379–87 (refers to Oxford meeting).

442. Elvin, L., *White Paper or Black Reaction?* (Huxley Memorial Lecture 1973).

443. Eng, E., "Thomas Henry Huxley's Understanding of Evolution," *Hist. Sci.* 16 (1978): 291–303.

444. Fiske, J., "Reminiscences of Huxley," *Ann. Rep. Smithsonian Inst.* (1901): 713–28.

445. Falconer, H., "On Professor Huxley's Attempted Refutation of Cuvier's Laws of Correlation in the Reconstruction of Extinct Vertebrate Form," *Ann. Mag. Nat. Hist.* 17 (1856): 476–93.

446. Flower, W. H., "Reminiscences of Professor Huxley," *North Am. Rev.* 161 (1895): 279–86.
447. Foden, F. E., "Popular Science Examinations of the Nineteenth Century," *J. Royal Inst. Chem.* 87 (1963): 6–9.
448. Foskett, D. J., "Wilberforce and Huxley on Evolution," *Nature* 172 (1953): 920.
449. Foster, M., "Obituary Notices of Fellows Deceased: Thomas Henry Huxley," *Proc. Royal Soc.* 59 (1895–96): xlvi–lxvi.
450. _____, "A Few More Words on Thomas Henry Huxley," *Nature* 52 (1895): 318–20.
451. _____, "Recent Advances in Science and Their Bearing on Medicine and Surgery," *Nature* 54 (1896): 580–83.
452. _____, "Thomas Henry Huxley," *National Rev.* 43 (1904): 421–39.
453a. Friday, J., "A Microscopic Incident in a Monumental Struggle: Huxley and Antibiosis in 1875," *Brit. J. Hist. Sci.* 7 (1974): 61–71.
453b. Gardner, J. H., "A Huxley Essay as 'Poem'," *Vict. Stud.* 14(1970): 177–91.
454. Geddes, P., "Huxley as Teacher" in "The Centenary of Huxley," *Nature* 115 (1925): 697–752: 740–43.
   Geison, G. L. *See* 693.
455. Gill, T. R., "Huxley and His Work," *Ann. Rep. Smithsonian Inst.* (1895): 759–79.
456. Gilmour, T. S. L., *British Botanists* (London, 1944), pp. 43–45 (Huxley).
457. Godkin, E., "Professor Huxley's Lectures," *The Nation* (28 Sept. 1876).
458. Gordon, J. D., "Doctors as Men of Letters," *Bull. New York Publ. Lib.* (1964) (Huxley, pp. 589–90).
459. Gray, P. H., "Prerequisite to an Analysis of Behaviourism: The Conscious Automaton Theory from Spalding to William Jones," *J. Hist. Beh. Sci.* 4 (1968): 365–76.
459a. Greene, J. C., *Science, Ideology and World View* (Berkeley, Los Angeles, and London, 1981), pp. 128–57 ("Darwinism as a World View") and 158–93 ("From Huxley to Huxley: Transformation in the Darwinian Credo").
460. Haeckel, E., "Thomas Henry Huxley," *Nature* 9 (1871): 257–58.
461. _____ "Thomas Huxley and Karl Vogt," *Fort. Rev.* 58 (n.s.) (1895): 464–69.
462. Hahn, G., *Thomas Henry Huxley*, pamphlet, extract from *Rev. Quest. Sci.* (Louvain, 1895).
463. Helfand, M. S., "T. H. Huxley's 'Evolution and Ethics': The Politics of Evolution and the Evolution of Politics," *Vict. Stud.* 20 (1977): 159–77.
464. Holmes, S. J., "Life, Morals and Huxley's 'Evolution and Ethics'," in *Science in the University* (Los Angeles, 1944), pp. 319–32.
465. Houghton, W. E., "The Rhetoric of T. H. Huxley," *Univ. Toronto Quart.* 18 (1949): 159–75.
466. Hunter, W., *Historical Account of Charing Cross Hospital and Medical School* (London, 1914), ch. 6.

467. Hutton, R. H., "The Great Agnostic," in *Aspects of Religious and Scientific Thought* (London, 1899); reprinted from *The Spectator* (6 July 1895): 10–11.

468. Huxley, A., *T. H. Huxley as a Man of Letters* (London, 1932).

469. _____ "T. H. Huxley and the Development of Physiology in Britain," *J. Physiol.* 263 (1976): 41P–45P.

470. Huxley, H. A., *Aphorisms and Reflections from the Works of Thomas Henry Huxley* (London, 1907).

471. Huxley, J. S., *T. H. Huxley: A New Judgment* (London, 1945); transcription of BBC broadcast.

472. Huxley, L., *The Life and Letters of Thomas Henry Huxley,* 2 vols. (London and New York, 1900).

473. Huxley, L., "Professor Huxley's Start in Life," *McClure's Mag.* 14 (1900): 564–72.

474. _____, *Thomas Henry Huxley: A Character Sketch* (London, 1920).

475. _____, "Home Memories," in "The Centenary of Huxley," *Nature* 115 (1925): 697–752, 698–702.

476. *Irish Church Society's Journal,* "Professor Huxley on the Hypothesis That Animals Are Automata," *Journal* 3 (1875): 1–12.

477. Irvine, W., *Apes, Angels and Victorians: A Joint Biography of Darwin and Huxley* (London, 1955).

478. _____, *Thomas Henry Huxley* (London, 1960).

479. Jensen, J. V., "The Rhetorical Influence of Thomas Henry Huxley on the United States," *Western Speech* (1967): 29–36.

480. _____, "The X-Club: Fraternity of Victorian Scientists," *Brit. J. Hist. Sci.* 5 (1970): 63–72.

481. _____, "Thomas Henry Huxley's 'Baptism into Oratory'," *Notes Rec. Royal Soc.* 30 (1976): 181–207.

482. _____, "The Most Intimate and Trusted Friend I Have," *Hist. Stud.* 68 (1977): 315–32 (on Ellen Busk, Huxley's confidante).

483. Johnstone, J., "An Unappreciated Side of Huxley's Public Life," *Royal Coll. Sci. Mag.* 15 (1903): 131–34 (on the Fisheries).

484. Jordan, A., *The Significance of Thomas Henry Huxley* (Hull, 1910, pamphlet).

485. Keith, A., "Huxley as Anthropologist," in "The Centenary of Huxley," *Nature* 115 (1925): 697–752, 719–23.

486. _____, "An Account of Five Unpublished Huxleyan Plates," *Proc. Zool. Soc.* 119 (1948–49): 839–60.

487. Kingsley, C., *Speech of Lord Dundreary in Section D: on the Great Hippocampus Question* (London, 1862).

488. Kirsch, A. M., "Professor Huxley on Evolution," *Am. Cath. Quart. Rev.* (1887): 644–64.

489. Kowalewsky, A., "Abstract of a Speech on Huxley Delivered at the Zoological Congress of 1895," *Nature* 52 (1895): 651.

490. Kropotkin, P., "Mutual Aid Among Animals," *Nin. Cent.* 28 (1890): 337–54.

491. Lankester, E. R., "Instruction to Science Teachers at South Kensington," *Nature* 4 (1871): 361–64.

492. _____, "Huxley," *Nat. Sci.* 7 (1895): 119–21.

493. _____, "Huxley's Eyes," *Nat. Sci.* 8 (1896): 285 (letter correcting T. J. Parker, 528 [1896], q.v.).

494. _____, "Huxley," in "The Centenary of Huxley," *Nature* 115 (1925): 697–752, 737–40.

495. La Vergata, A., "L'ipotesi di derivazione delle specie: l'evoluzionismo' di Charles Lyell. Due sue lettere, del 1859 e del 1862, a T. H. Huxley," *Ann. Ist. Fil. Univ. Fir.* 2 (1980):289–310.

496. Leighton, G., *Huxley: His Life and Work* (London and New York, 1912).

497. Lloyd Morgan, C., "Processes of Life and Mind," in "The Centenary of Huxley," *Nature* 115 (1925): 697–752, 737–40.

498. Lodge, O., "Introduction" to reprint of *Man's Place in Nature* (London, 1906).

Lubbock, J., *See* Avebury, 377.

499. MacBride, E. W., "Huxley's Contribution to Our Knowledge of the Invertebrates," in "The Centenary of Huxley," *Nature* 115 (1925): 697–752, 734–37.

500. _____, *Huxley* (London, 1934).

501. McCartney, J. F., "The Pedagogical Style of T. H. Huxley in 'On the Physical Basis of Life'," *Southern Quart.* 14 (1976): 97–107.

502. McCosh, J., *Agnosticism of Hume and Huxley* (Edinburgh, 1886).

503. MacLeod, R. M., "Government and Resource Conservation, the Salmon Act's Administration, 1860–1886," *J. Brit. Stud.* 7 (1968): 114–50.

504. _____, "The X–Club: A Social Network of Science in Late Victorian England," *Notes Rec. Royal Soc.* 24 (1970): 305–22.

505. Mallock, W. H., *Studies in Contemporary Superstition* (London, 1895): 48–93 (against Huxley, "Cowardly Agnosticism").

506. Marsh, O. C., "Thomas Henry Huxley," *Am. J. Sci.* 50 (3rd ser.) (1895): 177–83.

507. Marshall, A. J., *Darwin and Huxley in Australia* (Sydney, 1970).

508. Minney, R., *The Two Pillars of Charing Cross: The Story of a Famous Hospital* (London, 1967): 82–88 (Huxley).

509. Minot, C. S., "Huxley's Writings," *Int. Rev.* 11 (1881): 527–37.

510. Mitchell, P. C., "Professor Huxley on Evolution and Ethics," *Nat. Sci.* 3 (1893): 62–66.

511. Mitchell, P. C., *Thomas Henry Huxley: A Sketch of His Life and Work* (London, 1901).

512. Mivart, St. G. J., "Some Reminiscences of Thomas Henry Huxley," *Nin. Cent.* 42 (1897): 985–98.

513. _____, "Huxley as a Zoologist," *Nat. Sci.* 7 (1895): 121–25.

514. _____, "Evolution and Its Consequences: A Reply to Professor Huxley," *Essays and Criticisms* (London, 1892), 2 vols. Vol. 2, pp. 66–102.

515. Montague, A., "Introduction" to paperback edn. of *Man's Place in Nature* (Ann Arbor, 1959).

516. _____, "Introduction" to *On the Origin of Species or the Causes of the Phenomena of Organic Nature* (Ann Arbor, 1968).

517. Newth, D. R., "The Drawings of T. H. Huxley," *Med. Biol. Ill.* 6 (1956): 71–76.

518. Noland, R. W., "T. H. Huxley on Culture," *The Personalist* 42 (1964): 94–111.

519. Osborn, H. F., "Memorial Tribute to Professor Thomas H. Huxley," *Science* 3 (n.s.) (1896): 147–54.

520. _____, *Huxley on Education* (1910) (pamphlet).

521. _____, *Impressions of Great Naturalists* (New York, 1924; 2nd edn. 1928): 74–91 (Huxley).

522. _____, "Enduring Recollections" in "The Centenary of Huxley," *Nature* 115 (1925): 697–752, 726–28.

523. Ospovat, D., "Darwin on Huxley and Divergence," *Abstracts of Scientific Papers, 15th International Congress of the History of Science* (Edinburgh, 1977).

524. *Oxford Magazine* 11 (1893): 380–81 (on Huxley's *Evolution and Ethics*).

525. Padoa, G., "Introduzione" to "Il Posto dell'Uomo nella Natura" (Milan, 1961).

526. Paget, S., "Truth and Righteousness," in "The Centenary of Huxley," *Nature* 115 (1925): 697–752, 748–50.

527. Paradis, J. G., *T. H. Huxley: Man's Place in Nature* (Lincoln, Neb., 1978).

528. Parker, T. J., "Reminiscences of Huxley," *Nat. Sci.* 7 (1895): 297–98.

529. _____, "Professor Huxley: from the Point of View of a Disciple," *Nat. Sci.* 8 (1896): 161–67 (see also Lankester, 488).

530. Peterson, H., *Huxley, Prophet of Science* (London, 1932).

531a. Pingree, J., ed., *T. H. Huxley: A List of His Scientific Papers* (London, 1968).

531b. _____, *Thomas Henry Huxley: List of His Correspondence with Miss Henrietta Heathorn, Later Mrs. Huxley, 1847–54* (London, 1969).

532. *The Phoenix*, "Huxley Centenary Celebrations, by an Unscientific Observer," *Phoenix* 10 (1925): 130–32.

533. Poulton, E. H., "Professor Huxley," *Quart. Rev.* 193 (1901): 258–78.

534. _____, "Huxley and Natural Selection," *Sci. Am.* 59 (1905): 415–16 (lecture at Birmingham, rev.).

535. _____, "Thomas Henry Huxley," in "The Centenary of Huxley," *Nature* 115 (1925): 697–752, 704–08.

536. Querner, H., "Karl Ernst von Baer und Thomas Henry Huxley," *Südhoffs Archiv*, Band 62, Heft 2 (1978), pp. 131–47.

537. Randel, W. P., "Huxley in America," *Proc. Aus. Phil. Soc.* 114 (1970): 73–94.

538. Reeks, M., *Register . . . and History of the Royal School of Mines* (London, 1920).

539. Reeve, L., ed., *Portraits of Men of Evidence in Literature, Science and Art* (London, 1963): pp. 127–34 (Huxley).

540. Rehbock, P. F., "Huxley, Haeckel and the Oceanographers: The Case of *Bathybius haeckelii*," *Isis* 66 (1975): 504–33.

541. Renner, S., "The Garden of Civilization: Conrad, Huxley, and the Ethics of Evolution," *Conradiana* 7 (1975): 109–20.

542. Ritchie, J., "A Natural History Interlude: Huxley's Teaching at Edinburgh University," *Univ. Edin. J.* (1940): 206–12.

543. Roos, D. A., "Neglected Bibliographical Aspects of the Works of Thomas Henry Huxley," *J. Soc. Bibliography Nat. Hist.* 8 (1978): 401–20.

544. _____, "Matthew Arnold and Thomas Henry Huxley: Two Speeches at the Royal Academy, 1881 and 1883," *J. Mod. Philol.* 74 (1977): 316–24.

545. Rose, P., "Huxley, Holmes, and the Scientist as Aesthete," *Vict. Newsl.* 38 (1970): 22–24.

546. Rupke, N. A., "*Bathybius haeckelii* and the Psychology of Scientific Discovery," *Stud. Hist. Phil. Sci.* 7 (1976): 53–62.

547. Russell, E. F., "A Student's Reminiscences," in "The Centenary of Huxley," *Nature* 115 (1925): 697–752, 751–52.

548. Seth, A., "Man's Place in the Cosmos," *Blackwood's* 154 (1893): 823–34 (on *Evolution and Ethics*).

549. Smalley, G. W., "Mr. Huxley," *Scrib. Mag.* 38 (1895): 514–24.

550. Smith, G. E., *The Place of T. H. Huxley in Anthropology* (London, 1935).

551. Smith Woodward, A., "Huxley as a Palaeontologist and Geologist," *Nat. Sci.* 7 (1895): 125–28.

552. _____, "Contributions to Vertebrate Palaeontology," in "The Centenary of Huxley," *Nature* 115 (1925): 697–752, 728–30.

553. Sollas, W. J., "The Master," in "The Centenary of Huxley," *Nature* 115 (1925): 697–752, 747–48.

554. Stanley, O., "T. H. Huxley's Treatment of Nature," *J. Hist. Ideas*, 18 (1957): 120–27.

555. Stephen, L., "Ethics and the Struggle for Existence," *Cont. Rev.* 64 (1893): 157–70 (on evolution and ethics).

556. _____, "Thomas Henry Huxley," *Nin. Cent.* 40 (1900): 905–18.

557. Stirling, J. H., *As Regards Protoplasm in Relation to Professor Huxley's Essay on the Physical Basis of Life* (London, 1869).

558. Stoddard, D. R., "'That Victorian Science': Huxley's Physiography and Its Impact on Geography," *Trans. Inst. Brit. Geog.* 66 (1975): 17–40.

559. Strauss, W., Jr., "Huxley's *Evidence as to Man's Place in Nature*—A Century Later," in L. G. Stevenson and R. P. Multhauf, eds., *Medicine, Science and Culture* (Baltimore, 1968): pp. 160–67.

560. Teller, J. D., "Great Teachers of Science: 1. Thomas Henry Huxley," *Sci. Ed.* 25, no. 5 (1941).

561. _____, "Huxley's 'Evil' Influence," *Sci. Mon.* 56 (1943): 173–78.

562. Tener, R. H., "R. H. Hutton and 'Agnostic'," *Notes and Queries* 11 (n.s.) (1964): 429–31.

563. Thistleton-Dyer, W. T., "The First Volume of Huxley's Memoirs," *Nature* 58 (1898): 613–14.

564. _____, "Huxley," *Encyclopedia Britannica* (1902), 9th edn., supplement, pp. 368–72.

565. _____, "Plant Biology in the Seventies," in "The Centenary of Huxley," *Nature* 115 (1925): 697–752, 709–12.

566. Thompson, W. H., *Professor Huxley and Religion* (London, 1905).
567. Thomson, J. A., "Huxley as Evolutionist," in "The Centenary of Huxley," *Nature* 115 (1925): 697–752, 717–18.
568. ———, *The Great Biologists* (London, 1932): 145–50 (Huxley).
569. Turner, D. M., "The Philosophical Aspect of Education in Science," *Isis* 9 (1927): 402–19.
570. Tylor, E. B., "Professor Huxley as Anthropologist," *Fort. Rev.* 58 (n.s.) (1895): 311–12; the same issue contains an article entitled "Professor Huxley as a Biologist," by "A Student of Science," 313–16.
571. Uschmann, G., and I. Jahn, eds., "Der Briefwechsel zwischen Thomas Henry Huxley und Ernst Haeckel," *Wiss. Zeitschr. der Friedrich-Schiller Uni. Jena* 9 (1959–60): *Mathem.-Naturwiss. Reihe* 1 (2): 7–33.
572. Van Doren, C., ed., *Letters to Mother* (New York, 1959), part of section 2 (Huxley).
573. Veitch, J., "Professor Huxley's *Hume*," *Nature* 19 (1879): 453–56.
574. Vines, S. H., "The Beginnings of Instruction in General Biology," in "The Centenary of Huxley," *Nature* 115 (1925): 697–752, 714–15.
575. Ward, W., "Thomas Henry Huxley: A Reminiscence," *Nin. Cent.* 40 (1896): 274–92.
576. Watson, D. M. S., "Structure and Evolution in Vertebrate Palaeontology," in "The Centenary of Huxley," *Nature* 115 (1925): 697–752, 730–32.
577. Watts, W. W., "Geological Thought and Teaching," in "The Centenary of Huxley," *Nature* 115 (1925): 697–752, 732–34.
578. Weldon, W. F. R., "Thomas Henry Huxley," *Dictionary of National Biography*, vol. 3 (suppl.) (London, 1901), pp. 22–31.
579. Wenley, R. M., "Huxley in His Epoch," *The Monist*, 35 (1925): 347–71.
580. Williams, W. C., "Huxley," in *Dictionary of Scientific Biographies* (New York, 1970), vol. 6, pp. 589–97.
581. Winsor, M. P., *Starfish, Jellyfish, and the Order of Life* (New Haven and London, 1976), esp. pp. 73–97 (Huxley).
582. Woodward, H., "An Uncrowned King in Science: In Memoriam Thomas Henry Huxley," *Geol. Mag.* 374 (1895): 337–41.
583. Anonymous, "Messrs. Goschen and Huxley on English Culture," *Nature* 37 (1888): 337–40.

Section D

584. Agassiz, L., "Prodrome d'une monographie des radiares ou échinodermes," *Mem. Soc. Sci. Nat.* 1 (1835): 168–99.
585. ———, *Recherches sur les poissons fossiles* (Neuchâtel, 1833–43).
586. ———, *Monographie des poissons du Vieux Rouge ou système dévonien (Old Red Sandstone) des îles Britanniques et de Russie* (Neuchâtel, 1844).
587. ———, *An Essay on Classification* (London, 1859).
588. Allen, G. E., "Naturalists and Experimentalists: The Genotype and the Phenotype," *Stud. Hist. Biol.* 3 (1979): 179–209.

589. Allman, G., "On the Anatomy and Physiology of Cordylophora, a Contribution to Our Knowledge of Tubolarian Zoophytes," *Phil. Trans. Royal Soc.* 143 (1853): 367–84.

590. ———, "Additional Observations on the Morphology of the Reproductive Organs in the Hydroids Polypes," *Proc. Royal Soc. Edin.* 4 (1857–62): 123–45.

591. ———, "On the Structure of the Reproductive Organs in Certain Hydroid Polypes," *Proc. Royal Soc. Edin.* 4 (1857–62): 50–64.

592. ———, "The Genetic Succession of the Zooïd in the Hydroida," *Trans. Royal Soc. Edin.* 26(1872): 97–106.

593. Anderson, J., "On Dura Den Sandstone," *Brit. Ass. Rep.* (1859), part ii, p. 97.

594. ———, "Report on the Excavations in Dura Den," *Brit. Ass. Rep.* (1860): 32–34.

595. Argyll, G. D. Campbell, 8th Duke of, *The Reign of Law* (London, 1867).

596. Baer, K. E. von, *Über Entwickelungsgeschichte der Thiere*, 2 Theile (Königsberg, 1828–37); *Schlussheft* of 2nd part, ed. by L. Stieda (Königsberg, 1888).

597. ———, "Über Darwins Lehre," in *Reden gehalten in wissenschaftlichen Versammlungen und kleine Aufsätze vermischten Inhalts*, 3 Theile (St. Petersburg, 1864–76), 2. Theil, *Studien aus dem Gebiete der Naturwissenschaften* (1876): 235–480.

598. Baker, T. R., "The Cell-Theory: A Restatment, History and Critique," *Quart. Rev. Micro. Sci.* 89 (1949): 103–25; 90 (1949): 87–108; 93 (1952): 157–90; 94 (1953): 407–40; 96 (1955): 449–81.

599. Bakker, R. T., and P. M. Galton, "Dinosaur Monophily and a New Class of Vertebrates," *Nature* 248 (1974): 168–72.

600. Ball, W. P., *Effects of Use and Disuse* (London, 1890).

601. Bancroft, J., *Lessons in Elementary Physiology. See* Huxley, T. H. (1866), 132.

602. Barlow, N., ed., *The Autobiography of Charles Darwin, 1809–1882, with Original Omissions Restored* (London, 1958).

603. Barry, M., "On the Unity of Structure in the Animal Kingdom," *Edin. New Phil. J.* 22 (1836–37): 116–41, 345–64.

604. Bartholomew, M., "Lyell and Evolution: An Account of Lyell's Response to the Prospect of an Evolutionary Ancestry of Man," *Brit. J. Hist. Sci.* 6 (1972–73): 261–303.

605. Barzun, J., *Darwin, Marx, Wagner: Critique of a Heritage* (London, 1942).

606. Bate, C. S., and J. D. Westwood, *A History of the British Sessile-Eyed Crustacea*, 2 vols. (London, 1894).

607. Bateson, W., *Materials for Study of Variation, Treated with Special Regard to Discontinuity in the* Origin of Species (London, 1894).

608. Bather, F. A., *The Echinodermata*, "General Description," part 3, pp. 1–37, of E. R. Lankester, ed., *A Treatise of Zoology* (London, 1909).

609. BBC, *Horizon*, "The Hot-Blooded Dinosaurs" (transcription of television broadcast).

610. Beale, L. S., "What is 'Protoplasm'?" *Med. Times Gaz.* 39 (1869): 296.

611. Bell, T., *A Monograph of the Fossil Malacostracous Crustacea of Great Britain* (London, 1858–1913).
612. Ben-David, J., *The Scientist's Rôle in Society* (Englewood Cliffs, N.J., 1971).
613. Bevington, M. M., *The Saturday Review, 1855–1868* (New York, 1941).
614. Bichât, X., *Anatomie Générale* (Paris, 1801).
615. Blake, C. C., "The Negro's Place in Nature," letter to *The Reader* 3 (19 March 1864): 367–68.
616. ———, *Zoology for Students* (London, 1875); with Owen's preface.
617. Bolt, C., *Victorian Attitudes to Race* (London and Toronto, 1971).
618. Bosanquet, R. S., *Vestiges of the Natural History of Creation: Its Arguments Examined and Explained* (London, 1845).
619. Brickenden, "Notice of the Discovery of Reptilian Foot-tracks and Remains in the Old Red or Devonian Strata of Moray," *J. Geol. Soc.* 8 (1852): 100–05.
620. *The Bridgewater Treatises* (London, 1833).
     Bronn, H. G. *See* Gesstaeker, A., and A. E. Ortsmann, 698 (1859).
621. Brooke, J. H., "Richard Owen, William Whewell and *The Vestiges*," *Brit. J. Hist. Sci.* 10 (1977): 132–45.
622. Broom, R., "On the Early Development of the Appendicular Skeleton of the Ostrich with Remarks on the Origin of Birds," *Trans. S. Afr. Phil. Soc.* 16 (1906): 355–68.
623. Brown, A. W., *The Metaphysical Society: Victorian Minds in Conflict, 1869–1880* (New York, 1947).
624. Brullé, A., "Observations sur l'absence de tarses dans quelques insectes," *Ann. Sci. Nat.* (1 ser. zool.) 8 (1837): 246–49.
625. Buchdahl, G., "Inductivist Versus Deductivist Approaches in the Philosophy of Science, as Illustrated by Some Controversies Between Whewell and Mill," *The Monist* 55 (1971): 343–67.
626. Budd, S., *Varieties of Unbelief* (London, 1977).
627. Büchner, L., *Kraft und Stoff. Empirisch-naturphilosophische Studien. In allgemein verständlicher Darstellung* (Frankfurt am Main, 1855); English translation by F. Collingwood, *Force and Matter* (London, 1864).
628. Burchfield, L. D., "Darwin and the Dilemma of Geological Time," *Isis* 65 (1974): 301–21.
629. ———, *Lord Kelvin and the Age of the Earth* (London and New York, 1975).
630. Burkhardt, F., "England and Scotland: The Learned Societies," in T. F. Glick, ed., *The Comparative Reception of Darwinism* (Austin and London, 1972), pp. 32–74.
631. Burkhardt, R. W., Jr., *The Spirit of System: Lamarck and Evolutionary Biology* (Cambridge, Mass., and London, 1977).
632. Burrow, J. W., "Evolution and Anthropology in the 1860s: The Anthropological Society of London, 1863–71," *Vict. Stud.* 7 (1963): 137–54.
633. Burn, W. L., *The Age of Equipoise* (London, 1964).
634. Bynum, W. F., "The Anatomical Method, Natural Theology and the Functions of the Brain," *Isis* 64 (1973): 445–68.

635. ———, "Time's Noblest Offspring: The Problem of Man in the British Natural Historical Sciences" (unpublished Ph.D. thesis, Cambridge University, 1975).

636. Calman, W. T., *Crustacea*, part 7; fasc. 3 of E. R. Lankester, ed., *A Treatise of Zoology* (London, 1909).

637. Canguilhelm, G., "La Théorie cellulaire," in *La Connaisance de la vie* (Paris, 1967), pp. 43–80.

638. Cardwell, D. S. L., *The Organisation of Science in England* (London, 1972).

639. Carpenter, W. B., *Principles of General and Comparative Physiology* (London, 1939).

640. ———, *Nature and Man: Essays Scientific and Philosophical* (London, 1887).
     Chadwick, J., *See* Rutherford, E., 878 (1962).

641. Chadwick, O., *The Secularization of the European Mind in the Nineteenth Century* (Cambridge, Eng., 1975).

642. Chambers, R., *Vestiges of the Natural History of Creation*: 642a, 1st edn. (London 1844); 642b, 10th edn. (1854); 642c, 6th edn. (Darwin's copy, 1848).

643. Coleman, W., *Georges Cuvier, Zoologist* (Cambridge, Mass., 1964).

644. ———, *Biology in the Nineteenth Century: Problems of Form, Function and Transformation* (New York, 1971).

645. ———, "Morphology Between Type Concept and Descent Theory," *J. Hist. Med.* 31 (1976): 149–75.

646. Cope, E. D., "An Account of the Extinct Reptiles Which Approached the Birds," *Proc. Philad. Acad. Nat. Sci.* (1867): 234–35.

647. ———, "Synopsis of the Extinct Batrachia and Reptilia of North America," *Trans. Am. Phil. Soc.* 14 (1871): 1–252.

648. ———, "The Systematic Arrangement of the Order Peryssodactyla," *Proc. Am. Phil. Soc.* 19 (1882): 377–401.

649. Crow, D., *The Victorian Woman* (London, 1971).

650. Cuvier, G., *Leçons d'anatomie comparée* (Paris, 1805).

651. ———, *Histoire naturelle des poissons* (Paris, 1821–49) (continued by A. Valenciennes).

652. Dana, J. D., "On the Higher Subdivisions in the Classification of Mammals," *Am. J. Sci. Arts* 35 (2nd s.) (1863): 65–71.

653. Darlington, C., *Darwin's Place in History* (London, 1959).

654a. Darwin, C., *A Monograph of the Sub-Class Cirripedia, with Figures of All the Species: The Lepadidae, or Peduncolated Cirripedes* (London, 1851).

654b. ———, *A Monograph of the Fossil Lepadidae; or, Peduncolated Cirripedes* (London, 1851).

655a. ———, *A Monograph of the Sub-Class Cirripedia, with Figures of All Species: The Balanidae (or Sessil Cirripedes), the Verrucidae ℰ c.* (London, 1854).

655b. ———, *A Monograph of the Fossil Balanidae and Verrucidae of Great Britain* (London, 1854).

656. _____, *On the Origin of Species by Means of Natural Selection, or Preser-vation of Favoured Races in the Struggle for Life*: (a) 1st edn., (London, 1859); (b) 6th edn., (1872).

657. _____, *The Variation of Animals and Plants under Domestication* (London, 1868).

658. _____, *The Expressions of the Emotions in Man and Animals* (London, 1872).

659. _____, *The Descent of Man, and Selection in Relation to Sex* (London, 1874).

_____, *Autobiography: See* Barlow, N., 602 (1958).

"Darwin's Journal": *See* De Beer, G., 666 (1959).

"Darwin's Notebooks": *See* De Beer, G., 667 (1960).

660. Darwin, C., and A. R. Wallace, "On the Tendency of Species to Form Varieties; and on the Perpetuation of Varieties and Species by Natural Means of Selection," *J. Linn. Soc. (Zool.)* 3 (1858): 45–62.

661. Darwin, F., *The Life and Letters of Charles Darwin* (London, 1887).

662. Darwin, F. , and A. C. Seward, *More Letters of Charles Darwin* (London, 1903).

663. Davidson, T., *British Fossil Brachiopoda* (London, 1851–86).

664. _____, "A Monograph of Recent Brachiopoda," *Trans. Linn. Soc. (Zool.)* ser. 2, 4 (1886–88): 1–248.

665. De Beer, G., "Darwin's Views of the Relations Between Embryology and Evolution," *J. Linn. Soc. (Zool.)* 44 (1958): 15–23.

666. _____, ed., "Darwin's Journal," *Bull. Brit. Mus. (Nat. Hist.) Hist. Ser.* 2 (1960): 3–21.

667. _____, "Darwin's Notebooks on Transmutation of Species," *Bull. Brit. Mus. (Nat. Hist.) Hist. Ser.* 2 (1960): 23–200.

668. _____, *Charles Darwin, Evolution by Natural Selection* (London, 1964).

669. De Giustino, D., *Conquest of Mind: Phrenology and Victorian Social Thought* (London, 1975).

669a. Desmaret, E., "Note sur la vie et les travaux d'Auguste Brullé," *Annales de la Société entomologique* 2 (1872): 513–16.

669b. Desmond, A., *Archetypes and Ancestors: Palaeontology in Victorian London 1850–1875* (London, 1982); I regret that I could not discuss this book in my work, since it appeared when mine was already in progress.

670. Desmond, A. J., *The Hot-Blooded Dinosaurs* (London, 1975).

671. Dollo, L., "Première note sur les dinosauriens de Bernissant," *Bull. Mus. r. Hist. nat. Belg.* 1 (1882): 161–80.

672. _____, "Troisième note sur les dinosauriens de Bernissant," *Bull. Mus. r. Hist. nat. Belg.* 2 (1883): 85–126.

673. Duff, P., *Sketch of the Geology of Moray* (London, 1842).

674. Durant, J., "The Meaning of Evolution: Post-Darwinian Debates on the Significance for Man of the Theory of Evolution, 1858–1908," (unpublished thesis, Cambridge University, 1978).

Eddington, A. S. *See* Cohen, C., 424 (n.d.).

675. Egerton, F., "Refutation and Conjecture; Darwin's Response to Sedgwick's Attack on Chambers," *St. Hist. Phil. Sci.* 1 (1970): 176–83.

676. Egerton, Ph. G., "Catalogue of Fossil Fish in the Collections of Lord Cole and Sir Philip Gray Egerton, Arranged Alphabetically; with References to the Localities, Geological Positions, and Published Descriptions of the Species," *Phil. Mag.* 8 (1836): 366–73.

677. _____, "Observations on Mr. M'Coy's Paper on Some Fossil Fish of the Carboniferous Period," *Ann. Mag. Nat. Hist.* 2 (n.s.) (1848): 189–90.

678. Ehrenberg, C. G., "Über die Akalephen des Rothen Meeres und den Organismus der Medusen der Ostsee," *Abh. K. Akad. Wiss. Berlin* (1835): 181–260.

679. Eiseley, L., *Darwin's Century: Evolution and the Men Who Discovered it* (London, 1959).

680. Ellegård, A., "The Darwinian Revolution and Nineteenth-Century Philosophies of Science," *J. Hist. Ideas* 18 (1957): 362–93.

681. _____, *Darwin and the General Reader* (Gøteborg, 1958).

682. Etheridge, R., "On the Stratigraphical Position of Acanthopholis horridus (Huxley)," *Geol. Mag.* 4 (1867): 67–69; reprinted in T. H. Huxley, *Scientific Memoirs*, vol. 3, pp. 235–38.

683. Farber, P. L., "The Type-Concept in Zoology During the First Half of the Nineteenth Century," *J. Hist. Biol.* 9 (1976): 93–119.

684. _____, "The Transformation of Natural History in the Nineteenth Century," *J. Hist. Biol.* 15 (1982): 145–52.

685. Fawcett, H., "A Popular Exposition of Mr. Darwin on the Origin of Species," *Macmillan's Mag.* 3 (1860): 81–92.

686. Fisher, R. A., *The Genetical Theory of Natural Selection* (London, 1929).

687. Flower, W. H., "Observations on the Posterior Lobes of the Cerebrum of the Quadrumana, with a Description of the Brain of a Galago," *Proc. Royal Soc.* 11 (1860–63): 376–81; *Phil. Trans. Royal Soc.* 152 (1862): 185–201.

688. Forbes, E., "On Some Important Analogies Between the Animal and Vegetable Kingdoms," *Ann. Nat. Hist.* 15 (1845): 210–12.

689. _____, *A Monograph of the British Naked-Eyed Medusae* (London, 1848).

690. _____, "On the Supposed Analogy Between the Life of an Individual and the Duration of a Species," *Edin. New Phil. J.* 53 (1852): 130–35.
    Foster, M., and E. R. Lankester, eds. See 355 (1898–1903).

691. Fothergill, P., *Historical Aspects of Organic Evolution* (London, 1952).

692. Gasman, D., *The Scientific Origins of National Socialism: Social Darwinism in Ernst Haeckel and the German Monist League* (London and New York, 1971).

693. Geison, G. L., "The Protoplastic Theory of Life and the Vitalist-Mechanistic Debate," *Isis* 60 (1969): 273–92.

694. _____, *Michael Foster and the Cambridge School of Physiology* (Princeton, 1978).

695. Fürbringer, M., *Untersuchungen zur Morphologie und Systematik der Vögel* (Amsterdam, 1888).

696. Gegenbaur, C., *Grundzüge der vergleichenden Anatomie* (Leipzig, [a] 1859; [b] 1870).

697. _____, *Grundriss der vergleichenden Anatomie* (Leipzig, 1878).

698. Gesstaeker, A., and A. E. Ortmann, *Arthropoden* (Leipzig, 1901); Band 5, *H. G. Bronns Klassen und Ordnungen des Thier-Reichs* (Leipzig and Heidelberg, 1859–19   ).

699. Ghiselin, M. T., *The Triumph of the Darwinian Method* (Berkeley and Los Angeles, 1969).

700. Gillespie, C. C., *Genesis and Geology* (Cambridge, Mass., 1951).

701. Glass, B., O. Temkin, and W. L. Strauss, Jr., eds., *Forerunners of Darwin* (Baltimore, 1959).

Glick, T. F. *See* Burkhardt, F., 630 (1972).

702. Gordon, G., "A List of the Fishes That Have Been Found in the Moray Firth, and in the Fresh Waters of the Province of Moray," *The Zoologist* 10 (1852): 3454–62.

703. _____, "On the Geology of the Lower or Northern Part of the Province of Moray; Its History, Present State of Enquiry, and Points for Future Examination," *Edin. New Phil. J.* 9 (1859): 14–58.

704. _____, "Note upon the Geological Structure of the Elgin District," in T. H. Huxley, *Scientific Memoirs,* vol. 4, pp. 242–47.

705. Gould, S. J., *Ontogeny and Phylogeny* (New York, 1977).

706. _____, *Ever Since Darwin* (London, 1978).

707. Grassé, P. P., ed., *Traité de zoologie, anatomie, systématique, biologie* (Paris, 1960), tome 5, fasc. 2.

708. Greene, J., *The Death of Adam: Evolution and Its Impact on Western Thought* (Ames, Iowa, 1959).

709. Greenwood, P. H., "Macroevolution—Myth or Reality?" (presidential address to the Linnean Society of London), *Biol. J. Linn. Soc.* 12 (1979): 293–305.

710. Gregory, F., *Scientific Materialism in Nineteenth-Century Germany* (Dordrecht and Boston, 1977).

711. Gruber, H., and P. Barnett, *Darwin on Man* (London, 1974).

712. Gruber, J. W., *A Conscience in Conflict: The Life of St. George Jackson Mivart* (New York, 1960).

713. Gunther, A., "Ichthyology," *Enc. Brit.,* 9th edn. (1881), vol. 12, p. 634.

714. Haber, F. C., "Fossils and the Idea of Process of Time in Natural History," in B. Glass et al., *Forerunners of Darwin,* pp. 222–61.

715. Haeckel, E., *Monographie der Radiolarien* (Berlin, 1862).

716. _____, *Generelle Morphologie der Organismen* (Berlin, 1866).

717. _____, *Natürliche Schöpfungsgeschichte* (Berlin, 1868).

718. _____, *The Evolution of Man* (English translation, London, 1910).

719. _____, *Freedom in Science. See* Huxley, T. H., 260 (1879).

720. Haldane, J. B. S., *The Causes of Evolution* (London, 1932).

721. Hancock, A., *On the Organisation of the Brachiopoda* (London, 1857).

722. _____, "On the Organisation of the Brachiopoda," *Phil. Trans. Royal Soc.* 148 (1859): 791–871 (communicated by Huxley).

Harland, W. B., et al. *See* Snelling, 896 (1964).

723. Hartmann, R., *Anthropoid Apes* (London, 1889).

724. Heilmann, G., *The Origin of Birds* (London, 1926).

Henfrey, A. *See* Huxley, T. H., 24 (1853).

725. Herschel, J., *A Preliminary Discourse of the Study of Natural Philosophy* (London, 1831).

726. Hodge, M. J. S., "England," in T. F. Glick, ed., *The Comparative Reception of Darwinism* (Austin and London, 1972), pp. 3–31.

727. _____, "The Universal Gestation of Nature: Chambers' Vestiges and Explanations," *J. Hist. Biol.* 5 (1972): 127–52.

728. Holmes, A., "A Revised Geological Time-Scale," *Trans. Edin. Geol. Soc.* 17 (1959): 183–216.

729. Houghton, W. E., *The Victorian Frame of Mind, 1830–70* (New Haven, 1970 [1957]).

730. _____, ed., *The Wellesley Index to Victorian Pediodicals* (Toronto, 1966–79).

   Howes, G. B. *See* Huxley, T. H., 353 (1902).

   Howes, G. B. and D. H. Scott. *See* Huxley, T. H., and H. N. Martin, 360 (1888).

731. Hull, D., *Darwin and His Critics* (Cambridge, Mass., 1973).

732. Hume, D., *An Enquiry Concerning Human Understanding* (London, 1748).

733. Hunt, J., *On the Negro's Place in Nature* (London, 1863).

734. _____, "The Negro's Place in Nature," letter to *The Reader* 3 (19 March 1864): 368.

735. Hutton, F. W., "Some Remarks on Mr. Darwin's Theory," *The Geologist* 4 (1861): 132–88.

736. Huxley, A. F., "Evidence, Clues and Motives in Science," presidential address to the British Association for the Advancement of Science, 1977, *THES* (2 Sept. 1977): 4–6.

737. _____, "Fact and Value Must Not Be Confused," *THES* (7 Oct. 1977): 21.

738. Huxley, H. A., *Poems* (with three by T. H. Huxley) (London, 1913).

739. Huxley, J. S., *The Uniqueness of Man* (London, 1941).

740. _____, *Evolutionary Ethics* (London, 1943).

741. _____, *Essays of a Biologist* (London, 1923).

742. _____, *Evolution: The Modern Synthesis* (London, 1942).

743. _____, *T. H. Huxley's Diary . . . . See* 354 (1902).

744. Huxley, L., *The Life and Letters of Joseph Dalton Hooker* (London, 1918).

745. Jackson, J. W., *Ethnology and Phrenology as an Aid to the Historian* (London, 1863).

746. Jenkin, F., "The Origin of Species" (review), *North Brit. Rev.* 46 (1867): 277–318.

747. Keith, A., *A New Theory of Human Evolution* (London, 1948).

748. Kelvin, W. T., Lord, "On Geological Time," *Trans. Glas. Geol. Soc.* 3 (1868): 1–28.

749. Kettlewell, H. B. D., "The Phenomenon of Industrial Melanism in Lepidoptera," *Ann. Rev. Ent.* 6 (1961): 245–62.

750. King, W., "The Reputed Fossil Man of Neanderthal," *Quart. J. Sci.* 1 (1864): 88–97.

751. Kottler, M. J., "Alfred Russel Wallace, The Origin of Man, and Spiritualism," *Isis* 65 (1974): 145–92.

752. Knox, R., *The Races of Men* (London, 1850).

753. Kulp, J. L., "Geological Time Scale," *Science* 133 (1961): 1105–14.

754. Kühne, W., *Untersuchungen über das Protoplasma und die Contractilität* (Leipzig, 1864).

755. Lankester, E. R., "On the Use of the Term Homology in Modern Zoology, and the Distinction Between Homogenic and Homoplastic Agreements," *Ann. Mag. Nat. Hist.* 6 (1870): 34–43.

756. _____, "Karl Ernst von Baer," *The Academy* 10 (1876): 608.

757. _____, *Extinct Animals* (London, 1909).

758. _____, *A Treatise of Zoology. See* Calman, 636 (1909), and Bather, 608 (1909).

759. La Vergata, A., ed., *L'evoluzione biologica da Linneo a Darwin, 1755–1871* (Turin, 1979).

760. _____, "Darwin, Lamarck and MacLeay," unpublished paper read at the International Conference in Florence, 1981.

761. Lawrence, W., *Lectures on Physiology, Zoology and the Natural History of Man* (London, 1819).

762. Leach, W. E., "A Tabular View of the External Characters of Four Classes of Animals, Which Linné arranged under Insecta; with the Distribution of the Genera Composing Three of the Classes into Orders," *Trans. Linn. Soc.* 11 (1815): 306–400.

763. Leakey, L., *Unveiling Man's Origins* (London, 1970).

764. Leuckart, G. C. F. R., *Über die Morphologie und die Verwandtschaftsverhältnisse der wirbellosen Thiere* (Braunschweig, 1848).

765. Lewontin, R., "Testing the Theory of Natural Selection," *Nature* 236 (1972): 181–82.

766. Linnaeus, K., *Systema Naturae*, 1st edn. (Lund, 1735).

767. Lloyd, G., "On a New Species of Labyrinthodont from the New Red Sandstone of Warwickshire," *Brit. Ass. Rep.* (1849): 56.

768. Locke, J., *An Essay Concerning Human Understanding* (London, 1690).

769. Lorimer, D. A., *Colour, Class and the Victorians* (Leicester and New York, 1978).

770. Lubbock, J. (later Lord Avebury), "On the Evidence of the Antiquity of Man, Afforded by the Physical Structure of the Somme Valley," *Nat. Hist. Rev.* 2 (n.s.) (1864): 244–69.

771. _____, "Cave-Men," *Nat. Hist. Rev.* 2 (n.s.) (1864): 407–28.

772. _____, *The Origin of Civilisation and the Primitive Condition of Man* (London, 1870).

773. Lurie, E., *Louis Agassiz, a Life in Science* (Chicago, 1960).

774. Lyell, C., *The Principles of Geology* (London 1830–33).

775. _____, *The Geological Evidence of the Antiquity of Man* (London, 1863).

776. McCoy, F., (a) "On Some New Fossil Fish of the Carboniferous Period," *Ann. Mag. Nat. Hist.* 2 (n.s.) (1848): 1–10, 115–33. (b) Reply to P. G. Egerton's letter, ibid., 277–80 (*see* 677 [1848]).

777. McKinney, H. L., *Wallace and Natural Selection* (New Haven and London, 1972).

778. MacLeay, W. S., *Horae Entomologicae* (London, 1819).

779. MacLeod, R. M., "Evolutionism and Richard Owen," *Isis* 56 (1965): 259–80.

780. Mandelbaum, M., "Scientific Background of Evolutionary Theory," *J. Hist. Ideas* 18 (1957): 342–61.

781. _____, *History, Man and Reason: A Study in Nineteenth-Century Thought* (Baltimore and London, 1971).

782. Mantell, G. A., "Description of the Telerpeton Elginense, a Fossil Reptile Recently Discovered in the Old Red Sandstone of Moray," *J. Geol. Soc.* 8 (1852): 100–05.

783. Marcou, J., *Life, Letters and Works of Louis Agassiz* (New York and London, 1896).

784. Marsh, G. P., *Man and Nature; or, Physical Geography, as Modified by Human Action* (London, 1864).

785. Marsh, O. C., "Notice of a New and Diminutive Species of Fossil Horse *(Equus parvulus)* of Nebraska," *Am. J. Sci. Arts* 46 (1868): 374–75; *Ann. Mag. Nat. Hist.* 3 (1868): 95–96.

786. _____, "Fossil Horses in America," *Am. Nat.* 8 (1874): 288–94.

787. _____, "Small Size of the Brain in Tertiary Mammals," *Am. J. Sci. Arts* 8 (1874): 66–67; *Nature* 10 (1874): 273.

788. _____, "Introduction and Succession of Vertebrate Life in America," *Proc. Am. Ass. Adv. Sci.* (1877): 211–58.

789. _____, "Classification of Dinosauria," *Am. J. Sci. Arts* 23 (1882): 79–84; *Nature* 25 (1882): 244–46.

790. Mayr, E., *Animal Species and Evolution* (Cambridge, Mass., 1963).

791. _____, *Systematics and the Origin of Species* (New York, 1964).

792. _____, "Introduction" to C. Darwin, *On the Origin of Species, a Facsimile of the First Edition* (Cambridge, Mass., and London, 1975 [1964]); also in *Evolution and Anthropology* (Washington, 1959).

793. Meldola, R., "Evolution: Old and New," *Nature* 80 (1909): 481–85.

794. Mendelsohn, E., "The Emergence of Science as a Profession in Nineteenth-Century Europe," in K. Hill, ed., *The Management of Scientists* (Boston, 1964).

795. Meyer, A. W., *The Rise of Embryology* (Stanford, 1939).

796. _____, *Human Generation* (Stanford, 1956).

797. Meyer, H. von, "Reptilien aus dem Stubensandstein des obern Kempers," *Palaeonthographica* 7 (1859–60): 253–346; 14 (1865–66): 99–124.

798. Mill, J. S., *A System of Logic, Ratiocinative and Inductive* (London, 1843); several edns.

799. _____, "The Negro Question" (letter to the editor), *Fraser's Mag.* 41 (1850): 25–31 (signed "D.").

800. Mill, J. S., and H. Taylor, "Enfranchisement of Women," *West. Rev.* 55 (1851): 289–311.

801. Miller, H., *The Old Red Sandstone* (Edinburgh, 1841).

802. Millhauser, M., *Just Before Darwin: Robert Chambers and Vestiges* (Middleton, 1959).

803. Milne-Edwards, H., *Histoire naturelle des crustacées* (Paris, 1836).

804. _____, "Considérations sur quelques principes relatifs à la classification naturelle des animaux, et plus particulièrement sur la distribution méthodique des mammifères," (a) *Ann. Sci. Nat.* 1 (Zool.) (1844): 68–99; (b) report in *Ann. Mag. Nat. Hist.* 2 (1848): 70–78.

805. Mivart, St. G. J., "Notes on the Crania and Dentition of the Lemuridae, ' *Proc. Zool. Soc.* 32 (1864): 611–48.

806. _____, "On the Use of the Term Homology," *Ann. Mag. Nat. Hist.* 6 (1870): 113–21.

807. _____, "Darwin's Descent of Man" (review), *Quart. Rev.* 131 (1871): 47–90.

808. _____, *On the Genesis of Species* (London, 1871).

809. _____, "On Lepilemur and Cheirogaleus, and on the Zoological Rank of the Lemuroidea," *Proc. Zool. Soc.* 41 (1873): 484–510.

810. _____, "Sir Richard Owen's Hypotheses," *Nat. Sci.* 2 (1893): 18–23.

811. Murchison, R. I., "On the Coal-Field of Brora in Sutherlandshire, and Some Other Stratified Deposits in the North of Scotland" (1827), *Trans. Geol. Soc.* 2 (2nd s.) part ii (1829): 293–326.

812. _____, "Supplementary Remarks on the Strata of the Oolitic Series, and the Rocks Associated with them, in the Counties of Sutherland and Ross, and in the Hebrides," (1828), *Trans. Geol. Soc.* 2 (2nd s.), part iii (1829): 353–68.

813. _____, "On the Succession of the Older Rocks in the Northernmost Counties of Scotland, with Some Observations on the Orkney and Shetland Islands," *J. Geol. Soc.* 15 (1858): 353–418.

814. _____, "On the Sandstones of Morayshire (Elgin &c.) Containing Reptilian Remains; and on Their Relations to the Old Red Sandstone of That Country," *J. Geol. Soc.* 15 (1858): 419–39.

815. Murchison, R. I., and A. Sedgwick, "On the Structure and Relations of the Deposits Contained Between the Primary Rocks and the Oolitic Series in the North of Scotland," *Trans. Geol. Soc.* 3, 2nd s. (1835): 125–60 (written 1828).

816. Müller, J., (a) "Über den Bau und die Grenzen der Ganoiden und über das natürliche System der Fische," Abh. K. Akad. Wiss. Berlin (1844): 117–26; (b) "Nachtrag zur Abhandlung 'Über den Bau der Ganoiden'," ibid. (1845): 33–35; (c) translated by J. W. Griffith as "On the Structure and Characters of the Ganoidei, and on the Natural Classification of Fish" (*Taylor's*) *Sci. Mem.* 4 (1846): 499–558.

817. Müller, F., *Facts and Arguments for Darwin* (London, 1869); English translation of *Für Darwin* (Leipzig, 1864).

818. Needham, J., *A History of Embryology* (Cambridge, Eng., 1959).

819. Oppenheimer, J., "An Embryological Enigma in the Origin of Species," in B. Glass et al., *Forerunners of Darwin*, pp. 292–322.

820. _____, *Essays in the History of Embryology and Biology* (Cambridge, Mass., 1967).

821. Osborn, H. F., *From the Greeks to Darwin: An Outline of the Development of the Evolution Idea* (New York, 1892).

822. Ospovat, D., "The Influence of Karl Ernst von Baer's Embryology, 1828–1859: a Reappraisal in Light of Richard Owen's and William B. Carpenter's 'Palaeontological Application of "von Baer's Law"'," *J. Hist. Biol.* 9 (1976): 1–28.

823. _____, *The Development of Darwin's Theory* (Cambridge, Eng., 1981).

824. Ostrom, J. H., "The Ancestry of Birds," *Nature* 242 (1973): 136.

825. _____, "The Origin of Birds," *Ann. Rev. Earth and Plan. Sci.* 3 (1975): 55–77.

826. _____, "The Osteology of *Compsognathus longipes* (Wagner)," *Zitteliana: Abhandlungen der bayerischen Staatssammlung für Paläontologie und historische Geologie* 4 (1978): 73–118.

827. _____, "*Archaeopterix* and the Origin of Birds," *Biol. J. Linn. Soc.* 8 (1976): 91–182.

828. Owen, G., and A. Williams, "The Caecum of Articulate Brachiopoda," *Proc. Royal Soc., ser. B* 172 (1964): 187–201.

829. Owen, R., "On the Anatomy of the Brachiopoda of Cuvier," *Trans. Zool. Soc.* 1 (1835): 145–64.

830. _____, *Odontography* (London, 1840–45).

831. _____, "Report on British Fossil Remains," *Brit. Ass. Rep.* (1841): 60–204.

832. _____, *Lectures on the Comparative Anatomy and Physiology of the Invertebrate Animals*: (a) (London, 1843); (b) (London, 1855).

833. _____, *The Archetype and Homologies of the Vertebrate Skeleton* (London, 1848).

834. _____, *On the Nature of Limbs* (London, 1849).

835. _____, *On Parthenogenesis* (London, 1849).

836. _____, "On Dinornis," *Trans. Zool. Soc.* 4 (1850): 1–20.

837. _____, *Geology and Inhabitants of the Ancient World: The Animals Constructed by B. W. Dawkins* (London, 1854).

838. _____, "On the Characters, Principles of Division and Primary Groups of the Class Mammalia," *J. Proc. Linn. Soc.* 2 (1858): 1–37.

839. _____, *On the Classification and Geographical Distribution of the Mammalia* (London, 1859).

840. _____, "Lectures at the Royal Institution on the Brain," *The Athenaeum* (23 March 1861): 395–96 (report).

841. _____, "Letter to the Athenaeum on the Brain," *The Athenaeum* (7 April 1861): 467.

842. _____, "On the Archaeopterix of von Meyer, with a Description of the Fossil Remains of a Long-Tailed Species from the Lithographic Stone of Solenhofen," *Phil. Trans. Royal Soc.* 153 (1863): 33–47.

843. _____, "On the Aye-Aye," *Trans. Zool. Soc.* 5 (1866): 33–101.

844. _____, *On the Anatomy of Vertebrates* (London, 1866–68).

845. _____, "Letter to the *London Review*," *Lond. Rev.* 12 (1866): 516.

846. Owen, Rev. R. S., *The Life of Richard Owen* (London, 1894).

847. Paley, W., *Natural Theology* (London, 1802).

848. Pander, C., *Über die Saurodipterinen, Dendrodonten, Glyptolepiden und Cheirolepiden des devonischen Systems* (St. Petersburg, 1860).

Parker, T. J. *See* Huxley, T. H., 341 (1893).

849. Parker, W. M., "On the Morphology of Birds," *Proc. Royal Soc.* 42 (1887): 52–58.

850. Passmore, J., "Darwin's Impact on British Metaphysics," *Vict. Stud.* 3 (1959): 41–54.

851. _____, *The Perfectibility of Man* (London, 1970).

852. Peckham, M., ed., *A Variorum Text (of the Origin of Species)* (Philadelphia, 1959).

853. Perkin, H., *The Origins of Modern English Society* (London and Toronto, 1969).

854. Perry, J., "On the Age of the Earth," *Nature* 51 (1895): 224–27.

855. Phillips, J., "Oxford Fossils," *Geol. Mag.* 2 (1865): 292–93; 3 (1866): 97–99.

856. _____, "Notice of Some Specimens of Megalosaurian Bones in the University Museum of Oxford," *Quart. J. Geol. Soc.* 26 (1870): 13–16; reprinted in T. H. Huxley, *Scientific Memoirs,* vol. 3, pp. 466–70 (written 1868).

857. Pictet, J., "Agassiz," in *Album de la Suisse Romande* (Geneva, 1847).

858. Poliakoff, L., *The Aryan Myth* (London, 1974); English translation from original French.

859. Poole, W. F., ed., *Index to Periodical Literature* (Boston, 1882; London, 1908).

860. Poulton, E. B., *Charles Darwin and the Origin of Species* (London, 1896).

861. _____, *Charles Darwin and the Theory of Natural Selection* (London, 1896).

862. Pratt, V., "Biological Classification," *Brit. J. Phil. Sci.* 23 (1872): 305–27.

863. Rádl, E., *Geschichte der biologischen Theorien seit dem Ende des siebzehnten Jahrhunderts* (Leipzig, 1905).

864. Raikov, B. E., *Karl Ernst von Baer 1792–1876: sein Leben und sein Werk* (Leipzig, 1968; German translation from Russian).

865. Rathke, H., "Kiemen bei Vögeln," *Isis* (1825): 1100–01.

866. _____, "Kiemen bei Säugethier," *Isis* (1825): 747–49.

867. Reichert, K., *Vergleichende Entwickelungsgeschichte des Kopfes der nackten Amphibien* (Königsberg, 1838).

868. Rensch, B., *Evolution above the Species Level* (New York, 1960).

869. Roger, J., *Les Sciences de la vie dans la pensée française du XVIIIe siècle* (Paris, 1963).

870. Romanes, G. J., *Animal Intelligence* (London, 1882).

871. _____, *Mental Evolution in Animals* (London, 1883).

872. Rothschuh, K. E., *History of Physiology* (New York, 1973; English translation from German).

873. Rudwick, M., "The Inference of Function from Structure in Fossils," *Brit. J. Phil. Sci.* 15 (1964): 27–40.

874. _____, *Living and Fossil Brachiopods* (London, 1970).

875. _____, *The Meaning of Fossils* (London and New York, 1972).

876. Ruse, M., "Darwin's Debt to Philosophy: An Examination of the Influence of the Philosophical Ideas of John F. W. Herschel and William

Whewell on the Development of Charles Darwin's Theory of Evolution,"
Stud. Hist. Phil. Sci. 6 (1975): 159–81.

877. _____, "Darwin and Herschel," *Stud. Hist. Phil. Sci.* 9 (1978): 323–32.

878. Rutherford, E., "The Radiation and Emanation of Radium" (1904), in
J. Chadwick, ed., *The Collected Papers of Lord Rutherford of Nelson*, vol.
1 (London, 1962), pp. 650–57.

879. Russell, E. S., *Form and Function* (London, 1916).

880. Salisbury, Lord, *Evolution: A Retrospect* (London, 1894).

881. Salter, J. W., "British Fossils, Part 2—Description of the Species of
Pterygotus," *Mem. Geol. Surv. U.K.*, vol. 1 (1859), pp. 37–105; reprinted
in T. H. Huxley, *Scientific Memoirs*, vol. 2, pp. 203–62.

882. _____, "On the Identity of the Upper Red Sandstones with the Upper-
most Devonian (the 'Marwood Beds' of Murchison and Sedgwick) and of
the Middle and Lower Devonian," *Brit. Ass. Rep.* (1862), part ii, pp.
92–94.

883. Salvadori, M., *Liberal Democracy* (London, 1958).

884. Schleicher, A., *Über die Bedeutung der Sprache für die Naturgeschichte
der Menschen* (Weimar, 1858).

885. Sedgwick, A., "Natural History of Creation," *Edin. Rev.* 82 (1845): 1–8.
Sedgwick and Murchison. *See* Murchison, 815 (1835).

886. Semmel, B., *The Governor Eyre Controversy* (London, 1962).

887. Sharlin, H. I., "On Being Scientific: A Critique of Evolutionary Geology
and Biology in the Nineteenth Century," *Ann. Sci.* 29 (1972): 271–85.

888. Simpson, G. G., *The Major Features of Evolution* (New York, 1953).

889. _____, *This View of Life: The World of an Evolutionist* (New York, 1960).

890. Sleeth-Moredale, S., "Science Corrupted: Victorian Biologists Consider
the 'Woman Question'," *J. Hist. Biol.* 11 (1978): 1–56.

891. Smith, C. U. M., *The Problem of Life* (London, 1976).

892. _____, "Charles Darwin, the Origin of Consciousness and Panpsych-
ism," *J. Hist. Biol.* 11 (1978): 245–67.

893. Smith, R., "Alfred Russel Wallace: Philosophy of Nature and Man," *Brit.
J. Hist. Sci.* 6 (1972): 177–99.

894. Smith, S., "The Origin of 'The Origin'," *Adv. Sci.* 16 (1959–60): 391–401.

895. _____, "The Darwin Collection at Cambridge, with One Example of Its
Use: Charles Darwin and Cirripedes," *Actes du XIᵉ Congrès International d'Histoire des Sciences* (Warsaw-Cracow, August 1965), pp. 96–
100.

896. Snelling, N. J., "A Review of Recent Phanerozoic Time-Scales," in W. B.
Harland, et al., eds., *The Phanerozoic Time-Scale*, pp. 29–42.

897. Stafleu, F. A., *Linnaeus and the Linnaeans* (Utrecht, 1971).

898. Stauffer, R. C., *Charles Darwin's Natural Selection, Being the Second
Part of His Species Book Written from 1856–58* (Cambridge, Eng., 1975).

899. Steenstrup, J. J., *Om Forplanting og Udvikling gjennem vexlende Gener-
ationsraekker, en saegeren Form for Opfostringen i de lavere Dyreklasser*
(1840); English translation from German version by G. Busk (London,
1845).
Stieda. *See* Baer, K. E. von, 596 (1888).

900. Stocking, G. W. Jr., *Race, Culture and Evolution: Essays in the History of Anthropology* (London, 1968).
901. ———, "What's in a Name? The Origins of the Royal Anthropological Institute (1837–71)," *Man* 6 (1971): 369–91.
    Symondson, A. *See* Young, R. M., 943 (1970).
902. Taton, R., ed., *A General History of the Sciences* (English translation), vol. 3, *Science in the Nineteenth Century* (London, 1965).
903. Tax, S., ed., *Evolution after Darwin* (Chicago, 1960).
904. Temkin, O., "The Idea of Descent in Post-Romantic German Biology," in B. Glass et al., *Forerunners of Darwin*, pp. 323–55.
905. ———, "Basic Science, Medicine, and the Romantic Era," *Bull. Hist. Med.* 37 (1963): 97–129.
906. Thagard, P. R., "Darwin and Whewell," *Stud. Hist. Phil. Sci.* 8 (1977): 353–56.
907. Thompson, J. V., "On the Cirripedes or Barnacles; Demonstrating Their Deceptive Character; the Extraordinary Metamorphosis They Undergo, and the Class of Animals to Which They Belong," *Zool. Res.* 1 (1830): 69–88.
908. Thomson, J. A., *The Science of Life* (London, 1899).
909. ———, *Darwinism and Human Life* (London, 1909).
    Thomson, W. *See* Kelvin, 748 (1868).
910. Tiedemann, F., "Hirn des Horang-Outangs mit dem des Menschen verglichen," *Zeitschr.* 2 (1826): 17–28.
910a. Trevelyan, G. M., *English Social History* (London, 1967).
911. Tribolet, M., *Louis Agassiz et son séjour à Neuchâtel* (Neuchâtel, 1907).
912. Tylor, E. B., *Research into the Early History of Mankind and the Development of Civilization* (London, 1865).
913. Uschmann, G., *Geschichte der Zoologie und der zoologischen Anstalten in Jena, 1779–1919* (Jena, 1959).
914. Vogt, K., *Untersuchungen über die Entwickelungsgeschichte der Geburtshelferkröte* (Solothurn, 1842).
915a. ———, *Vorlesungen über den Menschen, seine Stellung in der Schöpfung und in der Geschichte der Erde* (Giessen, 1863); [915b] English translation and preface by J. Hunt, *Lectures on Man* (London, 1864).
916. Vorzimmer, P. J., "Charles Darwin and Blending Inheritance," *Isis* 54 (1963): 371–90.
917. ———, *Charles Darwin: The Years of Controversy* (London, 1972).
918. Vries, H. de, *The Mutation Theory* (London, 1910–11); English translation from German, 1901.
919. ———, "The Principles of the Theory of Mutation," *Science* 40 (1914): 77–84.
920. Vrolik, G., "Über die Unmöglichkeit einer Ganzlinie zwischen Thieren und Pflanzen," *Holländ. Mag.* 1 (1803): 268–96 (written in 1799).
921. Vrolik, W., and J. L. C. Schröder van der Kolk, "Ostleedkundige nasporingen over de hersenen van den Chimpansé," *Amsterdam Verhand.* 1 (1849): 263–78.

922. _____, "Note sur l'encéphale de l'Orang-Outang," *Verslag. Amsterdam Acad.* 13 (1862): 1–10; *Nat. Hist. Rev.* (1862): 111–17.

923. Wagner, J. A., "Neue Beträge zur Kenntnis der umweltischen Fauna des lithographischen Schiefers: V. Compsognathus longipes Wagner," *Abh. bayer. Akad. Wiss.* 31 (1857–60): 413–528; 32 (1861–63): 65–124.

924. _____, "Über ein neues, angeblich mit Vogelfedern versehnes Reptil aus den Solenhofener lithographischen Schiefer," *Sitz. bayer. Akad. Wiss.* 2 (1861): 146–54.

925. Walker, A. D., "Evolution of the Pelvis in Birds and Dinosaurs," in S. M. Andrews, R. S. Miles and A. D. Walker, eds., *Problems of Vertebrate Evolution* (London, 1977).

926. Wallace, A. R., "On the Law Which Has Regulated the Introduction of New Species," *Ann. Mag. Nat. Hist.* 16 (1855): 184–96.

927. _____, "The Origin of Human Races and the Antiquity of Man deduced from the Theory of Natural Selection," *J. Anthro. Soc.* 2 (1864): clviii–clxx.

928. _____, "Geological Climates and the Origin of Species," *Quart. Rev.* 126 (1869): 187–205.

929. _____, "The Measurements of Geological Time," *Nature* 1 (1870): 399–401.

930. _____, *My Life* (London, 1905).

931. Wassermann, G. D., "Testability of the Rôle of Natural Selection within Theories of Population Genetics and Evolution," *Brit. J. Phil. Sci.* 29 (1978): 223–42.

932. Weismann, A., *The Germ Plasm: A Theory of Heredity* (English translation from German, London, 1893).

933. Wells, K. D., "Sir William Lawrence (1787–1867): A Study of Pre-Darwinian Ideas on Heredity and Variation," *J. Hist. Biol.* 4 (1971): 319–61.

934. Whewell, W., *History of the Inductive Sciences, From the Earliest to the Present Time* (London, 1837).

935. Wilberforce, S., "On the Origin of Species . . ." (review), *Quart. Rev.* 108 (1860): 225–64 (A).

936. Wilkie, J. S., "The Idea of Evolution in the Writings of Buffon," *Ann. Sci.* 12 (1956): 48–62, 212–27, 255–66.

937. Williams, E., *British Historians and the West Indies* (London, 1966).

938. Williams, W. C., "Chambers," in *Dictionary of Scientific Biographies* (New York, 1970), vol. 3, pp. 191–93.

939. Wilson, D., *Prehistoric Man: Researches into the Origin of Civilization in the Old and New World* (London, 1862).

940. Young, G. M., *Victorian England: Portrait of an Age* (Oxford, 1960 [1936]).

941. Young, J. Z., *The Life of Vertebrates* (Oxford, 1958 [1950]).

942. Young, R. M., *Mind, Brain and Adaptation in the Nineteenth Century* (Oxford, 1970).

943. _____, "The Impact of Darwin on Conventional Thought," in A. Symondson, ed., *The Victorian Crisis of Faith* (London, 1970), pp. 3–35.

944. _____, "Can We Really Distinguish Fact from Value in Science?" *THES* (23 Sept. 1977): 6.

INDEX

DATE DUE

JUL 0 5 2001				
Ill 8219806				

DEMCO, INC. 38-3012